CONTRIBUTIONS OF VOICE RESEARCH TO SINGING

Edited by

John Large, Ph.D.

School of Music
North Texas State University

College-Hill Press   ●   Houston, Texas 77035

College-Hill Press
P.O. Box 35728
Houston, Texas 77035

Library of Congress Number 79-57539
ISBN 0-933014-53-8
Printed in the United States of America

CONTENTS

Introduction 1

Aerodynamics

Vocal Registers

Vibrato

Singers' Formants

Intelligibility

Introduction

Contributions of Voice Research to Singing is intended as a reference collection for introductory courses in Research in Singing and Vocal Pedagogy. It is aimed primarily at singers and teachers of singing who, in the tradition of Manuel Garcia, are accepting more and more the responsibility for producing meaningful research in their own field. Also, it is hoped that the experiments reported here will prove useful to interested persons in related disciplines, e.g., physiology, acoustics, psychology, linguistics, speech and hearing sciences, experimental phonetics, laryngology, and voice therapy.

Until relatively recent times the singing voice was one of the most neglected areas of research. A new interest is manifested in today's programming of symposia on vocal research at national conventions of The National Association of Teachers of Singing and in the publication of a new Journal of Research in Singing by The International Association for Experimental Research in Singing. Significant contributions to the new body of knowledge, now called odology, are also being made at special conferences, e.g., the Conference on Research Potentials in Voice Physiology held in 1961 at The State University of New York Upstate Medical Center at Syracuse, the conference called Sound Production in Man sponsored in 1966 by The New York Academy of Sciences at New York City, the symposia on the

Care of the Professional Voice held annually at The Juilliard School in New York City, and the several international conferences of The International Association for Experimental Research in Singing held at various times in different locations--1975 in San Francisco, 1977 in Paris, 1978 in Houston, 1980 in Graz.

It would have been impossible to include in a book of these dimensions all of the pertinent research articles published within the last 125 years or so since the singing-teacher Garcia invented the laryngoscope. The 25 articles finally assembled here were selected on the basis of several criteria. First, the selection depended in part on a distribution of articles among the several areas in which researchers had been most active. These areas were found to be (1) aerodynamics, (2) vocal registers, (3) vibrato, (4) singers' formants, and (5) intelligibility. Second, the collection reflects an interest in the historical development of original ideas. Stetson, Garcia, Seashore (represented here by Kwalwasser), Bartholomew, and Delattre were pioneers whose ideas have taken hold and have been developed in subsequent investigations. Finally, an attempt has been made to include articles which are difficult to obtain. Teachers of singing and professional singers, in particular, do not have ready access to the Archives Neerlandaises de Phonetique Experimentale, for example, or to Soviet Physics-Acoustics.

Most of the articles in this collection have been used as the basis for courses in Research in Singing I have taught at San Francisco State University, The University of Southern California, The University of California at San Diego, and North Texas State University. A companion volume, Five Areas of Research in Singing, based on lectures from those courses, is being prepared for publication; a third volume, Building and Equalizing the Singing Voice, introducing practical applications of voice research to the teaching of singing, will follow.

I wish to thank all authors and publishers whose cooperation has made this anthology possible.

JOHN LARGE

Aerodynamics

The Breathing Movements in Singing

by R. H. Stetson

Psychological Laboratory, Oberlin College

Singing and speaking are in some sense variations of the same process. The breathing movements of singing and the breathing movements of speech are closely related; and the note in singing corresponds to the syllable in speech. In exclamations and in calling we come to a type of speech which is close to song. Speech at rapid rates proves to be very like singing in the coordinations of the breathing movements. The carefully cultivated and precise character of the singer's execution makes it possible to study his coordinations. He may sing actual songs under laboratory conditions and it is probable that he will not depart from the trained organization of his movements.

APPARATUS AND EXPERIMENTAL METHODS[1]

The methods used were those developed for the study of the breathing movements of speech. The chest pulse for each note was recorded by means of the negative pressure applicator, and the movements of the rib-cage, of the epigastric, mesogastric, navel-, and lower abdominal levels were recorded by means of tambours with bosses.[2]

Only labial consonants were used in order to simplify the matter of articulation. The usual mask gave the air-pressure just outside the mouth and served also to register the vibrations of the vowels.

In the case of figures 1, 2, 3, 14, 18 the radius of the recording lever has been indicated. In the other figures the tracings are near the base line and the deviation for arc is negligible. Simultaneous points are marked at the left end of the tracings.

The records from which figures 8 and 19 are excerpts were not taken with the pneumatic system; instead threads were attached directly to the body wall; styluses mounted on these threads traced the movements on the kymograph drum. The method has been described for the recording of rhythmic movements.[3] This method gives the actual displacement of the region without magnification, and as the stylus always moves in a vertical line there is no distortion due to the tambour and to the radial movement of the Marey stylus.

The tracings were made from subjects in the sitting position as described above and also in the standing position. A vertical support was arranged against which the subject stood so that the spine was in contact with a rigid bearing at a place in the lumbar and a place in the thoracic region. This stance was natural and comfortable though the support at the back made the position immobile. The tambours with their bosses were mounted on a heavy, braced standard placed in front of the subjects; tests showed that no artifacts were introduced from chance movements of the subjects or from a shifting of the supports for the tambours.

Of the twenty one records of breathing movements in singing from which excerpts were reproduced, eight are taken from subjects standing; of the three subjects two were trained singers. Records both sitting and standing were taken from two subjects. It appears that there is no perceptible difference in the fundamental coordinations, sitting and standing, in singing. The standing position affords better control and more power; but it is impossible to point out variations in the actual movements.

The excerpts reproduced are all taken from the records of male singers. Tracings were taken of the movements of breathing in singing from one woman; the coordinations did not prove to be essentially different, though the movements are somewhat slighter in force and excursion. The tracings of the woman's breathing movements are very like those of subject To., figures 3 and 25.

The scales sung were pitched on a tonic an octave below middle C. (128 d.v.)

and the two melodies, "Materna", and "Italian Hymn" were sung an octave lower than written in the staves given in the figures. No type of execution was prescribed except the styles "legato" and "staccato". In some cases the subjects were asked to bring out clearly the arresting consonant at the close of a long note. The apparatus did not interfere with the process of singing, but occasionally the mask made it difficult at first for the singer to get accurate intonation. Many tracings were taken from each subject, so that chance peculiarities or incidental difficulties with the adjustments did not figure in the tracings studies.

Four of the subjects (Wm., Huf., Ben., Ha.) were trained singers of some experience; four of them (To., Ow., Mo., Bah) were partly trained, and three of them (Ba., An., Y.) had had no training at all. The subject whose records of calling are reproduced (Cu, fig. s, 5, 8, 12, 15, 19, 24) does not sing at all. There are minor peculiarities, but distinct types of coordination appear, and the records from the different subjects corroborate each other; they are consistent.

A COMPARISON OF THE FUNDAMENTAL COORDINATIONS IN SPEAKING AND IN SINGING

Before speaking a "breath" is taken through the mouth and nose; the chest is slightly inflated but there is no sense of fullness or of strain. As the person speaks the syllables are grouped into short "breath-groups" during which the thoracic and abdominal muscles are slightly fixated. These groups do not involve intake of breath in every case; rather they are brief fixations for the organization of the movements involved; the grouping itself is due to the single large movement which appears in the general form of the movement curve for the group. When breath is taken during speech, it is taken rapidly between these "breath groups".

These groups of speech are seldom longer than six or eight syllables and they may be as short as one or two syllables; the muscles relax between the groups and the air-pressure in the chest falls to zero. In repeating syllables at low speed, the pressure falls to zero between each isolated syllable, and a steady tension and a steady pressure do not appear until the speed of the series has increased to 3-4 per sec.[4]

At speeds higher than 3-4 per sec. there is a continuing fixation of both thoracic and abdominal muscles, with a slight increase of air-pressure in the chest. The fixation does not involve high pressure, and it is possible to maintain the fixations of high-speed speech without any positive pressure in the chest; but to produce the requisite puffs of air for the syllables at high speed it is essential to have the air under slight pressure, as well as to have the muscles of the chest and abdomen fixated so that there is a support for the rapid chest-pulse movements which produce the pulses of the syllables.

In speech the rectus abdominis and the laterals (obliques and transversalis) work together as a unit and the contraction of the rectus determines the "abdominal support" in the sense of a progressive changing fixation against which the chest pulses play. Tracings from the rectus abdominis are adequate as a record of the abdominal movements of speech.[5]

In singing the fixation of the type in high-speed speech appears immediately; upon taking a breath and singing a scale softly and legato the chest and abdomen at once assume a posture like that of speech at high speed. Cf. fig.s, 1, 2, 3.

The abdominal muscles are kept poised and adjusted to the decreasing chest volume so as to make possible the rapid chest pulse for each note. The abdominal action is mainly supporting for the individual pulses (notes;) this slow respiratory movement is the main element in phrasing.

The "breath-group" in singing is longer than in speaking; the scale of eight notes is always sung as a single group, and groups of sixteen or more notes are very common. Cf. fig. 4

The fixation does not mean high air-pressure in the chest. It is easy to take a full breath for singing and yet hold the chest and abdomen in a position which leaves the air-pressure in the chest quite neutral. This is easily demonstrated by taking a normal breath for singing, and while maintaining the fixation, opening the glottis and drawing a little air in and out of the lungs in a panting action. It is evident that the pressure in the chest shifts from positive to negative in such a movement and that it passes through the neutral point at each change from expiration to inspiration and back again. Cf. fig. 5 .

All the movements of singing are executed from this posture of slight fixation. The individual notes are made by a chest pulse which occurs in the musculature of the chest, probably in the intercostal muscles; the note and the syllable are identical. Both occur so rapidly at high speed that it is impossible for the abdominal muscles or for the larger chest muscles to execute them.

Accentuation often shows in the contraction of abdominal muscles; this reinforces the chest pulse but does not replace it. The striking thing in legato

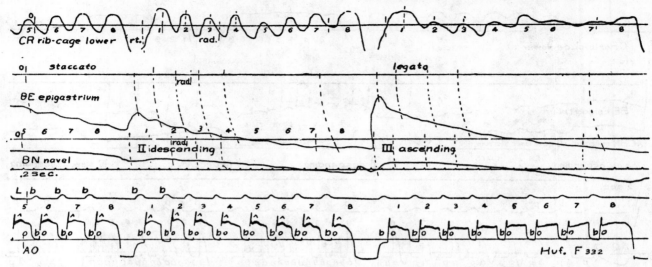

Figure 1. Orig. 35 x 15 cm. Singing scale with syl. "bo". Standing. Trained singer.

CR, Chest pulse, neg. press applicator, rib-cage, lower right: The phrases show a pronounced tension throughout, both the staccato and the legato. The pulses of the staccato phrases I and II are rather more marked than in the legato of III.

BE, Abdominal movement, boss, epigastrum: Phrases I and II are grouped together; the inception of the new phrase of II well defined, but the general recession of the epigastric region goes on throughout the two phrases. There is a slight pulse parallel with the chest pulse, but it is in phase showing that during the gradual descent of the rib-cage and the recession of the abdomen, the rectus abdominis is leading the abdominal musculature.

BN, Abdominal movement, boss, navel: There is a slow and steady recession of the navel region during the entire four phrases of the record (of which this excerpt shows only part). This slow inward movement is broken by the readjustments for the phrases, slight at the opening of II, and more pronounced at III. But the entire movement represents a slow change of posture rather than a breathing movement.

L, Lip movement: There are some variations in the length of the consonant; the first and the last consonants of the phrase tend to be more pronounced.

AO, Air pressure outside mouth: The accent of the staccato shows in each note of I and II, though in I, as often, the last notes of the phrase have the legato form. The vocalization immediately following the detente of the consonant is characteristic of the syl. with releasing consonant. In III the maintenance of the level of pressure throughout, though the line is broken by consonants, is striking; after notes 1, 2, it is very marked.

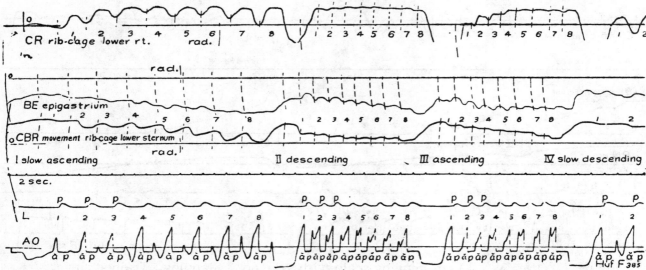

Figure 2. Orig. 34 x 16 cm. Singing scale with syl. "ap". Standing. Trained singer.

CR, Chest pulse, neg. press. applicator, rib-cage, lower right: Both the slow and rapid scale passages show the continuing tension for the entire phrase; it is more obvious for the rapid scales. In the rapid scales II, III, the tension is so high that the applicator barely responds.

BE, Abdominal movement, boss, epigastrium: Movements occur in the slow scales, and are more marked in the rapid scales II, III. Although II is a descending scale and III a rising scale there is little difference in the general form.

CBR, Movement of the rib-cage, boss, lower sternum: The sharp descent of the curve for each chest pulse is clear both in the slow and rapid scales; since it is the descent of the rib-cage which marks the pulse, the curve is in opposite phase to the chest-pulse curve, CR.

AO, Air pressure outside mouth: The sharp slant of the pressure curve in each syl. in I and IV is striking and characteristic of staccato. This is less true of the rapid scales II, III. At high speed the distinction between staccato and legato is lost. There is a frequent intake of air between the notes in the slow scales; but nothing of the sort is possible in the course of the rapid scales.

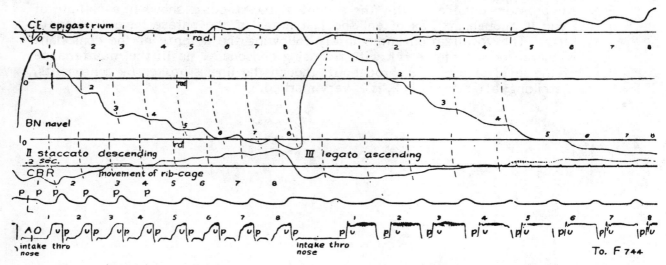

Figure 3. Orig. 35 x 15 cm. Singing staccato scale with syl. "up", legato scale with syl "pu". Standing. Partly trained singer.

CE, Chest pulse, neg. press. applicator, epigastrium: The pulses are sharper and more definite for the staccato than for the legato passage.

BN, Abdominal movement; boss, navel: Very large excursion of the breathing movements of the epigastrium; the breath is handled from the epigastric region. Definite pulses for each note, but the movements are inward, showing that the lateral muscles are primary in the movement.

CBR, Movement of rib-cage, boss, lower sternum: During phrase II the rib-cage actually expands. During III there is something the same movement. There are some indications of movements for the separate notes.

L, Lip movements: Consonants are long and vigorous. The lips are closed as if for double between the phrases, and the subject breathes through his nose at close of phrases I, II, etc.

AO, Air pressure outside mouth: The rapid rise in each syl. and the accent in the vocalization show the staccato type in II. In III singing "pu" legato, the uniform level of breath pressure is nicely maintained.

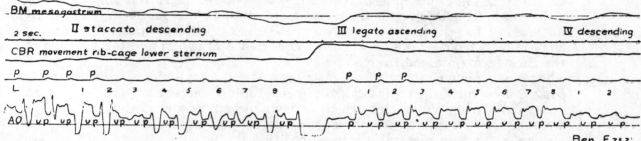

Figure 4. Orig. 35 x 8 cm. Singing scale with syl. "up". Staccato and legato. Trained singer.

BM. Abdominal movement, boss, mesogastrium: A gradual descent in II, though it is a staccato phrase, and there is some intake of breath during phrase. Individual movements of syl.s are not marked, and the descent is slight. During the legato, III, the mesogastric region shows little change. There is no break in the phrasing between I and II or between III and IV; each ascent-descent of the scale is handled as a unit.

CBR, Movement of rib-cage, boss, lower sternum: During the staccato scale II, the rib-cage is fixated throughout. This is associated with the intake of air during phrase, cf. AO below. In III, legato, there is expansion of the rib-cage at opening of phrase followed by a slight but definite, slow recession; there is no intake during the phrase.

AO, Air pressure outside mouth: The arresting function of the consonants is plain in II; the consonants vary as to the amount of air pressure behind them; in general they tend to be fairly light; the forms are varied and the line is irregular. There is a frequent intake of breath between the notes. In III the legato is plain. The average pressure is higher; the vowel begins immediately after the consonant, showing that the "up" has become "pu". There is no intake of air during the phrase, and the legato character shows in the uniformity of the pressure line especially notes 4-8.

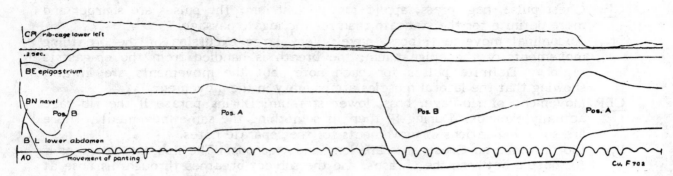

Figure 5. Orig. 61.5 x 15 cm. Neutral air-pressure maintained while the abdominal position is shifted from the normal position, A, to position B in which the abdomen is drawn in by the primary contraction of the lateral muscles.

CR,   Chest pulse, neg. press. applicator, rib-cage, lower left: The slight panting movements which drive air back and forth through the glottis are evidently initiated in the chest. The tensions in the chest shift from post. A to pos. B and are higher during pos. B when the abdomen is drawn in and the fixation of the chest is maintained from above.

BE,   Abdominal movement, boss, epigastrium: After a preliminary adjustment in pos. B in which the epigastrium moves rapidly outward there is a slow recession during the series which is undisturbed by the change to pos. A. When pos. B is assumed for the second time, the epigastrium recedes rather suddenly and then maintains a fixed position through the change back to pos. A. In all these changes the fact that air is being drawn back and forth through the glottis (AO) shows that there is no increase or decrease in air-pressure; the movements are due to changing fixations.

BN,   Abdominal movement, boss, navel: After the drawing in for pos. B the navel region is rapidly distended nearly to the normal position; only a slight change occurs when pos. A is assumed. When pos. B is assumed the seond time the change to nearly the normal position is very gradual after the drawing in; there is a pronounced distension of the region when the normal position if finally assumed.

BL,   Abdominal movement, boss, lower abdomen: movement is fairly regular, lower abdomen is drawn in during position B, and allowed to assume normal position during pos. A; the navel and lower abdominal levels tend to move together, though there may be independent action, as in second pos. B.

AO,   Air movement through mouth: The curve represents the drawing of air back and forth through the glottis to verify the equilibrium in the chest pressure. It is to be noted that the slight panting movement ceases during the actual shifts of position.

singing, whether fast or slow, forte or piano, is the absence of any such accentuation from the abdominal muscles.

THE MECHANISM OF BREATHING IN SINGING

When breath is taken for singing the rib-cage rises and expands by the familiar upward and outward movements of the ribs which are articulated to the spinal column and flexibly attached at the sternum. The diaphram lowers the floor of the thorax by a contraction dependent on the fixation of the rib-cage to the lower border of which the diaphram is attached.

It is sometimes said that the chest remains inflated, fixated, during the singing of a phrase, after a moderate breath has been taken. The inflation and slight tension in the chest walls is important for the production of the tone; in part because it makes possible the delicate changes of pressure of the outgoing air at the glottis for the control of the pulses and of the pitch; in part perhaps because the resonance of the singing tone is affected. The slight tension of the chest walls is maintained, as the chest-pulse tracings show, Cf. fig.s 6 and 7.

But there is nevertheless a steady recession of the rib-cage; this is apparent in tracings of the rib-cage taken with bosses or directly with threads attached to the chest wall. The gradual recession is plain. Cf. fig.s 2, 4, 8.

At the same time in several of the tracings the chest-pulse stroke shows in the movement of the rib-cage. Cf. fig. 2. It is a sharp, balistic stroke downward and inward followed by the slower relaxation phase; this stroke is synchronous with the chest pulse which is the wave of disturbance resulting from the movement. This rib-cage stroke appears in the tracings as in "opposite phase" to the chest pulse, but it constitutues the sudden contraction which produces the chest pulse. The recession of the rib-cage as a whole is clearly a slow movement, a changing fixation upon which are superposed the balistic movements of the individual strokes for each note (syllable).

The principal muscle of the abdomen is the heavy, two-columned rectus abdominis which extends from the public arch to the lower edge of the rib-cage; as it approaches the rib-cage it spreads fanwise to the ribs and sternum. The lateral muscles are made up of the two layers of the obliques and of the transversalis which are attached to the rib-cage, to the pelvis, or indirectly to the spinal column. These lateral muscles extend to the vertical columns of the rectus abdominis completing the walls of the abdomen.

The abdominal muscles and especially the rectus have to do with the fixation of the rib-cage. While the rib-cage is lifted and fixated by the scalenes, serrati, and the external intercostals, the rib-cage is drawn down by the abdominal muscles and their antagonism serves to fixate firmly the rib-cage for the action of the diaphram and of the internal intercostals.

The general contraction of the abdominal muscles draws down the rib-cage in deflation and expiration. Cf. fig. 2. And this general contraction of the abdominal muscles forces up the diaphram by pressure on the viscera; this action is sometimes called "the abdominal press".

TWO FUNDAMENTAL COORDINATIONS OF THE ABDOMINAL MUSCULATURE WITH THE THORACIC MUSCALATURE

The first coordination, the normal position.

In ordinary breathing in both singing and speaking, the abdominal walls expand, bulge, as the breath is taken and recede as the breath is expended. Cf. fig.s 9, 10, and 11.

It often happens that the first intake of breath does not involve a large outward abdominal movement; but with the gradual recession during the phrase sung, the abdominal wall will have receded beyond normal so that the breaths taken between phrases involve a pronounced expansion of the abdominal wall.

In breathing and phrasing of this general type, the rectus abdominis and the laterals work together just as in the usual form of abdominal action in speaking. It is probable that the movement is one of general contraction, though it does not result in a recession of the abdominal wall for each individual note or figure; instead each of these separate pulses is actually outward, and produces a bulging of the abdominal wall both in the rectus abdominis and in the lateral muscles. Cf. fig.s 12, 13, and 14.

The rectus leads in the contraction, bulging for each abdominal pulse because the heavy bellied muscle thickens both inward and outward, as it shortens and reduces the volume of the abdomen and draws down the rib-cage. The laterals contract in unison, evidently, but the pressure from the contracting rectus and their own thickening as they shorten result in outward movement for each abdominal pulse as often recorded in speech, in calling, and in singing.[6] Cf. fig.s 1, 14, and 15.

This slight outward movement for each note or figure at slow speed is accompanied by a gradual recession of the entire abdominal wall. In the slowly changing fixation the rib-cage descends and the diaphram arches higher and higher as the viscera move gradually upward and the volume of the thorax is reduced.

These abdominal pulses for each note or figure can occur only at moderate tempi. As soon as the speed increases, the abdominal wall becomes tense, and there is a slow, controlled movement of recession with little indication of separate pulses. This seems to be the common form of legato singing; the ideal toward which many singers strive. Cf. fig.s 16 and 17.

Just as the maximum breath in singing does not mean air-pressure in the chest, but rather an expanded rib-cage and large chest volume, so the descent of the rib-cage and the slow recession of the abdominal wall do not mean a steady pressure on the air in the chest. In speaking and in singing the fundamental function of the chest-abdominal coordination is not to expel air and still less to keep up an even pressure at the glottis or articulatory organs. Instead the abdominal musculature maintains a slowly changing chest-abdominal posture nicely adjusted so that the separate notes (or syllables) may be produced by the chest pulse acting against this slight tension of the posture to produce the separate expiratory puffs of air. It is essential that the rib-cage be somewhat fixated for the action of the rapid intercostal muscles which produce the chest pulses. The abdominal walls, the viscera and the diaphram must be under a certain tension to resist the pulse of air, so that it may run as a well-defined wave of compression through the glottis. This slowly changing posture with the descent and deflation of the chest may carry through a long phrase or section and lead to an indrawn position of the abdomen which is more than normal. Cf. fig.s 1 and 18.

At rapid tempi and with some singers at all rates, there may be a slight continuous air-pressure in the chest; this is indicated by the steady tension in the chest wall. Cf. fig. 6 and is clearly seen in rapid speech in tracings of the air-pressure in the chest taken from a tracheotomized subject.[7]

In this normal form of breathing the definite antagonism is between the rib-cage with its fixations plus the diaphram whose contraction tends to increase the chest volume on the one hand, and the abdominal muscles as a group on the other hand, contraction of which tends to draw down the rib-cage, force up the diaphram by pressure on the viscera and deflate the thorax. This antagonism may be developed into a powerful fixation, which does not however bring pressure to bear

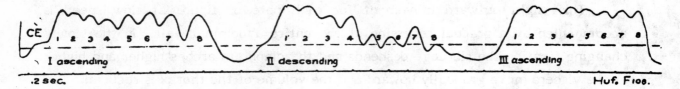

Figure 6. Orig. 35 x 5 cm. Singing scale with syl. "ah". Trained singer.

CE, Chest pulse, neg. press. applicator, epigastrum: Individual notes clearly marked. The grouping and the general tension throughout the phrase are evident; the elevation of the tracing marks a continuous pressure in the chest. Dynamic variations in the phrases are apparent. Phrase III is at fairly high speed, 5-5 per sec.; it is followed by three other phrases at 5.5, 6, and 7 per sec. which all show the same dynamic form, a uniform high level of pressure.

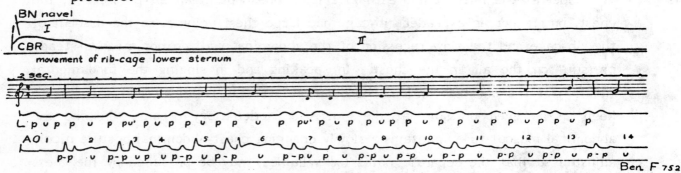

Figure 7. Orig. 35 x 9 cm. Singing 'pup' to mel. "Materna". Standing. Trained singer.

BN, Abdominal movement, boss, navel: A slight gradual recession during phrase I is followed by complete repose during phrase II.

CBR, Movement of rib-cage, boss, lower sternum: A slight expansion at the beginning is followed by a very slight and very gradual recession throughout the two phrases; very little movement indeed.

L, Lip movement: The doubles are clearly indicated, but they are distinct and have not quite fused. There is some indication of fusion, 8-9, 9-10, 12-13. The arresting consonant drops in the rapid notes 3 and 7, and in each case the following releasing consonant is prolonged.

AO, Air pressure outside mouth: Tracing is rather light. The puffs of air between the doublets is very clear, and often relatively high pressure shows behind the doubling consonant. The form is in general legato.

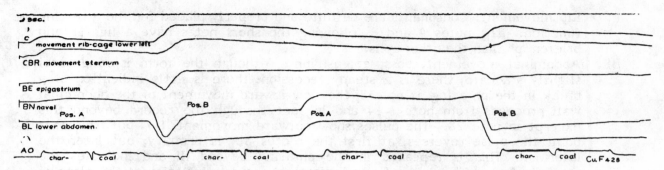

Figure 8. Orig. 61.5 x 15 cm. Calling the word "Charcoal" with changes from the normal position A, to the position B with the abdomen drawn in by the primary contraction of the lateral muscles. The tracings give a direct record of the actual amount of movement.

C,   Movement of the rib-cage recorded from thread attached to the lower left: The chest is slightly dilated during pos. B.

CBR, Movement of the sternum recorded from thread attached: Parallels the movement of the rib-cage, but the excursion is not as large.

BE, Abdominal movement, thread attached to epigastrium: Pronounced change when pos. B is first assumed, but there is no change at the resumption of pos. A, and the change when pos. B is assumed for the second time is only slight.

BN, Abdominal movement, thread attached at navel level:

BL, Abdominal movement, thread attached to lower abdomen: Movements are parallel and show the pronounced drawing-in prescribed by pos. B.

AO, Air pressure outside mouth: The calling tone is apparent in the regular vibrations. The articulation of the "I" shows at the end of the word.

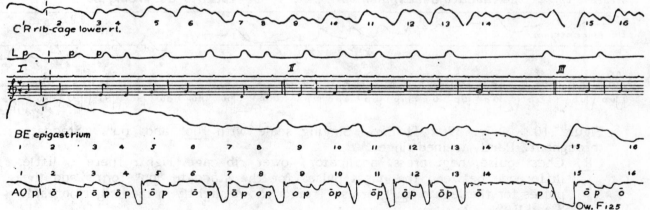

Figure 9. Orig. 35 x 12 cm. Singing syl. "ope" to mel. "Materia". Tremor very apparent. Slightly trained singer.

CR, Chest pulse, neg. press. applicator, rib-cage lower right: Pulses for the notes are clearly marked, except in the short notes 3, 4 and 7, 8 where the marked tremor obscures the division in the group. The slight pulse for the final "p" in note 14 is apparent.

The tremor in a series of notes 7-12, e.g. is marked enough so that it is easy to determine the rate, c. 7 per sec. The very apparent tremor of the long note 14 is at the same rate.

L,   Lip movement: Consonants are definite and properly placed for the arresting function. The notes 4 and 8 following the short notes have a lighter and briefer "p" than the other syl.s.

BE,   Abdominal movement, boss, epigastrium: Although the form is in general slightly staccato, there is a steady recession; there is little indication of a break in the phrasing at note 8; the slow inward movement of the abdominal wall proceeds from note I-14 and in fact through the record beyond this excerpt to note 28. The pulses show outward movement, I-7, but from that point the pulse reverses; at first the rectus ab. is primary, but later the laterals. This is repeated in the phrasing beyond III and indicates the staccato form. There is definite indication of a new inflation at the close of III. Tremor is apparent 9-13 and marked in 14; c. 7 per sec.

AO,   Air pressure outside mouth: The level of pressure is fairly even but broken at 7, 9, 11, e.g. by slight staccato pulses. There are frequent intakes of air, 4, 6, etc. which become more frequent at close of long phrase. The "p"s of notes 4, and 8 have very little pressure; in general the pressure on the consonants is light, although the arresting form is preserved. This light pressure on the consonant makes the pressure level more uniform than it could be with a heavy releasing consonant.
Vibrato, 7 per sec., evident in note 14.

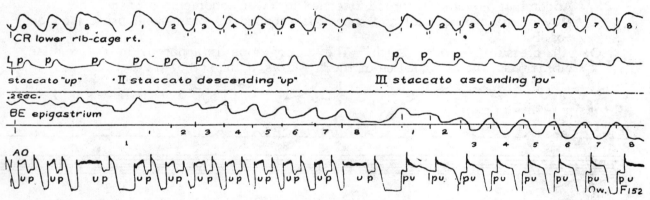

Figure 10. Orig. 35 x 11 cm. Singing scale with "up" and "pu". Staccato throughout. Partly trained singer.

CR,   Chest pulse, neg. press. applicator, lower rib-cage, right: There is little difference between the chest pulses for the staccato "up" forms and the pulses for the legato "pu" forms. Tremor shows slightly in the longer notes, I, 8 and II, 8.

L,   Lip movement: The lip movements are well defined. The arresting "p"s at the end of the longer notes, I, 8 and II, 8 are in the normal position and there is no tendency at this tempo to add an accessory pulse for the final "p".

BE,   Abdominal movement, boss, epigastrium: The indeterminate form of the curve at the close of phrase I is due to the change from a coordination in which the rectus ab. leads, to the later form in which the curve is in reverse to the chest-pulse tracing, showing that the laterals lead. This is the common form of coordination for staccato delivery.

AO, Air pressure outside mouth: In the form "up" the arresting consonants are very clearly indicated and there is considerable residual pressure at the detente. The "pu" forms on the other hand show the releasing consonant with a sharp accent on the beginning of the syl. and a striking decrease of pressure during the syl. Where the arresting form involves a sharp rise of pressure culminating at the "p", the releasing syl. when staccato shows a sharp maximum at the detente with a uniform and rapid decrease throughout the syl. In nearly all cases there is an intake of breath between the syl.s. The longest notes show the "vibrato".

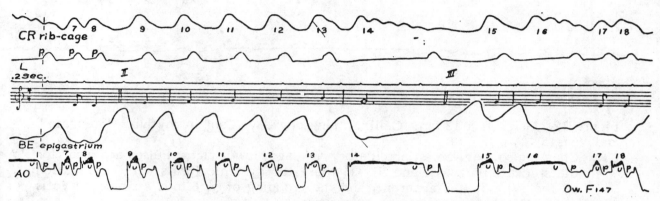

Figure 11. Orig. 35 x 11 cm. Singing "up" to mel. "Materna". Slightly trained singer.

CR, Chest pulse, neg. press. applicator, rib-cage, lower right: Notes 7, 8 and 17, 18 show the usual grouping of the short note with the following long note. Tremor is very obvious in 6, 14, 16, 7.5 per sec., apparent only in the longer notes.

BE, Abdominal movement, boss, epigastrium: The form is definitely staccato; energetic contractions for each note pulse, with the laterals leading; the rectus ab. is drawn in with each pulse. The pulses are obviously in reverse to the CR tracing. The pulses for the short note have nearly fused with that of the long, 7, 8 and 17, 18.

AO, Air pressure outside mouth: Short notes at the beginning of the phrases have staccato form. Intake of breath between each note in phrase II. Pressure on the arresting consonant rather light. Tremor (vibrato) apparent in the long notes, c. 7-5 per sec.

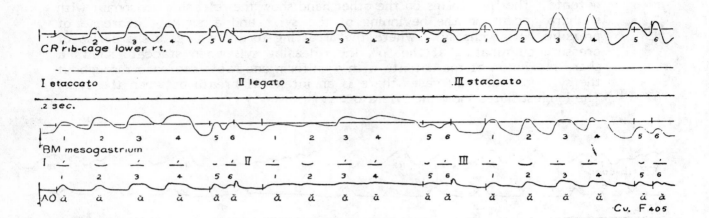

Figure 12. Orig. 34 x 12 cm. Calling, "singsong", syl. "ah" in rhythm. "Staccato", and "legato".

CR, Chest pulse, neg. press, applicator, rib-cage, lower right: Pulses are clear for the staccato phrases I and III. In these the dynamic forms with culmination on the syl.s 3, 4 is apparent, and the grouping of 5, 6 into a single curve is plain. Cf. short notes in singing records.
In II, "legato", the force is much less. The pulses can be made out, with the climax on 3, and 5, 6. There is a slight tension through the entire phrase which is not apparent in I, and III.

BM, Abdominal movement, boss, mesogastrium: Pronounced movements for each syl. In both the "staccato" and the "legato" the general contraction led by the rectus ab. is obvious; the outward bulges correspond to the chest pulses above. Again there seems to be a slight tension of the abdominal muscles throughout the "legato" phrase, II.

AO, Air pressure outside mouth: The "staccato" syl.s show more force but no sharp accents. The "legato" phrase, II, is very uniform indeed, with sustained vocalization throughout. It is interesting to note that there is a sharp rise in pressure after the last syl. 6, of each phrase, I, II, III, due apparently to release of a glottal stop.

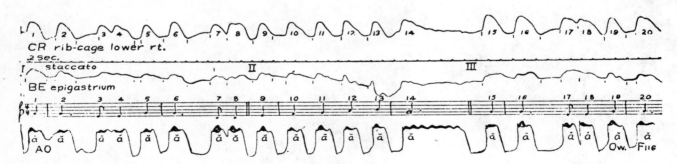

Figure 13. Orig. 35 x 8 cm. Singing "ah" to mel. "Ital. Hymn". Staccato. Slightly trained singer.

CR, Chest pulse, neg. press. applicator, rib-cage, lower right: Pulses for notes clearly marked. The short notes at 3-4, 7-8, 17-18 tend to form groups with the following notes, though the pulses are distinct. There is little continuous pressure during the phrases; as in speaking, the pressure returns to zero after each note or note-group. Tremor is marked, note 14. c. 8 per sec.

BE, Abdominal movement, boss, epigastrium: The separate notes are indicated by an outward thrust, which indicates primary contraction of the rectus ab., with the exception of notes 12, 13, where the curve reverses, the lateral musculature leads and the rectus ab. is slightly drawn in.

Notes 3-4 and 17-18 have nearly fused to a single pulse for the group. Notes 21-22, not shown in this excerpt have become a single pulse. This is inevitable as the speed of the chest pulse increases.

There is little indication of any gradual recession of the abdominal wall; the posture is maintained as often in "staccato" passages; this is associated with the intake of air during phrase, cf. AO below. Tremor shows plainly, notes 3-23, and 14.

AO, Air pressure outside mouth: The staccato character of the passage shows in the sharp and sudden pulses of the air and of the vibrations. In most cases there is an intake of breath between the notes; notes 1, 2 show but a slight relaxation of pressure; there is no intake at 3, 4 or 7, 8; but there is a momentary inhalation, 17, 18. Vibrato in note 14. c. 8 per sec.

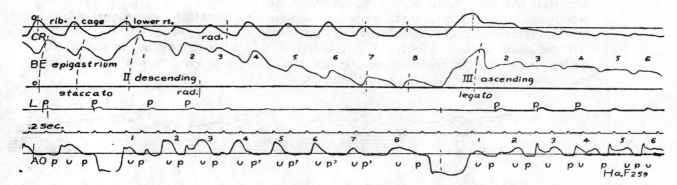

Figure 14. Orig. 35 x 9 cm. Singing scales with syl. "up", staccato and legato. Trained singer.

CR, Chest pulse, neg. press. applicator, rib-cage, lower right: The pulses are better defined for staccato, II, than for legato, III.

BE, Abdominal movement, boss, epigastrium: The action of the abdominal muscles is in phase with the chest pulse; the rectus ab. is leading and the outward movement of the entire abdominal wall occurs with each pulse, both staccato and legato.

L, Lip movement: The "p"s are rather faint strokes in the staccato parts, but are definite in the legato parts.

AO, Air pressure outside mouth: In the staccato portion, I and II there is very little pressure on the "p"s; it is doubtful if the consonant functions II 4-8; the lip stroke is very faint; the outside air shows no residual pressure at the detente. As the legato appears, III, the syl. is changed to "pu", the air pressure for the consonant is marked, and the lip movement corresponds.

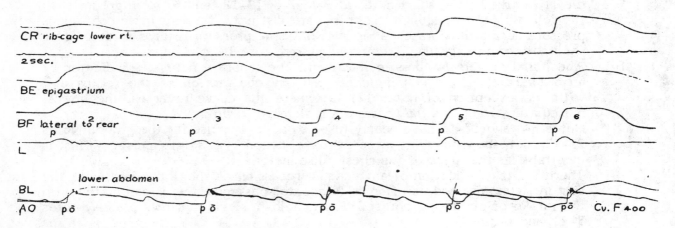

Figure 15. Orig. 34 x 12 cm. Calling syl. "pu".

CR, Chest pulse, neg. press, applicator, rib-cage, lower right: The ascent of the curve is sharply marked for the balistic stroke, but the tension is maintained for some. 4 sec. for each syl.

BE, Abdominal movement, boss, epigastrium: The tracing parallels the chest pulse, showing a primary movement of the rectus ab.

BF, Abdominal movement, boss, rear, flank: Bos applied to muscles in the back, parallels the movement of the rectus ab. in BE.

BL, Abdominal movement, boss, lower abdomen: The parallel movement of the lower abdominal region indicates the contractions of the rectus ab.

AO, Air pressure outside mouth: The prolonged syl. with releasing consonant is ended by a sudden release of air as the glottis opens, but there is no indication of breathing between the syl.s.

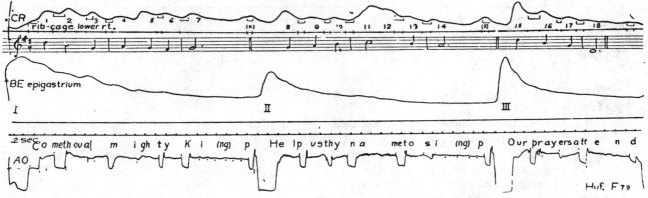

Figure 16. Orig. 35 x 12 cm. Singing words to mel. "Ital. Hymn". "Come Thou almighty Ki(ng)p - Help us Thy name to si(ng)p - Our prayers attend". "p" substituted for "ng" to mark the close of the long note. Trained singer.

CR, Chest pulse, neg. press. applicator, rib-cage, lower right: The notes are clearly marked, and there is indication of the dynamic changes; maximum is on notes 1 and 2 in phrase I, on 11-12 in phrase II, and on note 15 in phrase III. An accessory note at the close of the long notes, 7, 14, is clearly marked to give the arresting "p" its function; "nd" of note 18 also has a slight pulse but not so marked. Slight indications of tremor in notes 7, 14.

BE, Abdominal movement, boss, epigastrium: Some slight response to the individual notes, but in the main there is a steady recession of the abdominal wall, showing that the abdominal wall is receding with the contraction of the rectus ab., with the lateral muscles in synergy. The phrasing is clear and the movements uniform.

AO, Air pressure outside mouth: The consonants show clearly; even the "m", 3-4, and the "s", 13-14, and "rs", 16-17 are clearly articulated and interrupt the breath stream. The level of a normal legato is maintained throughout. Breathing is clearly marked, through the mouth. Note 5 shows the vibrato clearly, c. 5 per sec., rather slow.

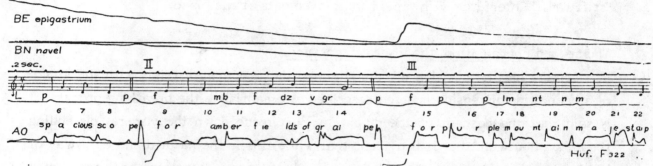

Figure 17. Orig. 35 x 11 cm. Singing modified words to mel. "Materna". Standing. Trained singer.

BE, Abdominal movement, boss, epigastrium: Although there is a phrase change at note 8, 9, the abdominal movement is continuous from I to II, indicating that as often happens the two phrases are grouped together in a movement for the section, note I-14. At 14, 15 there is a readjustment for phrase III.

BN, Abdominal movement, boss, navel: There is a very slow, steady recession of the abdomen at the navel level, broken by a slight readjustment, note 8, 9 and 14, 15. The change at 22, 23 is slightly more pronounced but the slow recession continues to the end of the record, 23-29 not shown in excerpt.

AO, Air pressure outside mouth: The general legato form is clear, breath is taken between the phrases. The consonants are well defined and the occlusives show definite pressure at the detente.

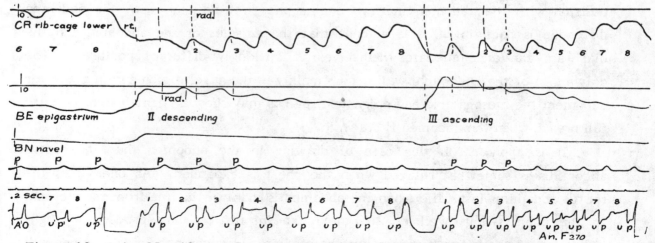

Figure 18. Orig. 35 x 13 cm. Singing scale with syl. "up". Untrained singer.

CR, Chest pulse, neg. press. applicator, rib-cage, lower right: Pulses are pronounced. Tendency for the tension to rise during the course of the phrase.

on the air in the lungs, although it does make a very tense chest-abdominal posture. When the subject has developed such a powerful fixation, it is possible to draw air back and forth through the glottis and demonstrate that there is neutral air-pressure in the chest in spite of the vigorous contractions.

Such an undue fixation of the muscles of the chest and abdomen is apparent in some forms of stammering in which the vocal canal is open, and yet the subject finds it difficult to execute a rapid series of syllables, especially with chest arrest; the powerful contraction interferes with the rapid balistic movement, just as the "stiff wrist" interferes with rapid hand movements at the piano.

The second coordination, the in-drawn position.

In the normal position discussed above the abdomen distends with the intake of air, and this distension is often described as essential to the breathing process; it is said that the descent of the diaphram must force down the viscera, distending the abdominal wall. But it is evident that while this is the natural and easy way of inspiration that it is not the only way. Lilli Lehmann describes the method of a horn player whom she consulted as to breathing in sustained phrases.[8]   He suggested the following procedure: draw in the abdominal muscles as much as possible and in that position take a full breath, then close the glottis and let the abdominal muscles out to their normal position. A trial will convince one that a full breath may be taken in that position; and moreover even if a maximum breath has been taken (far more than one would take in singing) one will find that after the abdominal muscles are returned to the normal position it is impossible to draw in much more air. The difference between the maximum capacity in the second position with the abdomen indrawn and in the first position with the abdomen distended is negligible. It is evident that the muscles of the abdomen and the diaphram can accommodate themselves to strikingly different postures. The drawing in of the abdominal wall occurs mainly in the navel region and in the lower abdomen; the mesogastric and epigastric regions may show a slight distension with full breath when the abdomen is drawn in.

It is apparent in this case of drawing in the abdomen that the rectus abdominis is somewhat relaxed when the chest is expanded. As one views the rectus abdominis in profile when the abdomen is indrawn the line from the sternum to the pubis swings well in; the maximum inspiration may produce a slight distension of the upper abdomen but the median and lower abdominal regions will be decidedly indrawn with only a slight swing outward of the rectus as it joins the pubic arch. This concave bowing in of the rectus must be due to the primary action of the lateral muscles; they actually draw the rectus in. The rectus abdominis is always somewhat contracted for it is a muscle of thrunk posture in sitting and especially in standing, but it must be pliant enough to yield to the lateral muscles. When a maximum breath has been taken with the abdomen indrawn and a slight panting movement is made drawing air in and out the glottis, the rib-cage remains fixated and the most obvious movement is in the upper abdominal region. This is due to the action of the lateral muscles reciprocating with the diaphram, for a contraction of the abdominal wall in that position must be due solely to the laterals; a primary contraction of the rectus would of course pull the abdominal outward, not inward. In this panting action it is apparent that the lateral muscles are capable of fairly rapid movements which have to do with the changing volume of the chest and the expulsion of air through the glottis.

The independence of the navel- and lower abdominal regions during the action of the chest in breathing is strikingly illustrated by the fact that a syllable may be repeated while the abdomen is being drawn in and again distended. Cf. fig.s 5, 8 and 19.

In such cases it is significant that the epigastric region shows a steady uniform recession; it is compensating for the change of volume in the chest. As the rib-cage is fixated as a whole, it is certain that the primary contraction of the lateral muscles is slowly forcing the diaphram upward, while the small muscles of the chest execute the individual pulses for each note (syllable). In fig. 20 the tracings for slow movements show that the displacement of the epigastric region cannot be due to the action of the thoracic muscles. The bulging of the epigastric muscles occurs between the rib-cage pulses. The chest pulse precedes the epigastric contraction by .4 sec. The epigastric region actually drives inward for the chest pulses and relaxes between the chest pulses. (On the tracing the rise of the curve indicates movement outward and the descent of the curve indicates movement inward.) This is the proper coordination since the contraction of the laterals in this position results in a movement inward which reduces the thoracic volume and accentuates the rib-cage stroke of the chest pulse. The curves of the chest pulse (CR) and of the epigastric musculature (BE) are apparently in "opposite phase", but the action of the chestpulse musculature and of the epigastric muscles is synergic.

It sometimes happens that the movement in "opposite phase" does not occur until the end of the phrase, when the conditions change and the laterals lead, causing a "reversal of phase", i.e. a movement inward, instead of outward, for each note. Cf. fig.s 10, 13, 18, 21.

This is probably a normal coordination showing in all powerful accentuation, so that vigorous staccato or sforzando involve this action of the abdominal laterals to reinforce the note. But it is difficult to get trained singers who know that tracings are being made of their singing to give such accented notes. Even when sharp and accented staccato is prescribed, there is a decided tendency to maintain a cautious, smooth, "legato" type of breathing which they believe to be the "true" breathing in singing. A slight primary movement of the lateral abdominal muscles is sometimes perceptible in the singing of the trained subjects (Huf., Ha., To., Wm.) but it is always slight unless powerful accentuation is demanded.

It is not possible to have such accentuation at rates of execution faster than 3-4 per sec. which is the maximum speed for the lateral muscles. At this rate staccato and legato must be indistinguishable, and the abdominal musculature sets with a slowly changing fixation. Cf. fig. 22.

In the singing of melodies it is often the case that the principal notes, especially if they are sung to syllables with arresting consonants, show a definite abdominal movement. But wherever the movement of the figure is too rapid the abdominal movement will be a single movement for two or more chest pulses (individual notes). Cf. fig.s 13 and 22.

PHRASING AND ITS RELATIONS TO BREATHING IN SINGING

It is a commonplace that the phrasing of singing depends on the breathing; if necessary the musical phrase may be broken for an intake of breath, and in some forms of staccato singing there is a slight intake before each note, but the normal phrase is marked and made by the slow continuous breathing movement. The phrase is a slowly changing chest-abdominal posture, a slow movement of expiration. There is a slow descent of the chest, and a recession of the abdominal wall (during which however the individual notes may appear as ripples of outward movement) until the end of the phrase. At that point a rapid movement of inspiration with compensatory movements of the abdominal wall restores the chest to the inflated position.

BE, Abdominal movement, boss, epigastrium: The pulses reverse the form of the curve in opposite phase to the chest pulse; the lateral muscles are leading and drawing in the rectus ab. Phrasing movement is normal.

BN, Abdominal movement, boss, navel: Only a slight readjustment of the navel region at the beginning of phrase. In general the musculature at this level is fixated.

AO, Air pressure outside mouth: Forms are a mixture of staccato, II, 1, 2, and most of III, and of legato forms, II, 4-8.

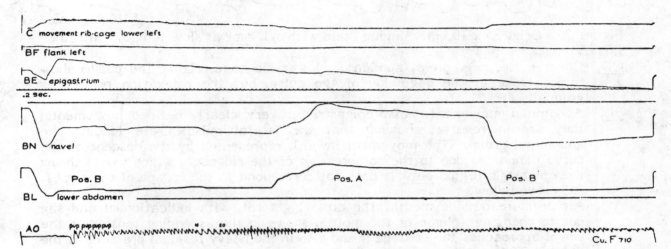

Figure 19. Orig. 61.5 x 22 cm. Repeating the syl. "pup" at high speed during changes from the normal position, A, to pos. B with abdomen drawn in by the primary action of the lateral muscles. The tracings give a direct record of the actual amount of movement.

C, Movement of the rib-cage recorded from thread attached to the lower left: There is but little change in the position of the chest throughout.

BF, Movement of the abdominal flank recorded from thread. No movement apparent.

BE, Abdominal movement, thread attached to the epigastrium: After readjustment at the beginning of pos. B there is little or no abrupt change. The slow recession is evidently the movement which supplies the steady support for the rapid chest pulses. The very gradual and continuous descent of the epigastrium is the striking thing in the record.

BN, Abdominal movement, thread attached at navel level.

BL, Abdominal movement, thread attached to lower abdomen. Movements are parallel and show the pronounced drawing in prescribed by pos. B.

AO, Air pressure outside mouth: "Pup" is at first repeated fairly slowly and then increased to high speed. The separate "p" strokes are apparent and also a few doubles, syl. 16-20 before the form "pu', pu'.." appears. There are slight readjustments during the long series, but they are not pronounced and they do not appear during the shifts from pos. A to pos. B. The series is continuous.

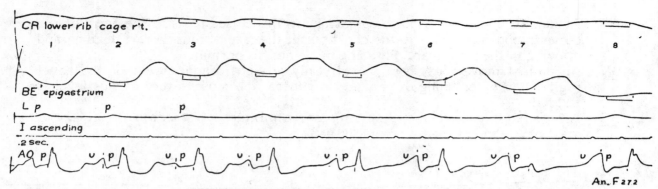

Figure 20. Orig. 35 x 10 cm. Singing scale with syl. "up" at slow tempo. Untrained singer.

CR, Chest pulse, neg. press. applicator, lower rib-cage, right: The pulses show rapid stroke at the beginning of the pulse, but the relaxation process is gradual.

BE, Abdominal movement, boss, epigastrium: Very clearly defined movements; they are in reverse, showing that the lateral muscles are leading the abdominal group. The movement inward, represented by the descent of the curve cannot be due to the compression of the rib-cage, which would throw the epigastric region out. It does not correspond to the escape of the air; cf. AO curve below.

AO, Air pressure outside mouth: The arresting form, with indication of mid-sag due to changing volume of the mouth, shows in the ascending tension as the vowel approaches the consonant and also in the heavy residual pressure at the detence of the "p".

Such heavy pressure on the consonant does not occur with trained singers.

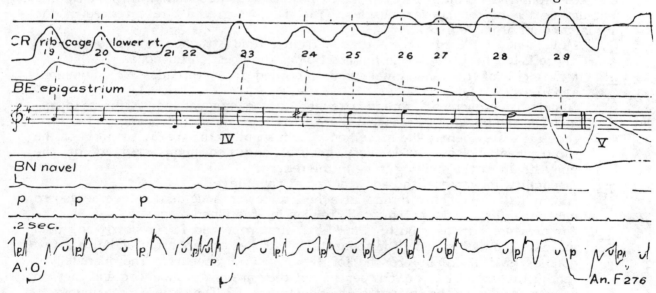

Figure 21. Orig. 27 x 12 cm. Singing "up" to mel. "Materna". Untrained singer.

CR, Chest pulse, neg. press. applicator, rib-cage lower right: Pulses well marked, though the rapid note 21 is not well defined, and there is a change of the coordination at note 27 for the heavier pulses of 28 and 29.

BE, Abdominal movement, boss, epigastrium: The pulses follow the chest pulse with an outward movement which indicates that the rectus ab. is leading up to the last two notes, 28, 29, when the curve reverses and the laterals are clearly making the primary movement, inward.

BN, Abdominal movement, boss, naval: The muscles at the navel level are fixated, with very slight change at note 23, and a more pronounced readjustment at the close of phrase, note 29.

AO, Air pressure outside mouth: The form is clearly arresting and the pressure drops to zero before the beginning of the vowel. The residual pressure at the consonant detente is high, except at note 29. Breathing is irregular, marking the end of a brief, irregular phrase just before 19, and again 22-23 where it closes the phrase apparent in CR, BE, BN.

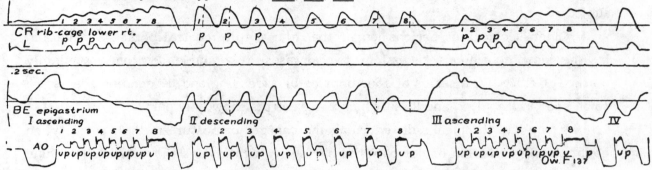

Figure 22. Orig. 35 x 10 cm. Singing scale with "up". Slightly trained singer.

CR, Chest pulse neg. press. applicator, rib-cage lower right: The rapid scales, I and III show the sustained tension throughout, while the slow scale II has the typical staccato form with the tension dropping to zero between the notes. Cf. BE and AO below.

BE, Abdominal movement, boss, epigastrium: There is definite expansion and steady recession for the rapid scales I and III. II, the slow scale, on the other hand shows the staccato form with a definite pulse for each note and no continuous recession. In II the lateral muscles are leading the contraction and drawing in the rectus ab. for each note.

AO, Air pressure outside mouth: The forms of the rapid scales I and III show that the arresting consonant has been shifted to releasing position; the series becomes "u, pu, pu .." closing with "pup", a legato form; the level of pressure is maintained. In II there is an intake of breath between each note, the pressure on the arresting consonant is very slight, there is little staccato accent, and the effect is only slightly staccato.

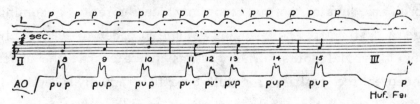

In staccato singing there is often a tendency to limit the phrasing to the single note or figure, thus maintaining a constant chest-abdominal posture apparent in the tracings of the air-pressure outside mouth and of the movement of the epigastric region. Cf. fig. 13. In some forms of staccato the intake between notes is not sufficient to restore the position and the phrasing shows the slow recession of chest and abdomen, and a definite inspiration at the end of the phrase. Cf. fig. 10. This type of phrasing with a slight intake between the individual notes but with a well-defined movement for the entire phrase shows in all the eleven subjects.

Often sections or periods longer than the simple musical phrase are marked by the slow continuous recession: two phrases in a single section are plainly marked, Cf. fig. 17; a series of four phrases of ascending and descending scales are to be seen in fig.s 1, 9, and 10, in which the excerpts show only parts.

If one had the means of recording the charges of posture in their entirety, no doubt the organization of not only the phrases (which always show in the breathing movements) but also of the sections and periods (which only occasionally show in the breathing movements) would be definitely indicated. As noted above the movements of breathing often make separate "breath groups" out of single notes or figures. Cf. fig. 13. It is the smaller unit, the note, the figure, and the phrase, which appear in the tracings taken of the breathing movements. Undoubtedly the melodic period has other tensions other types of postures and slow movement which bind it together.[9]

LEGATO AND STACCATO

The coordinations of singing present two types:

A. The ordinary, legato, "normal" type in which the rectus abdominis leads in the change of posture for the changing volume in order to support the chest pulse for the individual notes. The tracings indicate that the abdomen, slightly distended in the position for full breath, gradually recedes in a steadily changing fixation throughout the entire phrase. It is seldom that a single note gets a specific contraction of the abdominal musculature, and per contra seldom that the abdominal muscles relax between notes (syllables) as they often do between syllables in speech. All the fixations, coordinations and chest-pulse movements in this "normal" type can be likened to the conditions in rapid, free speech, and to the conditions in calling; the phrase is well-defined and the whole process is stereotyped although it resembles speech. This is the conventional form of breathing taught by teachers of voice.

B.   The staccato, intensive type in which the lateral muscles (obliques and transversalis) in the upper abdominal region lead and draw in the pliant rectus abdominis to which they are attached. Their action in this case can be seen in exaggerated form in the panting movements and in the general fixation of "Position B", figures 5, 8, 19. This vigorous, explosive type of delivery may occur with a few notes in the course of a phrase where the other notes of the phrase are supported by the normal chest-abdominal posture with positive, outward movements of the rectus - if any separate abdominal movements occur for these other notes.

The lateral musculature, especially in the upper abdomen, is shorter and more definitely attached than the rectus muscle, and therefore capable of faster and more precise movements.

LEGATO

Ever since the days of the Italian "bel canto" the essential of the singing style has been counted a "good legato". The adjectives ascribed to it have been "smooth", "flowing", "uninterrupted". And every effort has been made to leave the legato unbroken; consonants are to be given quickly, if they are unvoiced; and arresting consonants are to be minimized, to be light in stroke and as brief as possible. The ideal has been a continuous tone throughout the phrase. Admittedly the Italian has been an excellent medium for this legato with nearly continuous tone; most of the consonants are releasing consonants, and the few arresting consonants are mainly continuitives, m, n, l, r, s, z, and most of these are voiced so that they may continue the tone; the vowels are simple, there are few diphthongs and nothing of the peculiar "vanish" (change of quality, tendency to diphthongization) and there is little of the variation of the vowel quality with the accent so characteristic of the English (tendency to "dark e" in unaccented syllables) and prevalent in all the northern languages. And yet artists who sing English, Dutch and German make haste to say that these languages offer a variety and force which the more liquid languages lack, and assure one that a pure legato is possible in spite of the changing vowels and the arresting consonants.

And in fact tracings show that legato does not even in the most favorable conditions involve a really continuous vocalization throughout the phrase. Singing the syllable "po" to a slow scale gives an interupted tone; a phrase of 4.4. sec. duration is composed of 3. sec. vocalization; about one-fourth of the phrase is silence due to the interruption of the consonant "p". Cf. fig. 1. When the words of a favorable line of "America the Beautiful" is sung by a trained singer, at fairly slow tempo, a phrase of 4. sec. contains 2.2. sec. vocalization; about half the phrase is silence due to the interruption of the consonants. When the melody "Italian Hymn" is sung to the syllable "pup" so as to observe the double consonants, the effect is legato, but in a phrase of 3.6 sec. duration, there is but .74 sec. vocalization, the double consonants accounts for 2.86 sec. of silence. Cf. fig. 23. About three-fourths of the phrase is silence.

With increase in speed the relative duration of the consonant must increase; at maximum speed of execution the consonant must occupy at lease half the duration of each syllable.[10] It is true that if the vowel "ah" (Ital. a) is vocalized the result may be a continuous flow of tone with slight pulses for the individual notes; this is a good legato but the effect is no better than that of syllables with consonants. Cf. fig. 12.

An examination of the tracings makes it apparent that the "legato" is not due to the amount of vocalization during the phrase; it is not the mere continuity of the tone which is responsible for the "smooth, uninterrupted" effect. Instead the outstanding trait of "legato" singing is the unbroken level of the force of the tone indicated by the air-pressure just outside the mouth; it is dynamically uniform, steady. No matter how interrupted the tones may be, like a dotted line, the actual level is maintained throughout. It may be quite continuous, a straight, unbroken line with slight waves representing the individual notes. Or an interrupted tone with practically continuous, even, air-pressure as in the singing of "ha" to a scale. Or a series of notes to the syllable "po" giving a uniform series of note levels, each note slightly tilted downward, but the series lying in a definite, uniform dynamic line. Or there may be striking regularity and uniformity of level. Or in some cases the arresting consonants may demand a slight variation, and fricatives may vary the line somewhat. But in all these cases there is a clear, well-defined level of force which is strikingly apparent in the outside air-pressure, and in the character of the vibrations as they appear in the line AU.

During the legato phrases of a trained singer there is a steady and continuous recession of the rib-cage and abdominal wall; the chest pulse is slighter, the rib-cage and the upper abdomen often show no definite movements for single notes or figures, and there is a smooth, steady adjustment of the chest and abdomen to make possible this steady, uniform level of force in each chest pulse. There is never an intake of air during the phrase, and the slow movement, the smoothly changing posture of the chest and abdomen is obvious.

The tendency is always to mezzo forte or piano; consecutive staccato and legato phrases are nearly always sung so that the staccato is louder than the legato. The stroke of the consonant is made lightly and quickly, not so much to minimize the consonant duration as to avoid jolting and changing the steady dynamic level on which the "legato" depends.

Enunciation at high speed and the calling tone in speech also show this legato form as contrasted with the staccato. Cf. fig.s 12, 15, and 24.

STACCATO

The staccato note is usually isolated; interruption is part of the style of singing; but as we have seen above interruption is not the essential of staccato style. The essential lies in the dynamic character of the notes; they do not maintain a pressure level; instead there are sharp variations in the force of utterance; the line of the air-pressure outside the mouth is always disturbed. Cf. fig.s 12, and 13. The individual notes show peaks as a result of the sudden pulses which form them. The staccato is a matter of sudden, pointed pulses in the dynamic lines; these are necessarily made on isolated notes, but it is the sharp and sudden and irregular pulse which make the staccato and not the silence between the notes during which the abrupt, jerking blows of the staccato pulses are prepared. Sharp, diminuendo notes are a device of the subject Ow. for staccato. Cf. fig. 10.

A slight intake of air between the notes is very common in staccato series at slow and moderate tempi. Cf. fig.s 4, 10, and 13. This becomes an intake of breath between figures at a slightly higher speed. Often there is no general recession of the chest, the discrete notes are each phrased as a simple beat. On occasion the intake between notes is not sufficient to maintain the volume and there is a slow recession though the discrete notes are apparent in the chest-pulse tracing. Cf. fig. 10.

The chest pulses are always very pronounced and definite; the strokes are all sharp and clear, and in general staccato tends to mezzo forte and forte rather than to piano. Staccato may be described as a continuous slight sforzando.

The action of the abdominal muscles in staccato execution is characteristic. The upper abdominal musculature moves inward with each note or figure, giving a pronounced reinforcement to the chest pulse for the note. Cf. fig.s 10, 18, 21.

In this type of abdominal movement the laterals are the primary muscles in the movement, drawing in the pliant rectus abdominis. While this is the action which the trained singer tends to avoid - feeling that "legato" is the true style - there is no question that this coordination is valuable as a means of expression in singing, and certainly appears frequently in any animated style of execution.

While the releasing consonant is the easy and obvious form of the legato type of execution, the arresting consonant lends itself to the sudden jerk and dynamic crest of the staccato note. With the untrained singer the arresting consonant is apt to receive the staccato enunciation, and if legato is essential, he inclines to turn the releasing into an arresting consonant. In fig. 22 it is plain that the subject sings "op, op . ." as "o-po, po, ...". Although when carefully instructed to keep the arresting form he find it possible. Cf. fig. 10. The note with an arresting consonant is always sung with an increase of force as the singer approaches the consonant; they may be a sharp sudden increase which makes the note staccato, or it may be a gradual, steady inflexion of the note which does not break the legato line. Cf. fig. 16.

Some of the characteristics of staccato are those of slow or moderate speed of execution. Arresting consonants and separate pulses of the upper abdominal muscles are possible up to speeds of 3-4 per sec. At higher speeds of execution, consonants are forced into the releasing position, or must drop, and the abdo. minal muscles cannot follow. Cf. fig.s 13 and 24.

The familiar intake of breath between notes or figures is also possible at comparatively slow tempi.

At high speeds of execution the distinction between staccato and legato disappears leaving a form of enunciation which in the true singing style is nearer legato than staccato in many of its characteristics. For like high-speed it has the continuous rib-cage tension, and the steady recession of the legato style.

DICTION AS AFFECTED BY THE MOVEMENTS OF BREATHING
IN SINGING

The very important matter of the shading of the vowels for proper singing does not come within the scope of this study. The management of the resonant cavities is somewhat affected, to be sure, by the muscular state of the chest walls and the tension of the abdominal muscles, but much more than that is involved in the handling of the vocal canal for the vowels in singing as they are modified for various pitches and qualities.

The releasing consonant is usually followed immediately by the vowel tone. (The exceptions are cases of consonants with high air-pressure in mouth which give a puff of air at the detente; this puff of air is avoided by trained singers of English and other northern languages.) It is possible that the vowel sound extend through the entire interval between the consonants.

On the other hand the arresting consonant is followed by a period in which the air-pressure sinks to zero before the sounding of the vowel; therefore the arresting consonant is always followed by a relatively shorter vowel than is the releasing consonant. Cf. fig. 10. This shorter vowel duration with the greater interruption to the singing tone does not affect the legato as much as does the dynamic form of the syllable to which the arresting consonant tends. While it is possible to sing arrested syllables legato, the form lends itself to staccato execution.

As already noted, when the speed is increased to 3-4 per sec. the arresting consonant shifts to the releasing position or disappears.

The arrested form of syllable is satisfactory for a comparatively short note. But if the note is prolonged it is impossible to continue the rising pressure to a climax at the close of the syllable. The syllable has been drawn out into a slow movement and the syllable is not a closed syllable. This is the problem of the arresting consonant at the close of a sustained musical tone. If the consonant is articulated without breath pressure the chest pulse of the syllable is actually self-arrested and the consonant is unheard.[11] Cf. also fig. 11.

Two methods of making the articulation functional are possible when the consonant occurs at the end of a long note: 1. an added note is made just at the close in which syllable the consonant functions as arresting; 2. the consonant is sung as the releasing consonant of a whispered syllable following the sustained tone; this is at best artificial in English, Dutch or German, although the French lends itself to such practice.   The first method, the grace-note with arresting consonant is probably the better device.

The abutting and double consonants if essential to the meaning must be enunciated as prescribed.   In the mouth of a trained singer this means that the articulatory apparatus will remain closed throughout the pair of consonants and yet the stroke of the second consonant will be clear and definite as in speech.   There should be no escape of breath between the consonants in the case of abutting occlusives.   Cf. fig.s 23 and 25.   But it is no more necessary to "think and 'h' between them"[12] than it is in speech.   In singing as in speaking English the abutting and double consonants which are not essential to the sense are easily dropped; this is a common license.   Cf. fig.s 23 and 25.

TREMOR AND ITS EFFECT IN VIBRATO

The tracings in which the tremor and the resulting "vibrato" are conspicuous were not taken primarily for the study of tremor.   Three of the subjects produced tracings which show the tremor in the breathing muscles strikingly and often a corresponding vibrato appears in the tracings of the air-pressure outside the mouth.   There are indications of tremor in other subjects. Many of the tracings are clear enough so that it is possible to correlate the curves and show that the tremor of the chest is in phase with the vibrato of the air stream.

The tremor may appear in any of the tracings from bosses against the chest and abdominal walls, but it is usually most apparent in the tracings from the negative pressure applicator recording the "chest" pulse.   Cf. fig.s 9 and 26.   The natural periode of the negative-pressure system, and of the transmission system from the bosses is much higher than the frequency of the tremors recorded.   The tremors have a frequency of 6-11 per sec.   while the natural frequencies of the apparatus vary from 25-60 per sec. As the tremor shows at the same rate and in phase in the unlike and independent recording systems of 1. the negative-pressure apparatus, 2. the bosses applied directly to the body wall, and 3. the outside-air tracing which shows the variation of pressure at the glottis, there can be no question that the oscillations are not artifacts.

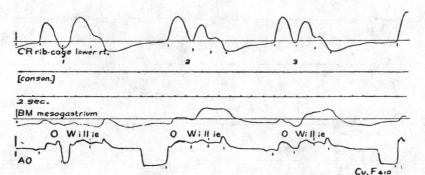

Figure 23. Orig. 23 x 5 cm. Singing "pup" to mel. "Ital. Hymn". Trained singer.

L,   Lip movement: The doubles are clear. The rapid notes 11, 12 drop the arresting "p"s giving "pu', pu'," which shows clearly in the consonant line. The doubles maintain contact throughout; there is no escape of air between the doublets.

AO,   Air pressure outside mouth: The syl. with releasing and arresting consonants has a mid-sag such as appears in speaking. Although the passage was sung legato and has a continuous effect, the vocalization fills but a small part of the duration. Three-fourths of the interval of the phrase is occupied by the consonants.

Figure 24. Orig. 25 x 10 cm. Calling syl.s "O Willie", without prelongation.

CR,   Chest pulse, neg. press. applicator, rib-cage, lower right: The three pulses of the phrase show grouping. The climax may be on the first syl., as in 2 and 3, or on the second syl, as in 1. The third syl. always groups with the second to form a single unit. In 1 it is very much subordinated. In 2 and 3 the phrase itself shows continuing tension in the group, but 1 has a drop to zero between the first and second syl.s.

BM,   Abdominal movement, boss, mesogastrium: The tracing shows two tendencies, 1) to fixate the abdomen during the group of chest pulses, as in 1; the release after the group is to be seen in a compensating after- pulse following the last vowel; and 2) to make two movements of the abdominal musculature for the three syl.s, phrases 2 and 3.

AO,   Air pressure outside mouth: The irregular, jerky outline of the breath tracing shows the "staccato" enunciation. The drop to zero in phrase 1, to be noted in CR, is apparent here in the intake of air between the first and second syl. of phrase 1. A full breath is taken between phrases 1 and 2, but there is no intake between 2, and 3. The sudden escape of air through the opening glottis is invariable. It appears in all nine phrases of this record of which the excerpt shows three.

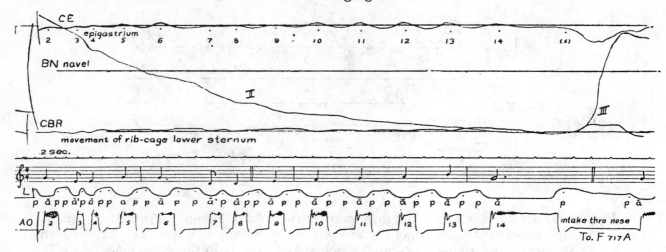

Figure 25. Orig. 35 x 13 cm. Singing "pap" to mel. "Materna". Standing. Partially trained singer.

CE, Chest pulse, neg. press. applicator, epigastrium: The curve shows the pulses but there is only slight indication of tension in the rib-cage; the change of fixation between II and III gives the extent. The arresting consonant of the last "pap" of II, syl. 14, shows a well defined accessory pulse for the arresting consonant.

BN, Abdominal movement, boss, navel: Very striking sweep of the curve of recession of the abdomen, from decided extension at note 2, to the final indrawn position at close of note 14. It is apparent that the laterals are primarily responsible for the breathing movement. The recession is fairly steady; there is some indication of the end of the phrase, note 8, 9 and the tracing may be slightly influenced by the pulses for the notes.

CBR, Movement of the rib-cage, boss, lower sternum: The rib-cage is fixated throughout; a slight change occurs at the new phrase III. The chest pulses show to some extent in the fixated rib-cage.

L,   Movement of the lips: The prescribed doubles show throughout. The components show clearly but there is no escape of air between the doublets. The rapid notes, 3 and 7, compel the dropping of the arresting consonant, so that the form runs "pa', pa'" for 3, 4 and 7, 8.

AO, Air pressure outside mouth: The legato level is well maintained. At opening of phrase III the intake of air through the nose is indicated by the continuing lip closure during the phrase pause.

The study of a group of records not reproduced shows that the variations in pressure at the glottis are always in phase with the tremor oscillations of the rib-cage. If the primary cause were the rarefactions and condensations produced by changes at the glottis, the puff of air which constituted an increase in the pressure in the outside-air tracing would be a wave of compression running to the outside, while a wave of rarefaction traveled inward, and the two tracings would be ninety degrees off phase. Such waves are transmitted through the systems with the speed of sound, so that the time of transmission is negligible.

This tremor and the resulting intensity vibrato appear whenever the rib-cage is fairly tense and the muscle groups are fixated, or there is a slowly changing posture. Cf. fig.s 9 and 26. It appears therefore in the prolonged notes, and often also in the entire phrase sung in the fairly tense position assumed in mezzo-forte or forte singing.

The tremor is undoubtedly due to the fixation of the muscles of the chest wall as a whole; it often characterizes the phrase from end to end, and it is sometimes difficult to distinguish the individual notes in the series of tremor oscillations of the tracing of the negative-pressure applicator. Where the notes are regular it is noteworthy that the number of oscillations per syllable is apt to be the same. Cf. fig. 9, notes 9-12. This striking regularity of pattern suggests some relation between the tremor process and the movement of the note-pulse. Investigators at the State University of Iowa have made much of the vibrato, especially of the variations in pitch involved; there is also a variation in intensity.[13] The pitch variation is very possibly due to the variations in pressure on the vocal folds which result from the tremor in the muscles of the rib-cage.

It is a familiar observation that the speed of tremor is the maximum speed of movement; and there are reasons for assuming that the maximum speed of repetition of a syllable with or without a releasing consonant often approaches a forced tremor. Individual lip movements are not possible above a speed of 8-9 per sec. But it is possible to have a tremor movement from the rib-cage which exceeds that, running up to 10-11 per sec. In such cases a series of syllables with releasing consonant may show a series of vowel pulses with which the lip movements do not coincide, and in which the number of lip movements is fewer than the number of chest pulses. Cf. fig.s 27 and 28.

The tremor rates in the subjects studied (Huf., Ba., Wm, and especially Ow and Mo) vary from 6-12 per sec. In the majority of cases, the tremor is from c. 8-10 per sec.

The concept of a "forced tremor" raises an interesting question as to "repetition time" or tapping time as the value is usually called from the familiar apparatus for recording it. Apparently the tremor differs from an ordinary movement in these two points: 1. the excursion of the tremor movement is necessarily small; 2. the muscles are tensely contracted against each other; there is always pronounced antagonism between the muscle groups. In the case of the voluntary movement at rates lower than that of the forced tremor, the movement may be of the balistic type in which the extent of the excursion does not affect the rate of the movement series, and in which the movement is "free", i.e. capable of variation of accentuation and of timing. This last condition is impossible with the forced tremor; it cannot run faster or slower; it is the last resort for speed and it is not variable at will. It can be turned on as it were for speed, but it cannot be regulated once it is started.

COMPARISON OF THE BREATHING MOVEMENTS OF TRAINED AND UNTRAINED SINGERS

The most obvious difference lies in the ability of the trained singer to achieve the legato type of execution throughout the entire phrase, and in spite of the vowels, and consonants arresting and releasing, which the words prescribe.

The staccato style with the trained singer is sharply differentiated, but often inclines to the staccato form, i.e. there is a slow, steady recession of the abdominal wall, and a steady descent of the rib-cage. But the individual notes are marked by inward pulses of the epi- and meso- gastric musculature in which the laterals must lead; and at the same time the separate pulses are apparent in the movement of the rib-cage. Cf. fig.s 2, 4 and 13.

In the matter of enunciation, the trained singer is able to follow a prescribed series of arresting and of double or abutting consonants. He is able to produce a legato in spite of the slight rise in intensity during the note sung to a syllable with an arresting consonant. And he is able to handle the abutting or doubled consonants clearly and cleanly. In certain details the arresting consonant may be modified, as will be seen later; but the consonant always retains its function. On occasion a certain type of trained singer will refuse to sing any consonant well; obsessed with the notion that "legato" means a <u>continuous</u> vocalization, all his "<u>p</u>"s become "<u>b</u>"s and all his "<u>b</u>"s become "<u>m</u>"s, and there is little of the true consonant function left; he is trying to make humming vowels of the consonants. Training of this sort is mistaken of course, but it is not unusual.

The untrained singer is often unable to produce a true legato. Cf. fig.s 18 and 22. The phrase may begin with a well defined legato movement, with a general abdominal contraction in which the rectus abdominis leads, but toward the end of the phrase the process reverses and the lateral musculature is primary, and the smooth, uniform recession of the abdomen has been interrupted. Sometimes the form is in effect a light staccato, in the handling of the pulses in both rib-cage and abdomen, but there is no intake of air between the notes, and the intensity level is that of the legato. In fig. 3 the legato phrase seems normal as it appears in the air-pressure outside <u>(AO)</u> but the breathing coordination is very like that of the preceding staccato phrase.

It is evident that with the rapid inspiration of the trained singer the rib-cage expands and becomes slightly tense. The expiration involves a general slight contraction; the expanded rib-cage sinks gradually during the course of the phrase without losing its "form" and tension. Cf. fig.s 2 and 7. This is the normal reaction for the decreasing volume of the thorax. Meanwhile the rectus abdominis leads in the general contraction of the abdominal musculature which draws down the rib-cage and by a slow, inward, receding movement forces the viscera and diaphram upward with the slow change in the rib-cage position. For the individual notes or figures, the abdominal pulse, if apparent, is <u>in phase</u> with the chest pulse, i.e. there is a slight <u>outward</u> movement for each note or figure, as in speech at slow and rapid rates of enunciation. Cf. fig.s 1 and 29. Owing to the gradual change - the general slow movement - of both rib-cage and abdomen, the phrase is executed with comparatively change in any one region. The recession and lowering of the rib-cage reduces the area of the floor of the thorax, and the corresponding recession of the upper abdomen automatically adjusts the diaphram to the changing volume. Cf. fig. 2. The steady contraction of the slightly distended rectus abdominis leads in this movement, and at the same time produce slight individual pulses for accented notes and figures at slow tempi. But the total recession of the abdomen is not large. Often the naval region is unaffected by the total expiration. Cf. fig.s 1 and 17.

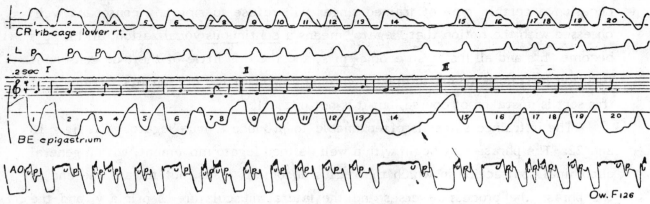

Figure 26. Orig. 35 x 11 cm. Singing "up" to mel. "Materna". Slightly trained singer.

CR, Chest pulse, neg. press. applicator, rib-cage, lower right: A vigorous pulse for each note; grouping of the short notes, 3, 7, 17 with the following notes. Tremor appears in the longer, accented notes, 2, 6, 14, 16, 20, c. 7 per sec. No mark of an accessory pulse for arresting "p", note 14. No maintenance of tension throughout the phrase; the pressure drops to zero between pulses as in speaking, a common mark of staccato execution.

L, Lip movement: Vigorous stroke. Both "p"s of the groups 3-4, 7-8, 17-18 are lighter and briefer than the other consonants.

BE, Abdominal movement, boss, epigastrium: Vigorous action for each pulse; the curve is the reverse of the chest pulse; this is striking for the groups 3-4 and 7-8 and 17-18; tempo is slow enough so that the abdominal muscles can respond. The vigorous movement inward is produced by the lateral muscles which draw in the rectus ab. Very slight, gradual recession during II and III; the form is staccato. Slight tremor, 14.

AO, Air pressure outside mouth: Form shows marked pressure for each arresting consonant, and the line of pressure has the characteristic upward slant in each syl., save for the long notes 2, 6, 14, 16, 20. The form tends decidedly to staccato; and notes 3, 7, 8, 9, 10, 17, 18 show the sudden accent in the vibrations. With the exception of the groups 3-4, 7-8, 17-18 there is a definite intake of breath between each note. The length of the consonants, compared with the length of the tone, is pronounced, and in most cases the residual pressure at the detente is apparent. Vibrato shows in the long notes, c. 7 per sec.

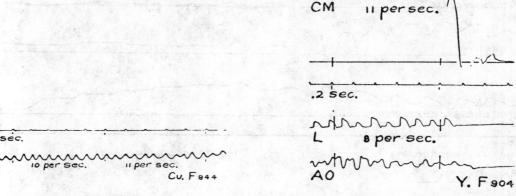

Figure 27. Orig. 12.5 x 3 cm. Syl. "ah" said at maximum speed.

AO, Air pressure outside mouth: The movements are clearly marked, of the type of a forced tremor. They are not as regular as definite balistic movements would be. Vocalization runs throughout the tracing. The forced tremor is probably due to the chest musculature.

Figure 28. Orig. 8 x 9 cm. Syl. "pup" said at increasing speed. Excerpt taken at maximum speed. The tracing CM has been retouched.

CM, Chest pulse, neg. press. applicator, mesogastrium: A movement of the type of a forced tremor runs at a speed of 11 per sec.

L, Lip movement: The movements are irregular in duration and excursion, and are not coordinated with the chest pulses. The lip movement occurs at a speed of 8 per sec.

AO, Air pressure outside mouth: The pulses are no longer defined, the coordination has been lost and it is not possible to trace individual syl lables.

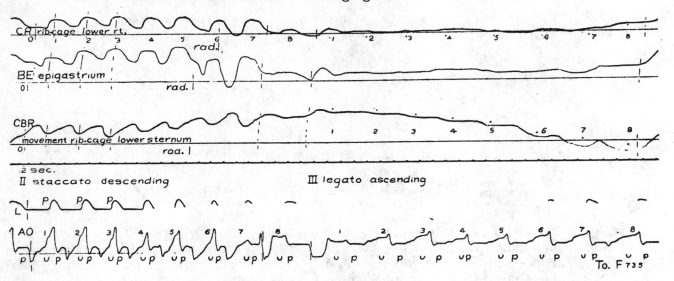

Figure 29. Orig. 35 x 15 cm. Singing scale with "up". Staccato, legato. Standing. Partially trained singer.

CR,   Chest pulse, neg. press. applicator, rib-cage, lower right: Pulses sharply marked, staccato; but much slighter and a little slower in tempo, legato.

BE,   Abdominal movement, boss, epigastrium: The staccato forms repeat the chest pulses showing a vigorous contraction of the abdominal muscles in which the rectus ab. leads, as each pulse is an outward movement. During the legato phrase III there is little movement in the epigastric region, a fixation is maintained and the abdominal muscles do not assist in the chest pulse for each note.

CBR,   Movement of the rib-cage, boss, lower sternum: The movements for each note are apparent in both II and III; they are much more marked, staccato. The sharp movement of descent of the rib-cage marks the chest pulse. The movement of the rib-cage, therefore, gives a curve out of phase with the chest-pulse curve; the chest-pulse is the resulting outward movement due to the muscular contraction; the rib-cage curve gives the sharp downward movement of the ribs in response to the muscular contraction.   In the staccato phrase II there is actually slight expansion of the rib-cage, which is more pronounced at the end of the phrase.

AO,   Air pressure outside mouth: In II, staccato, the very steep rise of the line of pressure in each syl. is marked and gives a sharp accent.   There is a momentary intake of breath between each note, which makes it possible for the rib-cage and abdomen to maintain the expanded position.   During the legato, III there is no intake and the recession of the rib-cage is gradual.

The untrained singer often fails to achieve this general coordination. Sometimes the rib-cage is lifted instead of being expanded, with a resulting tension and effort. Sometimes the rib-cage is inert and the inspiration is due to the lowering of the diaphram with compensating abdominal movement. During the slow expiration there may be little or no rib-cage recession and the change in volume during the phrase is compensated by a pronounced recession of the upper abdomen. This may involve a pronounced movement in the navel region as well. Cf. fig. 3. Abdominal recession of this type must go well beyond any possible cooperation of the rectus and is due of course to the primary action of the lateral muscles drawing in the heavy bands of the rectus. This is always a weaker and more difficult action, and since the laterals are thus already involved in the general recession for the phrase, it leaves little resource in the way of vigorous lateral contraction for staccato and sforzando notes. The lack of expansion and recession of the rib-cage gives a sense of inertness to the tone, and the rather dead and mechanical fashion in which the notes are executed adds to this impression.

To say that the untrained singer tends to a staccato form of execution implies that the coordination of the breathing movements will be of the staccato type. The rib-cage may be well expanded and the "chest resonance" satisfactory, and the gradual recession without intake of breath may occur, but even in the simplest passages the individual notes or figures are formed by the action of the upper abdominal muscles which draw in the rectus with each chest pulse or small group of chest pulses. This is a partial synergy; the lateral muscles of the abdomen contract with the small muscles of the rib-cage which give the chest pulse; but the rectus abdominis does not work with the group, in fact the laterals must work against it, and there is not the general contraction of all the abdominal muscles which is characteristic of high-speed speech, of the calling tone, and of the trained type of singing. Cf. fig. 22.

The objection to this staccato type of breathing movements is obvious. The movements are not general and synergic and quiet, there is none of the ease of the ordinary breathing in rapid speech and in calling, and there is little reserve for expression. Such breathing movements require a pliant rectus and decided contractions of the upper-abdominal laterals so that the muscles are working at the extreme of the possible excursion of the movement; there is little opportunity for any vigorous accent because the accentual mechanism has already been employed to its limit, and it is difficult to have a delicate and responsive adjustment of abdominal movements when the rectus and the laterals are opposed to each other and when they work at the end of the phrase in strained and extreme conditions of contraction.

It is certain also that the singer will literally lack poise; the rectus abdominis is an important muscle of trunk posture either sitting or standing, and if the quiet, unagitated delivery of the singer involves partial relaxation of the rectus and its drawing in by the laterals, the posture of the singer must be constrained. Maintenance of the erect posture is forced on to the back muscles alone, the shoulder girdle is more or less fixated to maintain the expanded chest, and even the simplest, easiest execution is labored and stiff. The rib-cage form and the gradual recession of the rib-cage must be managed without the natural assistance of the rectus abdominis.

The normal breathing in which the rectus abdominis leads the abdominal musculature and works with the slowly sinking rib-cage maintains throughout the phrase a chest-abdominal coordination which is ready for any variation in movement however delicate or however vigorous.

None of the subjects presented the peculiar artificial form of breathing sometimes known as "abdominal breathing". It is evidently the result of express training. In this form the entire extent of the abdominal laterals is employed in producing each note or figure, with a striking abdominal deformation. Such breathing has all the disadvantages and difficulties of the untrained, staccato type of breathing. It demands the fixation of the rib-cage without the cooperation of the abdominal muscles; it involves an unsatisfactory posture; it precludes flexibility because of the awkward fixation of the rib-cage. In addition the continual churning of the viscera is pernicious. The difficulty with such "abdominal" breathing is not that it brings pressure to bear on the viscera, especially in the lower abdomen, Bonnier's objection is not quite to the point.[14] There is no possible way to spare the contents of the pelvic basin from the constant and severe presssure during the movements of singing. Any vigorous contraction of the abdominal muscles, any forced descent of the diaphram, must produce pressure. Pressure alone will not harm the most delicate; if the pressure is uniform and compensated on all sides so that there is no deformation there is no injury. But when there are rapid changes of pressure and the kidneys, ovaries and uteries are forced out of position and dragged to and fro by the breathing movements the results are bad.

REFERENCES

1.   Mr. C. V. Hudgins gave valuable assistance in securing the tracings studied.

2.   Stetson & Hudgins, Breathing Movements in Speech, Arch. neerl. de phon. exp. V, '30, p. 4 ff.

3.   R. H. Stetson, Mot. Theory of Rhythm, Psy. Rev. 12, '05; the apparatus is illustrated, W.V.D. Bingham, Stud.s in Melody, Psy. Mon.s, 12, '10, whole no. 50, p. 44.

4.   Mot. Phon. Arch. neerl. de phon. exp. III '28, p. 92 f. fig.s 41, 42. Breathing M'vts in Speech, ibid., V'30, p.12 fig.s 15, 16, 17.

5.   Breathing Movements in Speech, p. 9 fig. 3, p. 19, fig.s 13,14.

6.   Breathing Movements in Speech, p. 19 fig. 13, 14.

7.   Mot. Phon. p. 90 fig. 39, 40; p. 92/3 fig. 41,42.

8.   Lilli Lehmann, How to Sing, Macmillian, N.Y., '14, p. 25.

9.   W. V. D. Bingham, Studies in Melody, Psy. Mon.s 12, '10, whole No. 50.

10.   Mot. Phon. p. 87, fig. 33, etc.

11.   Mot. Phon. p. 102, Fig. 47, shows a functionless "t".

12.   E. Wilcke, German Diction in Singing, Dutton, N.Y., '30, p. 142.

13.   Schoen, M., Pitch Factor in Artistic Singing, Psy. Mon. 31, '22, No. 140;' Kwalwasser, J., The Vibrato, Psy. Mon. 36, '26, No. 167; Metfessel, M. F., What is Voice?, Psy. Mon. 39, '28, No. 2.

14.   Bonnier, P., La Voix, Alcan, Paris, '21, p. 75-6.

The
Bernoulli Effect
in Singing

William Vennard

For some years now, at workshops and conventions as well as in articles in The Bulletin and elsewhere, our colleague, Robert Taylor[1], has been calling attention to the Bernoulli Effect in singing. He makes the point that in this age of science it is easier to convince students of singing not to use excess muscularity if one proves that the glottis can be vibrated by breath alone, that even the closing of the glottis can be accomplished partly by flow of air.

If Taylor has been somewhat of a voice crying "Bernoulli" in the wilderness of voice pedagogy, he has not been alone in the world of voice science. Van den Berg, et al[2], wrote an abstruse article on the subject for the JOURNAL OF THE ACOUSTICAL SOCIETY OF AMERICA, and others have mentioned the Bernoulli Effect in explaining vibratory phenomena (Moore[3], Timcke[4], von Leden[5]).

The principle which Bernoulli enunciated has many applications. It is a lifting force in aviation, and it creates the suction needed in atomizers, as well as being a factor in the vibrators of wind instruments. An easy demonstration of it is illustrated in Fig. 1. If you will hold a letter-size sheet of paper against your chin (Fig. 1 A) and blow, the paper will rise to a horizontal position (Fig. 1 B). The reason for this is that when a gas (or a liquid, for that matter) is in motion it exerts less than its normal pressure upon its surrounding environment. In Fig. 1 A, atmospheric pressure (represented by the arrows) is normal on both sides of the paper, so gravity pulls it down. In Fig. 1B, pressure is reduced above the paper by the motion of the air, and therefore the normal pressure below is sufficient to raise the paper.

Fig. 2 is a diagram of an atomizer. Air (or water, as in the case of the insecticide spray often used with garden hose) is moving from left to right in the drawing. The tube narrows, which causes the flow to be even faster in passing this point. Just here is the opening of a tube which goes down into a jar containing the liquid that is to be sprayed. Reduced pressure caused by the flow of air (or water) above draws the liquid up into the current, and it is blown out of the atomizer.

Now turn Fig. 2 on its side and see how the atomizer parallels the cross-section of the windpipe and larynx shown in the tomogram (courtesy of van den Berg). The under surface of the vocal folds is funnel-shaped. Indeed, the membrane lining it is called the conus elasticus. When the vocal folds (vocal cords) are fairly close to each other there is a narrowing of the air passage sufficient for the Bernoulli Effect to draw them together, if the breath is flowing at the same time.

As a matter of fact, in laughter the vocal muscles are sucked together in just this way. Moore and von Leden[3] have published a careful study of the kind of laughter that is expressed in writing commonly as: "Ha-ha-ha". Fig. 3 shows frames from a high-speed motion picture taken by them of the closing of the glottis for one of these "Ha's". In these pictures the arytenoid cartilages are seen at the bottom and the vocalis muscles are at the top.

Remember that the vocal cords, as we call them, are complex structures the forward part of which is muscular (with ligamentous edges) and the rear part of which is cartilage. The muscles are always together at the front end (top of our pictures) since they arise from the angle of the thyroid cartilage, but the glottis is opened or closed by movements of the arytenoid cartilages, which are controlled by three sets of muscles other than the vocalis muscles.

In Fig. 3 A, the glottis is rather widely open, and throughout the series C-L the arytenoids are closing at a nearly constant rate, but the vocalis muscles are doing something else. The Bernoulli Effect is drawing them together more rapidly than the arytenoids are approaching each other. At D they almost touch. However, their elasticity is such that they pull apart again (E-H), after which the suction of the flow of air brings them toward each other again (I-L). In L the

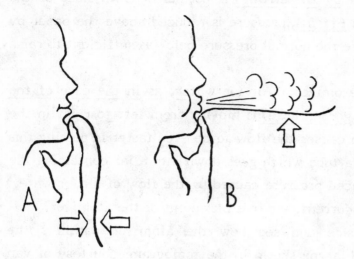

Figure 1: Demonstration of the Bernoulli Effect.

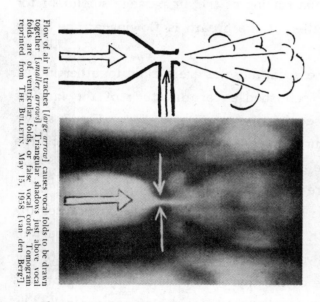

Flow of air in trachea [*large arrow*] causes vocal folds to be drawn together [*smaller arrows*]. Triangular shadows just above vocal folds are of ventricular folds, or false vocal cords. Tomogram reprinted from THE BULLETIN, May 15, 1958 [van den Berg].

Figure 2: Diagram of Atomizer Compared with Tomogram of Larynx.
Flow of air in trachea (large arrow) causes vocal folds to be drawn together (smaller arrows). Triangular shadows just above vocal folds are of ventricular folds, or false vocal cords. Tomogram reprinted from THE BULLETIN, May 15, 1958 (van den Berg[7]).

muscular glottis is closed, though the cartilaginous glottis is still partly open. Moore and von Leden report that actually the muscular glottis completed two more vibrations, closing tightly and remaining closed for a longer time than the open phase, before the cartilages came together (Fig. 4).

This is how vibration is initiated by the aspirate (h). Breath is flowing while the glottis is closing by action of the interarytenoid muscles. When the vocal muscles are nearly enough together, the Bernoulli Effect sucks them into fibration before the cartilages have fully closed. After the cartilages have been approximated (it may even be an imperfect approximation) the sequence of aerodynamic factors is as follows: first the flow of breath sucks the glottis shut; this stops the flow momentarily, whereupon breath pressure blows the glottis open again; air flow recommences and the cycle repeats.

This is rather different from the way the vibration has usually been described. In fact, I myself wrote, in 1949: "The lips hold back the breath until its pressure becomes greater than their tension. Then a minute puff of air escapes, reducing the pressure to the point where the lip tension can stop the flow of breath again", (Vennard[6] p. 34). The concept here is one of muscle tension resisting breath pressure. No account is taken of suction. The old idea is part myoelastic; the new one does not deny the muscular factors, but neither does it depend upon them - it is completely aerodynamic, throwing the emphasis upon breath flow.

You can demonstrate purely aerodynamic vibration by holding two sheets of paper to your lips and blowing between them. Hold the sheets vertically, one in each hand. They may fall apart, but when you blow they will be drawn together and will begin to vibrate. The Bernoulli Effect brings them together. This stops the flow of air, so they are blown apart only to be sucked together again immediately, and the cycle repeats itself as long as you keep blowing.

Actually we must combine both of these ideas in our concept of phonation. Voice is a myoelastic-aerodynamic phenomenon (van den Berg[7]). But our teaching should emphasize breath rather than muscle. The difference of emphasis is epitomized in the two different ways in which it is possible to attack a vowel. This is one detail of singing upon which I allow myself to be a perfectionist.

There are two acts which must synchronize in attacking a vowel. The interarytenoid muscles must close the glottis (with cooperation from other laryngeal muscles) and the breath must flow. If the two acts synchronize perfectly, we have the perfect simultaneous attack or instantaneous attack, as it is

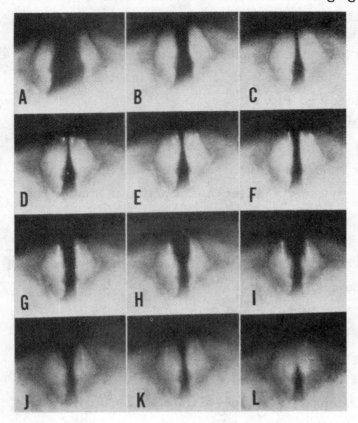

Figure 3: Vocal Folds in Aspirate Attack.
High-speed motion picture sequence reprinted by permission from Folia Phoniatrica, Vol. 10, No. 4, p. 209, 1958 (Moore and von Leden[3]). Several frames are omitted between the first three pictures, from C to L the pictures are roughly every other frame from the movie. See Figure 4.

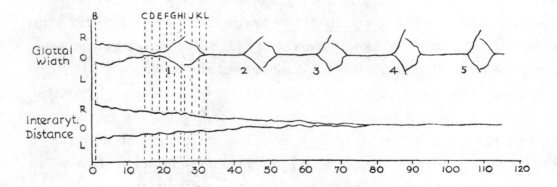

Figure 4: Graph Movements of Vocal Folds and Arytenoids in Aspirate Attack. Graph movements taken from high speed motion picture represented in Figure 3, reprinted by permission from FOLIA PHONIATRICA, Vol. 10, No. 4, p. 210 (Moore and von Leden[3]). Number of frames 0-120 indicated at bottom. Distance between mid-points of muscular folds as measured in each frame is shown in upper graph.

Five separate complete vibratory movements can be noted. Distance between arytenoid cartilages is shown in lower graph. Notice that there are three vibrations of the muscular (or ligamentous) glottis before the arytenoids are fully approximated. Figure 3A is a frame that came before this graph. Vertical broken lines show where the other frames belong on this graph. Figure 3B is frame 1; Figure 3C is frame 15, etc.

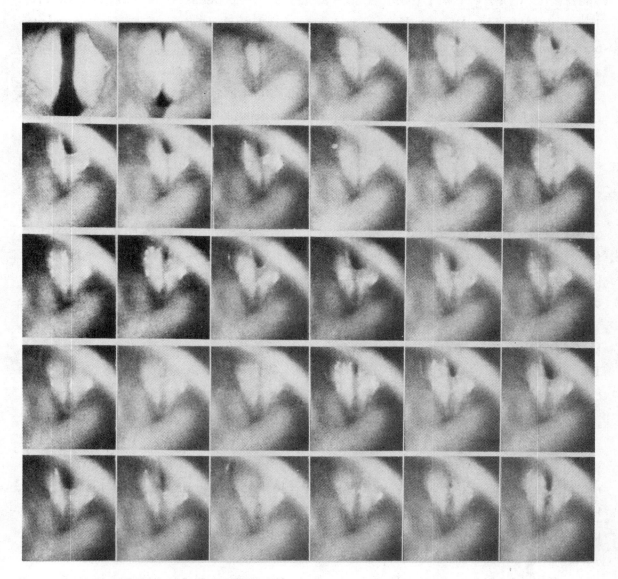

Figure 5: Vocal Folds in Glottal Plosive.
High-speed motion picture sequence prepared especially for THE BULLETIN by Dr. Paul Moore, Institute of Laryngology and Voice Disorders, Chicago. View from left to right, beginning with upper left. Frames are omitted between first four pictures, but beginning with fourth from upper left the frames are consecutive.

sometimes called. But assuming that a student will not achieve perfection, which act should come first? Upon which act should he concentrate, breathing or closing the throat?

If the glottis closes first, and then breath pressure is applied, the vibration will begin with an explosion of air as the pressure overcomes the muscular tension. The Bernoulli Effect will then become a part of the process, it is true, but too late. The muscular adjustment is not the same. Moore and von Leden have also photographed the glottal plosive (which is the phonetic term for this kind of attack) and shown how much more violent it is than an aspirate attack.

Fig. 5 was prepared by Dr. Moore especially for this article. The sequence of frames is from left to right, beginning at upper left. The first picture corresponds roughly to Fig. 3 B, and shows the glottis closing. Notice that the arytenoid cartilages are not parallel and meet at the vocal processes first, Fig. 5, second picture from upper left. Friction is thus created between the vocal processes as the cartilages are further drawn together, and sometimes repeated glottal plosives actually produce contact ulcers between the cartilages. In the third picture of Fig. 5 the closing of the glottis is complete and its tenseness is shown by the fact that the laryngeal collar is closing over the glottis. The epiglottis (upper right) is descending and the cartilages of Santorini are moving in (bottom of picture). The false cords, or ventricular bands, are closing over the true cords on each side. Dr. Moore writes that a few frames later the true cords were completely obscured. The glottal plosive is really a slight cough. The whole larynx tenses for it. The explosion is one which laryngologists agree is damaging to the delicate structures.

The remaining pictures in Fig. 5, beginning with the fourth from the left are consecutive frames taken at 4000 per second, and they show the first 3½ cycles of vibration. Notice the constriction. The glottis opens only partially, the cartilages remaining tightly held. Only in the 4th cycle (just beginning in the last picture, lower right) does the whole glottis open. Dr. Moore writes that in some films in his laboratory as many as 22 cycles of vibration elapse before the full cords become active.

The attack which develops freedom in the laryngeal adjustment is the one in which the flow of breath begins first, and then the glottis is closed to meet it. The vibration actually begins with the Bernoulli Effect, and the adjustment of the muscles that bring the vocal cords together need never be as tense as with the glottal plosive. The result is truly "singing on the breath". In the Bernoulli Effect, we find the scientific explanation of this classic empirical concept.

The objection is sometimes raised that an aspirate attack results in a breathy tone. I am willing to concede that in cases of extreme breathiness the glottal plosive may be a means of overcoming this fault, but it is a dangerous remedy. The glottal rattle, or "fry" as the speech authorities call it, is better. However, the aspirate attack need not be breathy. Indeed, there can be a very complete reaction from the breathiness of the (h) to the clarity of the vowel. Think of the laugh for a moment. Breath flows generously between the "ha's" but the vowel sounds themselves are loud and clear.

The attack by means of (h) can be every bit as crisp as the glottal plosive. In fact, one has a definite feeling of the breath striking something, even more than one does in the glottal plosive. In other words, the closing by means of the Bernoulli suction may well be what was originally intended by the expression "stroke of the glottis." The connotation was not objectionable at first, but as the expression became corrupted to mean glottal plosive, it lost favor. For this reason it is well to avoid using the phrase "glottal stroke," because one can never be sure what it means to the other person.

Garcia advocated the coup de glotte and described it as a plosive, comparing it to the consonant (p). However he also said: "It is very necessary to guard against confusing the articulation or stroke of the glottis with the stroke of the chest which resembles a cough, or the effort that one makes to expel from the gullet something that disturbs it." (Il faut bien se garder de confondre l'articulation ou le coup de la glotte avec le coup de poitrine qui ressemble a' la toux, ou a' l'effort que l'on fait pour expulser du gosier quelque chose qui le gene, Garcia[8], p. 11). We can see with the aid of Fastax photography that the glottal plosive really is a cough, the difference is only one of degree. On the other hand, the "imaginary aspirate" that I am about to describe, when seen with the unaided eye in the laryngeal mirror (which is all Garcia had) looks very much like lips making a plosive.

Of course, an audible (h) is only a crutch for learning the correct attack. Once there is a clear, crisp initiating of the vowel, the amount of time and breath that is wasted in the (h) should be reduced until finally there is only an "imaginary h". Mynard Jones calls this the "imaginary aspirate". I am sure that insistence upon this kind of vowel attack is the most direct means of teaching freedom, or "singing on the breath." The beginner may not achieve a much more pleasing tone with the "imaginary h" than he does with a careless glottal plosive, but vowels initiated with the "imaginary h" have a future. The glottal plosive only leads to more tension.

Van den Berg[9] has been experimenting for twelve years and more with excised larynges which he succeeds in making sing with compressed, preheated and humidified air. The interesting thing about such experimentation is that while in the living larynx all the muscles work at once, in the excised larynx one factor may be varied at a time. One of the many important findings of van den Berg is that both pitch and loudness can be varied either by varying myoelastic factors only, or by varying aerodynamic factors only. In the living larynx, then, one or the other of these elements may be said to predominate. I believe that when the aerodynamic factor is neglected, freedom is lost; and furthermore, the "imaginary aspirate" insures that this emphasis will not be lost.

The "imaginary h" is not limited in its usefulness to the attack alone. It promotes freedom wherever it may be needed. For example, one often hears a singer insert an aspirate in making an ascending leap on the same vowel. This is poor in performance, but profitable in practice. Without the aspirate the singer may simply drive to the upper tone with the same laryngeal adjustment as he had on the lower one, just by increasing the tension in it. With the aspirate the lower tone is released and a new adjustment is achieved for the higher one. When it has been learned, the aspirate becomes unnecessary, but it must still be imagined!

There are five different modes of execution (Garcia[10], p. 20): aspirato, staccato, marcato, legato, and portamento. I am sure that cleanness of articulation in a legato florid passage comes from practicing it aspirato first, that is, "Ha, ha, ha," and then making the (h)s imaginary. This may produce a marcato that must still be smoothed into a legato, but the more rapid the coloratura the more the transition from aspirato to legato becomes direct.

It would be interesting to see a Fastax camera study of these phases of singing. Meanwhile it may be said that the evidence points clearly to the value of the Bernoulli Effect in singing.

REFERENCES

1. Taylor, Robert M., Acoustics for the Singer, the Emporia State Research Studies, Kansas State Teachers College, Vol. 6, No. 4, June 1958.

2. van den Berg, Janwillem, J. T. Zantema and P. Doornenbal, "On the Air Resistance and the Bernoulli Effect of the Human Larynx," Journal of the Acoustical Society of America, Vol. 29, No. 5, pp. 626-631, May 1957.

3. Moore, Paul, and Hans von Leden, "Dynamic Variations of the Vibratory Pattern in the Normal Larynx," Folia Phoniatrica, Vol. 10, No. 4, pp. 205-238, 1958.

4. Timcke, Rolf, Hans von Leden and Paul Moore, "Laryngeal Vibrations: Measurements of the Glottal Wave, Part I", A.M.A. Archives of Otolaryngology, Vol. 68, pp. 1-19, July 1958. Ditto: Part II, Ibid., Vol. 69, pp. 438-444, April 1959.

5. von Leden, Hans, Paul Moore and Rolf Timcke, "Laryngeal Vibrations: Measurements of the Glottal Wave, Part III," A.M.A. Archives of Otolaryngology, Vol. 71, pp. 16-35, January 1960.

6. Vennard, William, Singing, the Mechanism and the Technic, pub. by author, Los Angeles, 1949.

7. van den Berg, Janwillem, "On the Myoelastic-Aerodynamic Theory of Voice Production," NATS Bulletin, pp. 6-12, May 1958.

8. Garcia, Manuel, Traite' Complet de l'Art du Chant, 3rd. edition, Heugel et Cie., Paris, 1911.

9. van den Berg, Janwillem, and T. S. Tan, "Results of Experiments with Human Larynxes," Practica Oto-Rhino-Laryngologica, Vol. 21, No. 6, pp. 425-450, 1959.

10. Garcia, Manuel, Hints on Singing, Edward Schuberth & Co., New York, 1894.

Kinetic Aspects
of Singing

Arend Bouhuys,[2] Donald F. Proctor,[3] and Jere Mead

Department of Physiology, Harvard School of Public Health, Boston, Massachusetts

Bouhuys, Arend, Donald F. Proctor, and Jere Mead. Kinetic aspects of singing. J. Appl. Physiol. 21(2): 483-496. 1966. - We analyzed volume events during singing, together with esophageal and gastric pressures, in pressure-volume diagrams. During singing and talking up to 90% of the vital capacity may be used without conscious efforts to increase tidal volume. Subglottic pressure (Ps) was obtained by subtracting, from pleural pressure (Ppl), the static lung recoil pressure at the same lung volume. Ps increased with loudness when sustained tones were sung; airflow rate increased in two and decreased in one subject. A steady Ps during sustained tones requires a continually and gradually changing effort, at first inspiratory and finally entirely expiratory. During singing of soft tones the diaphragm is often relaxed even though net inspiratory muscle effort is required. Apparently, the actions of the diaphragm and of other inspiratory muscles may become dissociated during singing in the upright posture: To maintain Ppl below relaxation values, even though the diaphragm is relaxed, inspiratory muscles other than the diaphragm increase rib-cage volume, the relaxed diaphragm ascends, the zero reference level for abdominal pressure descends, and the decreased Ppl is balanced by an increased hydraulic pull of the abdominal contents upon the diaphragm.

phonation; body plethysmograph; pressure-volume diagram; volume events during phonation; subglottic pressure during phonation; airflow rate during phonation; control of subglottic pressure; diaphragmatic function in phonation; abdominal pressures during phonation; singing during negative-pressure breathing; mechanical analysis of voice production; pleural pressure during phonation.

During phonation the vocal cords are periodically pushed apart by the increased subglottic pressure, and closed by their elastic recoil and Bernoulli forces. The periodic escape of air from the trachea, at the frequency of the vocal cord movements, causes longitudinal vibrations of the air above the glottis at this same frequency, the fundamental tone of the voice.

Phonation requires close coordination between two mechanical processes: 1) the movements of the vocal cords and of the supralaryngeal vocal tract, which together determine pitch, loudness, and quality of the resulting sound, and: 2) the movements of the respiratory bellows, which provide the subglottic pressure and glottal airflow needed to drive the sound generator.

We will refer to these two different processes as the acoustic and the kinetic aspects of phonation. The present paper discusses the kinetics of singing, about which few systematic studies are available, in spite of the vast lore on "breathing techniques" referred to by teachers of singing and speech.

To generate a tone of constant loudness and pitch it is necessary that subglottic pressure remains constant during phonation. The resulting airflow rate leaving the glottis is at each instant determined by the area of the glottal opening and the pressure difference across it. Thus, for a given tone at a given vibration pattern of the vocal cords the mean airflow rate is expected to remain constant as long as pitch and loudness are constant.

Subglottic pressures can be measured directly using needle puncture of the trachea (12-14, 26). Although this is a safe procedure in normal subjects there is an understandable reluctance among trained singers to submit to it. Van den Berg (27) devised a catheter which can be introduced through the glottis without impeding free movements of the cords; however, its introduction requires local anesthesia. Van den Berg (27) also introduced the use of intraesophageal pressure measurements to estimate subglottic pressure. After correction for the effect of long volume on esophageal pressure, Van den Berg found good agreement between subglottic pressures as measured by the esophageal balloon method and by his catheter technique. Other investigators (9, 10, 16) have attempted to obtain esophageal pressure records in which the effect of lung volume is minimized by placing a small balloon at the level of the tracheal bifurcation and filling it with 2 ml of air. Good agreement between subglottic pressures, estimated this way, and simultaneous mouth pressures during expiration against a fixed resistance was reported. These findings were not confirmed by McGlone (18), who varied balloon size, position, and air volume, but could not find any combination of factors which made esophageal pressure independent of lung volume. McGlone (18) concluded that the extent of variability both between and within subjects made the esophageal pressure method questionable in studies of the voice. This author did not realize, however, that one can take the lung volume changes into account, as done by Van den Berg and in the present studies.

During phonation lung volume decreases, and it is the task of the respiratory bellows to maintain subglottic pressure constant in the face of changing elastic recoil of the lungs and chest wall. A number of investigators (9, 10, 17) have recognized the general features of the manner in which this is accomplished, and have provided experimental data on several details of this mechanism, but no comprehensive analysis of the mechanical events in the lungs, chest wall, and abdomen has as yet been reported.

Recent years have seen major advances in respiratory mechanics. We have taken advantage of some modern techniques to attempt such an analysis of the kinetic aspects of singing. In essence these techniques combine old methods of measurement (Fig. 1) and long established mechanical principles - first applied extensively to the respiratory system by the Swiss physician-psychiologist Rohrer early in this century - with modern methods of recording. We begin by describing the volume events accompanying singing in some experienced and relatively inexperienced singers, and compare these to the volume events during speech. We next describe how measurements of these volume events combined with simultaneous measurements of esophageal pressures may be analyzed in the form of a pressure-volume diagram to estimate both subglottic pressures and the net forces developed by the respiratory muscles. We then present estimates of subglottic pressures and rates of airflow during the singing of sustained tones, and we also describe the net forces developed by the respiratory muscles in producing such tones. Finally, we extend the use of the pressure-volume diagram to include measurements of gastric pressures and show how these may be analyzed to indicate the relative roles of the diaphragm and of the other respiratory muscles during singing.

VOLUME EVENTS DURING SINGING

Subjects.

We first recorded volume events in one of the authors (DFP) an amateur singer who studied voice for 12 years. Later, we also studied eight amateur singers with different degrees of experience and professional training. These subjects were rated by the leader of their group as experienced singers with formal training (1-3 in Figure 4), experienced singers with good voices but without formal training (4 and 5), and untrained singers with some experience but no formal training (6-8).

Methods.

An air-conditioned volume-displacement body plethysmograph (19) was used to record lung volume changes. For the present experiments and dome of the plethysmograph was removed and replaced by a rubber dam membrane across the top. The subject entered the box and put his head through a suitably placed hole in this membrane, so that an adequate neck seal was obtained without discomfort. The rubber dam membrane was fixed to the sides around the top of the box and the seal completed by wetting it with water. Movements of the part of the membrane directly around the subject's neck were prevented by weighting this down with a thin rubber bag filled with polystyrene beads which was hardened by applying suction from a vacuum line (Fig. 2) (21). Control of temperature in the box by air conditioning was important both for the subject's comfort and for the stability of the volume recordings. The volume recordings, on a direct-writing recorder, were regularly calibrated by displacing known volumes of air into and out of the sealed body plethysmograph.

Results.

The volume events during performance by DFP, of three songs with different musical qualities are shown in Fig. 3. Like wing instrument players, (5), the singer adapts a breathing pattern consisting of rapid inspirations and prolonged expirations. He uses a large portion of his vital capacity during several phrases, in particular when singing loudly. A steady rate of airflow is maintained during most phrases, as shown by constant slopes of the expiratory volume record.

The volume events in eight other subjects, who all sang the same song together, with each subject sitting in turn in the body plethysmograph, show a

Figure 1:   Presumably, the first body plethysmograph was used in Edinburgh in 1790 by Menzies (22). The first application of the modern body plethysmograph to studies of the voice was also made at the University of Edinburgh, by Draper, Ladefoged, and Whitteridge in 1959(9).

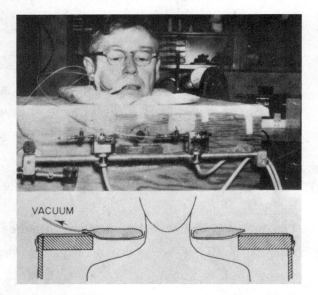

Figure 2:   Subject seated in the body plethysmograph; esophageal and gastric catheters are connected to pressure transducers in front of the plethysmograph. See schematic drawing of the neck seal and rubber dam bag filled with plastic beads which is hardened by suction from a vacuum line (21).

similar basic pattern (Fig. 4). For each rendition, the pitch was chosen by the individual in the box as one in a comfortable range. The first stanza was sung pianissimo and the second fortissimo. A strict rhythm was maintained with a metronome. Each subject, while in the plethysmograph, performed a vital-capacity (VC) maneuver immediately before and after the song. In addition, each subject sang one soft and one loud sustained tone, at a comfortable pitch, initiated from a near maximum lung volume. The subjects were not informed about the purpose of the measurements nor were they permitted to see any of the tracings obtained until all measurements had been completed.

In Fig. 4 the volume changes during singing are related to the vital capacity shown at the left in each curve. The individual breathing **patterns** differ considerably, as do the total volumes of air expired during singing of each stanza p or ff. As the time taken for each stanza was nearly the same in all renditions (36 sec), the latter values indicate the average airflows used by each singer for p or ff performance. Most subjects sing each of the phrases 1-4 during a single expiration, but others inspire briefly in the middle of one or more phrases. All subjects except two (4 and 7) use appreciably higher average expiratory airflow rates when singing ff than when singing p. The rating of the singers by their leader is indicated in Fig. 4. Independently, one of the authors (DFP) rated the same subjects as good or poor according to certain criteria of the volume record which a priori appeared to be desirable for efficient performance in singing. These criteria are: 1) good phrasing and absence of inspirations in midphrases; 2) use of a substantial portion of the VC during singing, without unnecessary use of the lowest part of the VC; 3) relatively constant airflow rates as evidenced by a smooth volume trace. On this basis two of the trained singers (2 and 3) have a poor quality volume trace. Both of these repeatedly break a phrase at lung volumes close to or higher than resting lung volume levels; 3 shows a fluctuating volume trace, and 2 uses only a small proportion of his vital capacity of 5-8 liters. On the other hand, two among the untrained singers (6 and 7) were considered to have good quality volume traces according to the same criteria.

The average airflow rates in Fig. 4 do not show any clear relation to the subject's VC which ranged from 3.0 to 5.9 liters. This was also true for airflow rates during the sustained tones sung by the same subjects. The changes in airflow rate with lung volume when singing a sustained soft or loud tone starting at a large lung volume, were of variable direction and magnitude. Cavagna and Margaria (7)

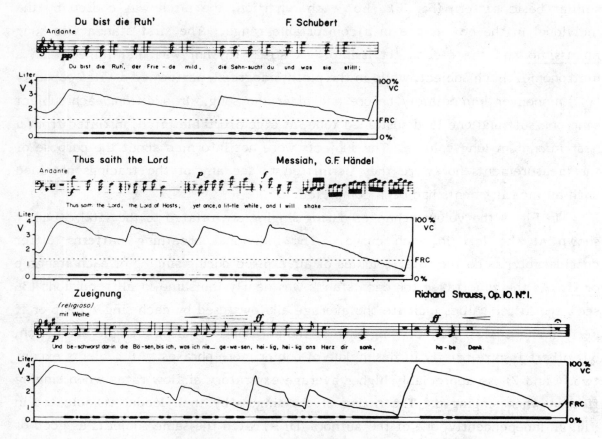

Figure 3: Musical score, text, and volume events during performance of parts of three songs by an experienced amateur singer (DFP). Marker bars below the volume traces indicate the syllables of the text. These signals do not correspond exactly to the timing or duration of the syllables; they were done with a hand switch while listening to the sound. The three songs are: A, Du bist die Ruh' (F. Schubert); B, Zueignung (R. Strauss); and C, Thus saith the Lord, from G. Handel's Messiah.

observed a systematic decrease of flow rates with decrease of lung volume during singing of soft tones; we observed this in only three out of our eight subjects.

For comparison, Fig. 5 shows the volume events during speech, recorded with the same method as used during singing. The subject read a text in English, first with a normal, conversational voice, and later again at two levels of increased loudness. The same experiment, using the same text, was performed in two other subjects. Figure 6 shows that a larger proportion of the VC is used when speaking loudly. However, airflow rates increased appreciably only at maximum loudness in one subject (Fig. 7). Lung volumes below functional residual capacity are frequently used during speech. This is particularly evident during spontaneous talk in the subject of Fig. 5 at the end of the experiment, and during laughing this subject expired nearly to residual volume (Fig. 5D).

Expiratory minute volumes (V$\underline{E}$) varied from 7.8–15.3 liters/min in the $\underline{p}$ stanzas of Fig. 4, and from 12.7–23.3 liters/ min in the $\underline{ff}$ stanzas. Breathing rates are low in most subjects (4 breaths in 36 sec, i.e., 6.7 breaths/min), so that alveolar ventilation can only be slightly lower than V$\underline{E}$. These values are higher than average resting ventilation rates. We have not investigated the regulation of ventilation during singing and speech in this study. It seems evident, however, that hyperventilation may occur at least during singing of loud phrases.

KINETIC ANALYSIS OF SINGING

Pressure-Volume Diagram

The pressure we measure (indirectly in terms of esophageal pressure) is pleural pressure relative to atmospheric. We must first develop the relationships between this pressure on one hand, and $\underline{a}$) subglottic pressure and $\underline{b}$) the mechanisms producing subglottic pressure, on the other hand.

The pressure differences between two points must equal the sum of the pressure differences across all intervening structures. In the present instance there are two sets of structures between the pleural surface and the body surface, depending on the pathway taken: the lungs and airways, in one direction, and the structures of the chest wall in the other. Accordingly there are two expressions for the pressure equalities:

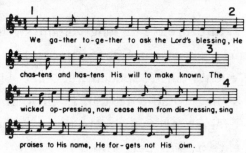

We ga-ther to-ge-ther to ask the Lord's blessing, He
chas-tens and has-tens His will to make known. The
wicked op-pressing, now cease them from dis-tressing, sing
praises to His name, He for-gets not His own.

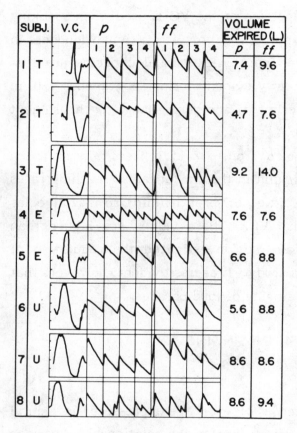

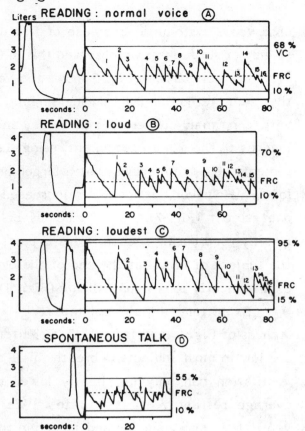

Figure 5: Volume events during reading of a written English text (subj AB) A: at normal voice; B: at increased loudness, "as if spesaking to an audience in a large room;" and C: at maximum loudness "as if addressing an audience in a stadium." D: spontaneous talking at the end of the experiment; at arrow the subject laughed.

Figure 4: Volume events during performance of the "Prayer of Thanksgiving" by 8 singers. Subjects were rated trained (T), experienced (E), and untrained (U). Each stanza (phrases 1-4 was sung twice, p and ff. Volume expired = sum of volumes expired during each of the phrases 1-4. The musical score (Valerius, 1597) and the four text phrases are shown for comparison.

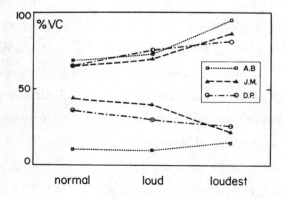

Figure 6: Percentage of vital capacity used during the experiment of Figure 5 by three subjects who read the same text at three different voice intensities.

$$Ppl = Palv - Pst(l) \qquad (1)$$

and

$$Ppl = Pmus + Pst(w) \qquad (2)$$

where:

Ppl = pressure between the pleural and body surface, herein referred to as pleural pressure

Palv = alveolar pressure

Pst(l) and Pst (w) = static recoil pressures of lungs and chest wall, respectively

Pmus = pressure caused by contraction of respiratory muscles

The minus sign for Pst(l) in equation 1 may be confusing to the reader. Clearly, pleural pressure should increase as alveolar pressure increases, but why should it decrease when the static recoil pressure of the lungs increases? The reason lies in the mechanical arrangement of the lungs and chest wall. The pleural surface is inside the chest wall; therefore any tendency of the chest wall to decrease in size will increase pleural pressure. However, the pleural surface is outside the lungs; therefore the tendency of the lungs to collapse reduces pleural pressure.

During phonation rates of gas flow and volume acceleration are so low that pressures related to the viscance and inertance of the lungs and chest wall are negligible compared to the other pressures. Hence corresponding dynamic terms are left out of the equations.

Equations 1 and 2 may be conbined as follows:

$$Palv = Pst(l) + Pmus \qquad (3)$$

During phonation most of the resistance to gas flow is offered by the glottis, and the pressure drop from the alveoli to the subglottic region is, as will be demonstrated, extremely small. Palv therefore approximates subglottic pressure. The terms on the right hand side of equation 3 represent the "driving forces" which together are responsible for subglottic pressure: the combined elastic recoil of the lungs and chest plus any pressure developed by contracting respiratory muscles.

In equations 1 and 2 we find four unknown quantities. Ppl alone is assumed to be known. By suitable respiratory maneuvers two of the quantities-one in each equation-can be made equal to o. In equation 1 Palv may be made equal to o by holding one's breath with the airways open. In that case Ppl = -Pst(l). In equation 2 Pmus may be made equal to o by voluntary relaxation against an obstructed airway,

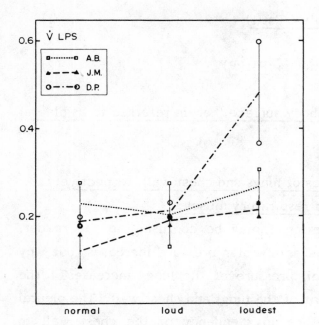

Figure 7: Airflow rates, calculated from the slopes of the volume recordings during the experiment of Fig. 5 in three subjects. The range of flow rates for each subject is shown at three different voice intensities.

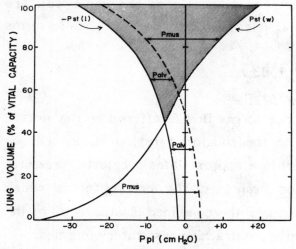

Figure 8: Campbell diagram. Drawn lines are the static characteristics of the lungs (-Pst (1)) and of the chest wall (Pst(w)). Broken line indicates pleural pressure during singing of a soft tone through the full vital capacity range. Graphical determination of Palv and of Pmus according to equations 1 and 2 is indicated. Shaded area: in this part of the diagram Palv is positive, i.e., expiration takes place if the airways are open, and Pmus is negative, i.e., inspiratory muscle effort keeps Ppl at lower than relaxation values. In this area of the diagram airflow and respiratory muscle effort are in opposite directions.

e.g., the closed glottis or an obstructed mouthpiece. In that case Ppl = Pst(w). With the unknowns now reduced to two, i.e., Palv and Pmus, a complete solution is possible.

Such a solution is readily accomplished with a volume-pressure graph in which pleural pressure is plotted against lung volume-the so-called "Campbell diagram" (6). This representation has been used extensively by Agostoni, Rahn, and co-workers (2, 3). Much of the present analysis, including the interpretation of abdominal and transdiaphragmatic pressures, is based on the work of these authors.

Figure 8 illustrates the Campbell diagram. The static characteristics of the lungs and chest wall are plotted as lines. The line -Pst(l) is drawn through points obtained by holding the breath, with the airways open, at various lung volumes over the full vital-capacity range; in that case, as shown above, Ppl = - Pst(l). To obtain the line Pst(w) the subject relaxes against an obstructed airway, in which case Ppl = Pst(w), again at different lung volumes over the full vital-capacity range. Equation 1 states that Ppl, whatever its value, will differ from -Pst(l) by a pressure equal to alveolar pressure, Palv. Whenever Ppl is to the left of the static characteristic of the lungs, Palv is negative in sign and gas will tend to flow into the lungs. For all values of Ppl to the right of the -Pst(l) line, Palv is positive and gas tends to flow out of the lungs. Similarly, equation 2 states that any value of Ppl differs from the Pst(w), at the same volume, by a pressure equal to Pmus. To decrease Ppl below the isovolume value of Pst(w) requires inspiratory muscle effort. For all values of Ppl to the left of the Pst(w) line, Pmus is negative in sign and the net muscle effort is inspiratory. To increase Ppl above the inovolume value of Pst(w) requires expiratory muscle effort. For all values of Ppl to the right of the Pst(w) line Pmus is positive, and the net muscle effort is expiratory. For certain areas of the graph these statements about the inspiratory or expiratory direction of the pressures appear to be in conflict. For instance, there is a triangular area between the Pst(l) and Pst(w) curves and above their point of intersection (Fig. 8; shaded area), where expiration should take place (Palv = positive) in the face of net inspiratory muscle effort (Pmus negative). In this region, the inspiratory muscles have a braking action and keep the static recoil of the lungs and chest wall from exerting their full effect. The muscles "let the air out"-slowly if Ppl is close to -Pst(l) and more rapidly if Ppl is close to Pst(w). In the triangular area below the intersection the direction of flow (inspiratory) is also opposite in sign to the direction of muscle effort (Pmus positive): the tendency of the chest wall to expand and cause inspiration is countered by the braking action of the expiratory muscles.

Since phonation occurs during expiration all values of Ppl during phonation will be to the right of the -Pst(l) line. As will be demonstrated, soft sustained tones initiated at high lung volumes require comparatively small and steady subglottic pressures. An example of such a tone is given in Fig. 8 (broken line). Initially, pleural pressures are in the region requiring continued inspiratory effort. As the tone continues, this effort must diminish to zero and be followed by progressive expiratory effort, if subglottic pressure is to be maintained nearly constant. It appears that a steady tone will require continuously changing muscular effort. This example serves to illustrate how the Campbell diagram will be used both to measure subglottic pressure and the net participation of respiratory muscles during singing.

MEASUREMENT OF SUBGLOTTIC PRESSURE
AND AIRFLOW RATE DURING SINGING

Subjects.

The kinetic aspects of singing were studied in three healthy, experienced, though not highly trained, singers, and in two healthy subjects untrained in singing.

Methods.

The volume events during singing were recorded as described earlier in this paper. Intraesophageal pressures were recorded with the methods described by Milic-Emili et al. (23). Intragastric pressures, used in conjunction with esophageal pressures to evaluate transdiaphragmatic pressure and hence the activity of the diaphragm (2, 11; see the next section of this paper) were measured from 5-cm-long balloons (circumference 3.5 cm) placed in the stomach and partially filled with 2 ml of air. Esophageal and gastric pressures were recorded with Sanborn 268B transducers. Airflow rates during singing were obtained in most experiments from the record of lung volume versus time. In some experiments, a continuous flow record was obtained with a full-face plastic mask provided with a circular wire screen (20); pressures inside the mask were recorded with a Sanborn 270 differential gas pressure transducer. All signals were amplified and recorded on a 4-channel direct-writing system. In addition, the output of the preamplifiers was fed into a tape recorder (tape speed: 7½ inch/sec). XY plots of pressures versus lung volume were made either directly by recording these events on a direct-writing XY recorder or by playing the tape recording back into the XY recorder. The pressure difference between esophagus and stomach was either computed from the two separate recordings versus time, or the difference was recorded directly with the esophageal pressure catheter connected to the positive and the gastric catheter to the negative side of a differential transducer.

The static pressure-volume relationships of the lungs were obtained as follows. The subject performed three full vital capacity maneuvers in order to standardize the volume history of the lungs (23). He then inspired maximally and held his breath at different lung volumes (glottis open) during the subsequent maximal expiration. This procedure was repeated at least once and gave consistent results in all subjects. To describe the static lung recoil curve we averaged the subatmospheric pressure at each lung volume at which the breath was held over the excursion corresponding to the heart beat, and drew the line of best fit freehand through the points obtained. In the same subjects, relaxation pressures of the chest wall (Pst(w)) were obtained while repeating the above maneuver; this time the subject relaxed against a closed airway at each lung volume.

To record the mechanical events during singing of single tones the subject was asked to inspire maximally and to phonate as long as possible at constant pitch (B♭2, 116.5 cycles/sec, or B♭3, 233 cycles/sec) and constant loudness during the subsequent expiration. Esophageal or gastric pressures, or the differences between the two, were recorded against lung volume on the XY recorder. Similar maneuvers were made in one subject with direct recording of airflow rate, using the wire-screen face mask.

The pressure transducers were calibrated against a water manometer. In addition, electrical signals corresponding to known quantities of each event were fed into the 4-channel recorder, the XY recorder, and the tape recorder at regular intervals to check the constancy of calibrations.

Results.

The mechanical events during singing of sustained tones are shown in Fig. 9. The vertical row of graphs marked C are the Campbell diagrams, with the Pst(l) curve shown as dashed line (cf. Fig. 8). The drawn lines in Fig. 9C represent Ppl during singing of sustained tones through a large part of the vital capacity. On some occasions esophageal contractions interfered with the Ppl recording during singing

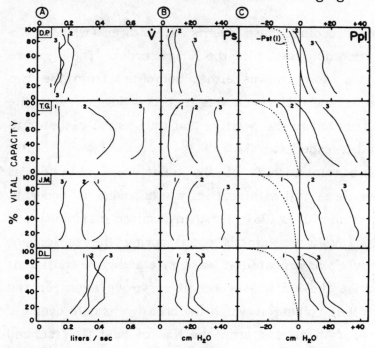

Figure 9: A: airflow rates; B: subglottic pressures; and C: pleural pressures during singing of sustained tones starting near maximum lung volumes, plotted versus lung volume, expressed as a percentage of VC. Dashed line in C: static recoil curve of the lungs. Subjects DP and TG are amateur singers with professional training; subjects JM and DL are inexperienced singers. Identical tones for each subject are indicated by numerals 1-3, in the order of increasing pitch (subj DP) or of increasing loudness (all other subjects).

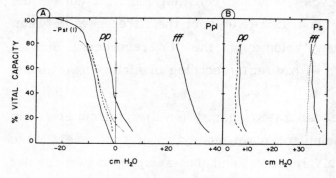

Fig. 10. A: Ppl versus lung volume (% of VC) during singing of a sustained tone pp and fff (subj DFP; solid lines). Ppl during expiration, without phonating, at the same flow rates, as observed on an oscilloscope screen, as when singing the pp tone is indicated by dashed line (----). Similarly, the dotted line (...) represents Ppl during expiration (without phonating) at the same flow rate as when singing the fff tone. Horizontal distance between the dashed or the dotted line and the Pst (l) curve represents the resistive pressure across the lungs and airways at each lung volume, and at the flow rate prevailing during singing of the two tones. B: Subglottic pressures for the same tones calculated as Ps = Palv = Ppl + Pst(l) (solid lines) and also as this value minus the resistive pressure drop across the lungs and airways, including the wide open glottis (dashed and dotted lines).

in the upper 10-20% of the vital capacity; these parts of the records have been omitted in Fig. 9C. For each subject, the tones are numbered, in order of increasing pitch (subj DP, upper row), or in order of increasing loudness (all other subjects).

At each lung volume, the horizontal distance between the drawn lines (tones) and the Pst(l) curve represents Palv, according to equation 1. Palv is the pressure head available for airflow through the airways, including the glottis. During phonation, the pressure drop across the glottis is large compared to the pressure drop across the rest of the airways. To demonstrate this, one subject (DFP) sang different tones while wearing the wire-screen face mask. Airflow during phonation was displayed on an oscilloscope in front of the subject, and the flow rate during phonation was marked on the screen. Ppl and lung volume were recorded simultaneously on the XY recorder (Fig. 10A, lines marked pp and fff). The subject was then asked to inspire maximally and expire at the same flow rates, but without phonating, while watching his airflow rates on the screen. Ppl during these maneuvers were again plotted on the pressure-volume diagram (Fig. 10A, dashed and dotted lines). The horizontal distances between these lines and the Pst(l) curve indicate the resistive pressure drip across the lungs and airways, including the wide-open glottis. This pressure drop increases as lung volume decreases. In Fig. 10B the solid lines pp and fff indicate the subglottic pressures Ps calculated as Ps = Palv = Ppl + Pst(l), while the dashed and dotted lines represent this value minus the resistive pressure drop across the rest of the airways and the lungs. As we assume the pressure directly above the glottis to be atmospheric, the latter values should represent the true subglottic pressure. However, the error introduced by assuming that Ps = Palv = Ppl + Pst(l) appears to be small, in particular at high lung volumes and for tones which require high subglottic pressures. In Fig. 9, this error has been neglected in calculating subglottic pressures Ps in Fig. 9B from the Campbell diagrams for each subject. The graphs of Fig. 9B show that subglottic pressures are kept relatively constant over a major portion of the vital capacity in all subjects, in spite of the large increase in Ppl with decreasing lung volume. That is in subject TG, tone 2, Ppl increases from -3 to +25 cm H_2O during phonation from 95% of VC down to 10% of VC, while subglottic pressure Ps varies only between +18 and +24 cm H_2O.

Airflow rates during singing of the same tones have been plotted in Fig. 9A. The variability of flow rate over the range of lung volumes used appears larger, at least for some subjects and some tones, than the variability of Ps for the same tone. Tone 2 in subject TG is the most pronounced example for this statement. Also, the range of airflows used for comparable tones differed considerably among the subjects. When singing the same tone (B 2) with increasing loudness subject TG increased his airflow rate from 0.14 to 0.69 liters/sec, while subject JM decreased flow rate from 0.44 to about 0.17 liters/sec. In subject DP, flow rate changes relatively little when singing at increased pitch.

GENERATION OF SUBGLOTTIC PRESSURE

Net respiratory muscle effort.

Figure 11A is the same as Fig. 9C, with the addition of dashed lines corresponding to the static characteristic of the chest wall (Pst(w)). (Figure 11 contains data on an additional subject, ER, not included in Fig. 9 for lack of flow measurements.) As developed in conjunction with Fig. 8 the horizontal distance between such lines and observed esophageal pressures corresponds to the pressures developed by the respiratory muscles. The values for Pmus represent net inspiratory or expiratory effort. It cannot be excluded that, when Pmus is negative, some expiratory muscle contraction may take place, but we can merely state that the effort of the inspiratory muscles must preponderate, and vice versa when Pmus is positive. To maintain Ps approximately constant is it apparent from these diagrams that a continuously changing degree of respiratory muscle effort is required. The horizontal dashed line in Fig. 11A-D) corresponds to the lung volume at which Pmus is zero, i.e.,Ppl = Pst(w), for the lowest or softest tone for each subject. At all larger lung volumes net inspiratory muscle effort is required for these tones (Pmus negative; Fig. 11B). For loud tones, Pmus may be positive at all lung volumes, i.e., expiratory muscle effort is required as soon as the tone is started.

Action of the diaphragm.

Agostoni and Rahn have introduced the measurement of gastric pressure (Pga) in conjunction with esophageal pressure to estimate transdiaphragmatic pressures, Pdi, and intra-abdominal pressure, Pab (2). Figure 8C and D presents these pressures during the same tones for which Pbl is shown in Figure 11A and Pmus in Fig. 11B. The action of one particular respiratory muscle, the diaphragm, can be examined from the graphs of Pdi versus lung volume in Fig. 11C. Positive values of

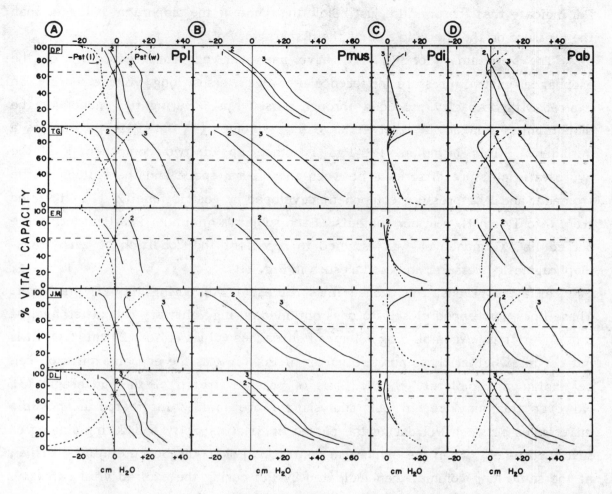

Figure 11: Generation of subglottic pressure during singing of sustained tones. Subjects are the same as those in Fig. 9, with the addition of ER, a trained female singer. A: Campbell diagrams: Ppl versus lung volume in percent of VC. Dashed lines represent the Pst(l) and Pst(w) curves. Ppl during sustained tones shown as in Fig. 9C. B: net muscular effort required for the tones in A: Pmus versus lung volume. Negative values of Pmus indicate net inspiratory muscle effort, positive values indicate net expiratory muscle effort. Pmus = o when Ppl = Pst(w). C: role of the diaphragm in producing the negative values of Pmus at large lung volumes: transdiaphragmatic pressure Pdi versus lung volume, for the same tones as in A and B. No evidence of contraction of the diaphragm for any tone is found in subjects ER and DL. Subjects DP, TG, and JM contract their diaphragm when singing tone 1; in TG and JM this contraction ends at a lung volume larger than that where Pmus = o for the same tone (horizontal dashed line through A-D. Curved dashed lines represent Pdi during performance of an expiratory vital capacity through pursed lips, a maneuver during which the diaphragm is relaxed except perhaps at very small lung volumes (3). D: abdominal pressures during performance of the same tones. Sloping dashed lines indicate relaxation values of abdominal pressure. During singing of soft tones at large lung volumes Pab is lower than the relaxation pressure at the same lung volume (tones 1). In the subjects who initiate this tone with a contraction of the diaphragm, Pab decreases as the diaphragm relaxes.

Pdi indicate that the pressure just below the dome of the diaphragm is higher than the pressure on the thoracic side of the diaphragm, Ppl.

The zero lines for Fig. 11C have been derived from recordings of the esophageal-gastric pressure difference Pes-Pga versus lung volume during an expired vital capacity ptoduced through pursed lips. During this maneuver the diaphragm is relaxed, at least at large lung volumes (3), and Pes-Pga reaches a minimum.   This minimum Pes-Pga is made up of two components: 1) the hydrostatic pressure difference between the pleural space and the balloon in the stomach, and 2) a pressure component developed by gastric tone (2, 11). It varied from 6 to 14 cm H_2O in our subjects. Each subject's minimum Pes-Pga during the pursed lip VC maneuver was assumed to represent the condition of zero trans-diaphragmatic pressure, and used as such in Fig. 11C.

In these graphs, the dashed lines represent Pdi during the VC maneuver. These lines correspond closely to ones obtained during voluntary relaxation against a closed glottis. At small lung volumes Pdi reaches values up to +28 cm H_2O. It is not certain whether these positive values of Pdi towards the end of expiration can be explained completely on the basis of passive stretch of the diaphragm (3). However this may be, in our analysis we are mainly interested in possible differences between Pdi during the pursed lip vital capacity and during singing of sustained tones. When the diaphragm contracts, Pdi should become more positive, at the same lung volume, than indicated by Pdi during the expired vital capacity. In Fig. 11C this is shown to happen at large lung volumes for tones 1 in subjects DP, TG, and Jm.

There is an evident discrepancy between the data for Pmus in Fig. 11B and those for Pdi in Fig. 11C. For tone 1 in all five subjects, the horizontal dashed line, referred to above indicates the lung volume at which Pmus is zero. At higher lung volumes inspiratory muscles must be contracting actively according to our analysis.   Nevertheless, we find no evidence for contraction of the diaphragm during these tones in two subjects (ER and DL), while in two others the diaphragm appears to relax at a lung volume well above that indicated by the horizontal dashed line (TG and JM). Only in subject DP does the diaphragm, for this tone, relax approximately at the lung volume where Pmus = o. Even in this subject, however, contraction of the diaphragm cannot account for more than a part of the negative value of Pmus, e.g., at 90% of vital capacity Pdi = +9 cm H_2O, while Pmus = -15 cm H_2O. In other subjects, the diaphragm was apparently relaxed while values of Pmus were as low as -13 cm H_2O (subj JM).

Net inspiratory forces at large lung volumes without recourse to the major inspiratory muscle, the diaphragm, are possible because of the hydraulic properties of the abdominal contents. Next we will briefly describe these properties. In Fig. 11D, Pab is the pressure existing in the abdomen just under the dome of the diaphragm, and has been calculated from gastric pressure by subtracting the difference between Pes and Pga under conditions of zero transdiaphragmatic pressure as discussed above for Pdi. The validity of this procedure is shown by the data for Pab during relaxation against a closed glottis (dashed lines in Fig. 11D). During this maneuver, Pab should be zero, if the diaphragm is relaxed and not passively stretched, at the same lung volume and where Pst(w) equals zero. Comparison of Fig. 11A and D shows this to be true for four subjects. In subject JM, Pst(w) is zero at a lung volume of 56% while Pab = o at a lung volume of 48%. This small discrepancy can be explained by the fact that at this lung volume his diaphragm is probably undergoing a slight passive stretch, as indicated by the simultaneous value of Pdi.

Duomarco and Rimini (11) were the first to show clearly that, with regard to pressures, the abdomen behaves as a container with partly elastic walls, and filled with a liquid of close to unit density. They showed that, in different postures, pressure in the abdomen increases with as many centimerters H_2O as one moves the point of measurement down in the direction of the force of gravity. The absolute pressure levels at each point can be obtained by referring to a zero reference level. The setting of the zero reference level is determined by the elastic recoil of the abdominal walls and by forces exerted by muscles of the chest and abdomen. Thus, for the conditions mentioned in the preceding paragraph, at a lung volume where Pst(w) is zero, and the diaphragm is relaxed, Pab = o at a point just below the dome of the diaphragm. In the concept of Duomarco and Rimini, recently reviewed by Agostoni and Mead (1), one may state that in these conditions the zero reference level for Pab is situated just below the dome of the diaphragm. At lower points in the abdomen, in the upright posture, pressure will be higher with as many centimeters H_2O as one moves downward.

At higher lung volumes, where Pst(w) assumes positive values, Pab becomes positive during relaxation (Fig. 11D). As long as transdiaphragmatic pressure remains zero, Pab will equal Pst(w) at each lung volume. The zero reference level for abdominal pressures is now situated in a plane above the diaphragm; e.g., when Pab = +8 cm H_2O just under the dome of the diaphragm, the zero reference level is situated 8 cm above that point. At lower lung volumes, where Pst(w) becomes negative, this negative chest recoil pressure, too, will be transmitted throughout the abdomen and decrease pressures at all points in it. In other words, the zero reference level for abdominal pressure moves down to a point below the diaphragm. At these smaller lung volumes, as the diaphragm ascends, an appreciable trans-diaphragmatic pressure develops (Fig. 11C), probably mostly because of passive stretch of the diaphragm. Thus, the decrease of Pab by the negative Pst(w) is partially offset by an increase due to the positive pressure contribution of Pdi. (Compare Fig. 11, A and D.) At these lower lung volumes, during relaxation, the zero reference level for abdominal pressure moves down, in the upright posture, with as many centimeters as indicated by the negative value of Pab.

We must now examine the various factors which cause deviations of Pab from the values obtained during relaxation. Contraction of the diaphragm or of abdominal muscles will increase Pab and move the zero reference level upwards. Also, if at a given lung volume one contracts expiratory rib cage muscles and thus decreases the rib cage contents, the diaphragm is pushed downward, and Pab increases. For the same lung volume, the rib cage volume will now be smaller and the abdominal volume larger, compared to these volumes during relaxation. This maneuver, too, will displace the zero reference level upward.

How is it possible for Pab to be less at a given lung volume than during relaxation? At large lung volumes, when soft tones are sung, this certainly occurs. The most likely explanation is as follows. If at the same lung volume one increases the rib cage volume by contraction of inspiratory muscles which operate on the rib cage, the relaxed diaphragm will be pulled upward and the abdominal wall will be sucked inward. The decrease of Ppl caused by the contraction of inspiratory chest muscles will be transmitted through the relaxed diaphragm to the abdomen and cause a downward movement of the zero reference level. At the same time, the relaxed diaphragm is displaced upward. These two factors together can produce a considerable decrease of Pab compared to its value during relaxation at the same lung volume. The hydraulic forces in the abdomen now exert a pull on the diaphragm, evidenced by a much lower Pab than during relaxation at the same lung volume, and this pull is caused both by the downward movement of the zero reference level and by the upward movement of the diaphragm itself.

On the basis of this discussion we can now examine the departures of Pab from its values during relaxation when sustained tones are being sung. For loud or high tones, at all lung volumes (tones 3, Fig. 11D) Pab is always more positive than its value during relaxation. These departures to the right of the relaxation curve for Pab can readily be accounted for by contraction of expiratory muscles, including both abdominal and chest cage muscles. At large lung volumes and for soft tones, the singer's problem is to maintain his Ppl at a lower value than would obtain during relaxation (Fig. 11A). Net inspiratory muscle force must be used to accomplish this (Fig. 11B). It is evident that this can be done by simultaneous contraction of inspiratory rib cage muscles and diaphragm. However, in several cases Pdi indicates that the diaphragm remains relaxed when soft tones are sung at large lung volumes (Fig. 11C), and in these cases the diaphragm does not contribute actively toward a decrease of Ppl below relaxation values. The mechanism discussed in the previous paragraph must then be called into operation: by contracting inspiratory chest muscles, the zero reference level in the abdomen is brought downward and the diaphragm ascends, resulting in a hydraulic pull of the abdominal contents on the relaxed diaphragm, which achieves the same purpose as active contraction of the diaphragm would, i.e., a Ppl lower than relaxation values, but only at lower values of Pab. For example, during relaxation at 90% of VC subject DL has a Ppl and Pabd of +5 cm H_2O, i.e., the zero reference level is situated 5 cm above the dome of the diaphragm. When a soft tone (tone 1) is produced at this lung volume, Ppl = -8 cm h_2O, Pdi remains zero (diaphragm relaxed) and thus Pab also equals -8 cm H_2O. Thus, the zero reference level has moved to a position 8 cm below the dome of the diaphragm, i.e., a decrease of the zero reference level of 13 cm.

Discussion

This paper is not concerned with the aesthetic qualities of the sound produced by the human voice. Such basic sound qualifies as pitch and loudness have been introduced as variables only to illustrate the mechanical behavior of the respiratory system during phonation. In fact, the monotonous appearance of the volume traces in Fig. 3 contrasts markedly with the widely variable content of the musical scores. Clearly, our measurements relate to phenomena which are, although necessities for sound production, infinitely coarse in comparison to the modalities of expression of which the human voice is capable.

In 1837, Johannes Muller (24) showed that, when he increased the subglottic pressure in phonating isolated larynges, both loudness and pitch increased. To sing a tone louder but at the same pitch, subglottic pressure must increase while vocal cord tension decreases in order to keep pitch constant. Good voice performance therefore requires fine coordination between intrinsic laryngeal and respiratory muscles. This paper reports experiments on the mechanical factors relating to control of subglottic pressure during singing. As yet, only a small number of subjects, not including any highly trained professional performers, has been studied, and we have not made recordings over the full range of the voice in any subject. We believe, however, that the mechanical principles discussed have a more general validity, and the methods presented may therefore be of use in future studies.

Recordings of volume events during singing showed no clear-cut differences between "trained" and "untrained" singers (Fig. 4). None of these subjects was highly trained, however, and the comparison is further complicated by the apparent fact that some persons are naturally endowed with a good voice and adapt a suitable breathing pattern even without formal training. Also, the song chosen may have been too easy to bring out differences between the subjects. Further studies with similar methods, and including highly trained professional singers, seem desirable. Both during singing (Figs. 3 and 4) and during speech (Figs. 5 and 6), one often uses 80% or more of one's vital capacity. The subglottic pressures produced are sufficiently low so that the limit of the expiratory maximum pressure-volume diagram (25) is not reached until the lung volume is close to residual volume, in contrast to the predicament of many brass wind instrument players who can only use a fraction of their vital capacity because of the high mouth pressures which they develop (5). How does it come about that such a complete use is made of one's vital capacity during singing and speech at rest, while on the other hand one rarely uses more than 50% of one's vital capacity during maximum physical exercise (4)? The answer probably lies in the area of energy expenditure; the maneuvers during phonation would become extravagant in this respect if used to accomplish high levels of ventilation.

Considerable discussion has arisen in the literature on phonetics concerning the estimation of subglottic pressures from esophageal pressure measurements (9, 10, 16-18, 26-28). The present study shows that subglottic pressures may be estimated during phonation, using the esophageal balloon technique as recently improved (23), if the elastic recoil (Pst(l)) curve of the lungs is determined separately in the same subject. This principle was applied by Van den Berg (27), who determined the difference between esophageal pressure during phonation and during breath holding with open glottis. The advantage of the present method is that subglottic pressure can be measured without interrupting phonation and at any lung volume. The relation between Van den Berg's method and the present technique is shown in Fig. 12. Here, the subject sang a tone, starting near the top of the vital capacity, interrupted phonation several times, and held his breath, glottis open, during these interruptions. At each interruption, Ppl decreases to the value of Pst(1) at the prevailing lung volume.

When singing sustained tones at constant pitch and loudness subglottic pressures and airflow rates are in many cases relatively constant through the full range of lung volume used (Fig. 9, A and B). In other cases either Ps or airflow rate, or both, are more variable during the same tone. We made no simultaneous recordings of pitch and sound pressure in these experiments and thus cannot verify to which extent the variability of Ps and flow rates is related to changes in pitch or sound pressure, or to other factors. For the same reason, we cannot yet evaluate the relationships between the power spent in producing tones (i.e., the product of subglottic pressure and flow rate) and the sound power produced. Such experiments have recently been done, using the techniques described in this paper, and these will be the subject of a separate communication. With increasing sound intensity subglottic pressure regularly increases (Fig. 9B), but the changes of flow rates seem to be more variable: increasing in some subjects (subj TG and DL in Fig. 9A), decreasing in another subject (subj JM, Fig. 9A). In wind instruments, airflow rates nearly always increase in a regular fashion when sound intensity is increased (Bouhuys (5), and unpublished observations).

To keep subglottic pressure constant over a wide range of lung volumes requires a finely graded muscular effort, in which both inspiratory and expiratory muscles participate. In this respect, our results agree with electromyographic studies of Draper et al. (9, 10), who found that inspiratory activity during phonation ceased at lung volumes close to FRC when subglottic pressures were low, and at gradually larger lung volumes when subglottic pressures increased, to be replaced by expiratory activity at lung volumes below these levels. Our observations also agree with their finding that the diaphragm does not play an important role during phonation in most persons (9). In their experience, diaphragmatic activity as measured by intraesophageal electrode usually diminished rapidly and ceased completely during the first 2 or 3 sec of an utterance after a maximal inspiration. In the present study, the relative lack of participation of the diaphragm in the

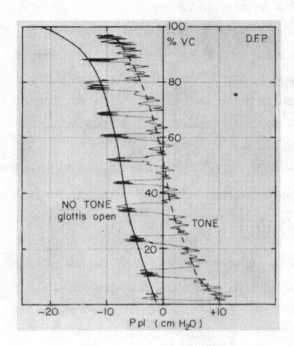

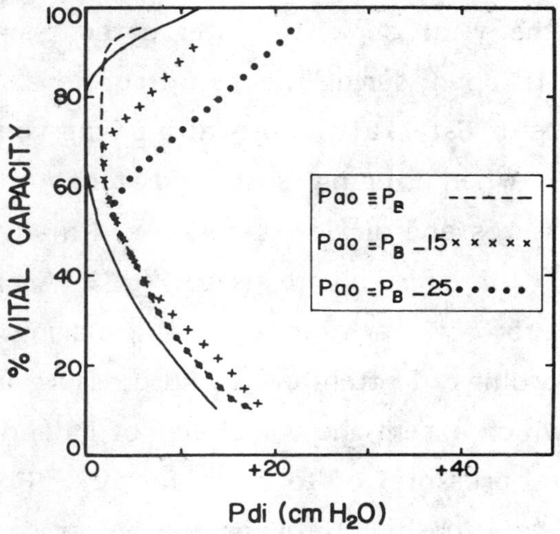

Figure 12:   Pleural pressure and lung volume recorded directly on an XY-recorder during singing of a tone at constant pitch and loudness. The subject initiated the tone at a lung volume close to 100% of VC and interrupted phonation 10 times. During the brief interruptions he held his breath with his glottis wide open. This is the maneuver used by Van den Berg (27) to estimate subglottic pressure from esophageal pressure readings.   The "noise" in the Ppl recording is the result of fluctuations in esophageal pressure caused by the heart beat. The course of Ppl during phonation is indicated by the dashed line. During the interruptions, Ppl decreases to the value of Pst(1) at the prevailing lung volume. Solid line: static recoil curve of the lungs (-Pst(1)) for this subject. Subglottic pressure = 7.5 cm H_2O at 50% of VC (horizontal distance between solid and dashed lines).

Figure 13: Subject DL: Pdi versus lung volume (%VC). Solid curved line: Pdi during performance of a "pursed lip VC." Other lines represent Pdi during singing of the same sustained tone, at the same loudness, at three different pressures at the airway opening as indicated in the box. When Pao is decreased, the singer has to resort to contraction of the diaphragm over a large proportion of the VC in order to decrease Ppl by the same amount as Pao has been decreased, and thus he is able to keep the subglottic pressure at the level required for this tone. Under conditions of decreased Pao the mechanism discussed in the text, i.e., decreasing Ppl below relaxation values by elevation of the rib cage and the hydraulic pull of the abdominal contents upon the diaphragm, is no longer sufficient.

process of developing a negative Pmus at large lung volumes is evident in most subjects who sang sustained tones (Fig. 11C), and it could also be demonstrated during performance of a song by DFP (Fig. 14). Ppl-volume and Pdi-volume loops are shown for three phrases of the song. During inspiration Palv is subatmospheric, and the inspiratory portion of the Ppl-volume loop is situated to the left of the Pst(l) curve. During inspiration the diaphragm contracts, resulting in transdiaphragmatic pressures of up to +15 cm H_2O, but when expiration and phonation begin the diaphragm relaxes almost instantaneously, as shown by the rapid return of Pdi, over a very small portion of the VC, to values equal to those obtained during a "pursed lip VC" with the diaphragm relaxed.

The function of the inspiratory muscles during phonation, i.e., to keep Ppl at levels below relaxation values whenever required, is to us one of the intriguing problems in the present study. This inspiratory muscle function may correspond to what is variously called "Atemstutze," "Appoggio," or breath support in the literature on singing. Winckel (29) defines "Atemstutze" as the support with which the inspiratory musculature opposes the collapse of the chest. Distinctions are made between tones sung "without support," "with chest support," and with "diaphragm support." If the concept of breath support corresponds to our notions about the function of inspiratory muscles during singing, the singer would have little voluntary choice as to the use of support by inspiratory muscles for a certain tone; some inspiratory muscle activity is required whenever Ppl has to be lower than Pst(w) at any given lung volume. Trained singers apparently experience different subjective sensations in connection with their breath support, which they interpret as being due to elevation of the chest or to contraction of the diaphragm. The present methods may enable one to demonstrate objective physiological differences between these, intuitively defined, methods of breath support.

The analysis of transdiaphragmatic and abdominal pressures has shown how a reduction of Ppl below relaxation values can be accomplished at high lung volumes without the use of the diaphragm, i.e., by expanding the rib cage beyond its relaxation volume, thus bringing the zero reference level for abdominal pressure down and elevating the diaphragm. However, the negative Pmus which can be exerted in this way must be limited by the maximum hydraulic pull of the abdominal contents, whichever is smaller. This limitation appears, for example, when singing tones while pressure at the mouth is decreased. When a tone requiring a certain Ps is being sung at decreased pressure at the airway opening,

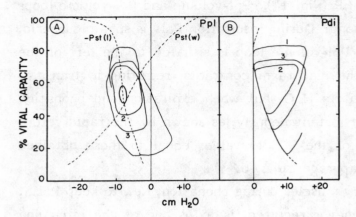

Figure 14: A: Ppl versus lung volume and B: Pdi versus lung volume for three phrases (1-3) of a song performed by DFP ("Du bist die Ruh'"; see Fig. 3 for volume events during this song). Dashed lines (-Pst(l) and Pst(w) in A, and Pdi during "pursed lip VC" in B) as in Fig. 11A and C for this subject. In A the pressure-volume loop during a tidal breath is shown for comparison. The portions of the loops to the left of -Pst(l) are inspirations. Contraction of the diaphragm during inspiration (positive values of Pdi) ceases very soon after initiation of expiration and phonation.

Pao (negative pressure breathing), Ppl must be lowered to the same extent as to Pao to keep Ps constant. Normally, subject DL did not contract his diaphragm when singing a soft tone from large lung volumes (Fig. 11C). When Pao was lowered by 15 cm H_2O the Pdi-volume diagram showed evidence of a diaphragm contraction over an appreciable proportion of the VC, and even more so when Pao was further lowered to -25 cm H_2O (Fig. 13).

The hydraulic pull of the abdominal contents is largest in the upright posture. In the supine position, Pab is always positive (11) and presumably one must contract the diaphragm to reduce Ppl to lower than relaxation values. Recent measurements by means of pneumographs and other devices to measure motion of the chest wall (15) have shown that during singing at large lung volumes the rib cage was invariably maintained at degrees of expansion which exceeded those occurring during relaxation at the same lung volume. This observation is consistent with the mechanism proposed in this paper to explain the decrease of Ppl below relaxation values at large lung volumes without the use of the diaphragm. Thus it appears that during singing the action of the diaphragm may become dissociated from the action of other inspiratory muscles.

Why whould the singer prefer not to use his diaphragm? It may be that use of the several inspiratory rib cage muscles affords a finer graded control of Pmus than the use of one large and strong muscle, the diaphragm. In this connection it may be of importance that the proprioceptive control of the diaphragm, at least in animals, appears to be different from that of the intercostal muscles; the paucity of proprioceptive afferents in the diaphragm of the cat has recently been confirmed (8). It is tempting to speculate that adoption of the upright posture has enabled man to achieve a fine control of subglottic pressure over nearly the full range of his vital capacity, by using his inspiratory rib cage muscles and the hydraulic pull of his abdominal contents to control Ppl at lung volumes above FRC, and that the development of this mechanism has greatly furthered man's capacity to communicate with his fellow man.

The authors are indebted to Adrienne Auerswald, who generated the interest which started this study, to Emily Romney, who was a subject and who helped in selecting members of the Harvard Medical Student Chorus who also served as subjects, to Dr. K Konno for his generous help with some of the experiments, and to Fenna G. Bouhuys who prepared the figures.

REFERENCES

1. AGOSTONI, E., and J. MEAD. Statics of the respiratory system. In: Handbook of Physiology. Respiration. Washington, D.C.: Am. Physiol. Soc., 1964, sect. 3, vol. 1, chapt. 13, p. 387-409.

2. AGOSTONI, E., and H. RAHN. Abdominal and thoracic pressures at different lung volumes. J. Appl. Physiol. 15: 1087-1092, Physiol. Soc., 1964, sect. 3, vol. 1, 1960.

3. AGOSTONI, E., G., SANT'AMBROGIO, and H. Del PORTILLO CARRASCO. Electromyography of the diaphragm in man and transdiaphragmatic pressure. J. Appl. Physiol. 15: 1093-1097, 1960.

4. ASTRAND, P.-O. Experimental Studies of Physical Working Capacity in Relation to Sex and Age. Copenhagen, Denmark: Munksgaard, 1952.

5. BOUHUYS, A. Lung volumes and breathing patterns in wind instrument players. J. Appl. Physiol. 19: 967-975, 1964.

6. CAMPBELL, E. J. M. The Respiratory Muscles and the Mechanics of Breathing. London: Lloyd-Luke Ltd., 1958.

7. CAVAGNA, G. A., and R. MARGARIA. An analysis of the mechanics of phonation. J. Appl. Physiol. 20: 301-307, 1965.

8. CORDA, M., C. Von EULER, and G. LENNERSTRAND. Proprioceptive innervation of the diaphragm. J. Physiol., London 178: 161-177, 1965.

9. DRAPER, M. H., P. LADEFOGED, and D. WHITTERIDGE. Respiratory muscles in speech. J. Speech Hearing Res. 2: 16-27, 1959.

10. DRAPER, M.D., P. LADEFOGED, and D. WHITTERIDGE. Expiratory pressures and air flow during speech. Brit. Med. J. 1: 1837-1843, 1960.

11. DUOMARCO, J. L., and R. RIMINI. La Presion Intra-Abdominal en el Hombre. Buenos Aires: El Ateneo, 1947.

12. FERRIS, B.G., J. MEAD, and L. H. OPIE. Partitioning of respiratory flow resistance in man. J. Appl. Physiol. 19: 653-658, 1964.

13. HYATT, R. E., and R. E. WILCOX. Extrathoracic airway resistance in man. J. Appl. Physiol. 16: 326-330, 1961.

14. ISSHIKI, N. Regulatory mechanism of voice intensity variation. J. Speech Hearing Res. 7: 17-29, 1964.

15. KONNO, K., and J. MEAD. Graphical analysis of chest wall motion. Federation Proc. 24: 138, 1965.

16. LADEFOGED, P. The regulation of sub-glottal pressure. Folia Phoniat. 12: 169-175, 1960.

17. LADEFOGED, P., M. H. DRAPER, and D. WHITTERIDGE. Syllables and stress. Misc. Phonetica 3: 1-14, 1958.

18. McGLONE, R. E. An Experimental Study of a Technique of Intra-Esophageal Pressure Measurement as a Method for Estimating Subglottic Pressure. (Ph.D. Thesis. State Univ. of Iowa.) Ann Arbor, Mich.: University Microfilms, 1963.

19. MEAD, J. Volume displacement body plethysmograph for respiratory measurements in human subjects. J. Appl. Physiol. 15: 736-740, 1960.

20. MEAD, J. Control of respiratory frequency. J. Appl. Physiol. 15: 325-336, 1960.

21. MEAD, W. J., and V. P. COLLINS. The principles of dilatancy applied to techniques of radiotherapy. Am. J. Roentgenol. Radium Therapy Nucl. Med. 71: 864-866, 1954.

22. MENZIES, R. Tentamen Physiologicum Inaugurale De Respiratione. Edinburgh: Creech, 1790.

23. MILIC-EMILI, J., J. MEAD, J. M. TURNER, and E. M. GLAUSER. Improved technique for estimating pleural pressure from esophageal balloons. J. Appl. Physiol. 19: 207-211, 1964.

24. MULLER, J. VON der Stimme und Sprache. Handb. d. Physiol. des Menschen. Coblenz: J. Holscher, 1837, vol. 2, book 4, 3rd Part, p. 133-245.

25. RAHN, H., A. B. OTIS, L. E. CHADWICK, and W. O. FENN. The pressure-volume diagram of the thorax and lung. Am. J. Physiol. 146: 161-178, 1946.

26. STRENGER, F. Methods for direct and indirect measurement of the subglottic air pressure in phonation. Studia Linguistica 14: 98-112, 1960.

27. VAN Den BERG, J. Direct and indirect determination of the mean subglottic pressure. Folia Phoniat. 8: 1-24, 1956.

28. VAN Den BERG, J. Myoelastic-aerodynamic theory of voice production. J. Speech Hearing Res. 1: 227-244, 1958.

29. WINCKEL, F. Elektroakustiche Untersuchungen an der menschlichen Stimme. Folia Phoniat. 4: 93-113, 1952.

Vocal Intensity, Subglottic Pressure and Air Flow Relationships in Singers

By H. J. Rubin, Beverly Hills, Cal., M. LeCover, Los Angeles,
W. Vennard, Los Angeles

The art of singing has achieved a high level of refinement and sophistication - not so the science. Controlled investigations to reduce all but the psychologic aspects of singing to their essential mechanics are relatively recent, and vocal pedagogy in such important matters as laryngeal dynamics, registers, and breath control remains based more on personal conviction than on experimental evidence.

This study is concerned with one facet of the singing voice - the effects of variable fundamental frequencies (pitch) and sound intensities (volume) on transglottic air flow and subglottic air pressure.

METHOD

The subjects of this investigation were three vocalists: baritone, bass, and soprano. Two were professional, the third (baritone) was an amateur and at a far lower level of training and ability. Each cooperated in the following procedure on several occasions: a needle was introduced into the trachea for measurement of subglottic pressures; a close-fitting mask was applied over the face for measurement of air flow; a microphone was placed in front of the mask to record sound intensity; the subject then vocalized a rehearsed exercise on command, and sound pressure levels, subglottic pressure, and rate of air flow were simultaneously recorded. The vowel (a) was used throughout.

INSTRUMENTATION

A schematic representation of the experimental set-up is presented in Figure 1. The technique was developed on patients with various pulmonary conditions and extended to vocalists only after it was well standardized. Singers do not lend themselves kindly to puncture of their tracheas, and it was essential that experiments be conducted without a minimum of delay.

MONITORING METHOD

A special housing unit was built to contain all the amplifiers and recording channels in one unit so as to facilitate monitoring. The Honeywell Visicorder 1508 (five channels) recorded all events simultaneously on a continuous roll of photo-sensitive graph paper. Tracings were visible within ten seconds after emerging from the machine. The high intensity spots of light that are used to expose the graph paper in the Visicorder are clearly visible during recording, and the subject can react instantly to changes in any parameter. This provides a unique feature since a subject can hold either air flow or subglottic pressure constant during vocalization by observing the light spot and not allowing it to move. This requires a degree of tone control that the average person, as contrasted with a trained vocalist, does not possess.

A pitch pipe was used to clue the subject as to fundamental frequency. Type of voice production (full voice, falsetto, etc.) was designated by the vocalists and noted on the graph paper.

MEASUREMENT OF SUBGLOTTIC PRESSURE

Direct:

A 22 gauge hypodermic needle having an outside diameter of 7 mm was introduced into the trachea through the cricotracheal ligament and maintained in perpendicular position by a plastic block shaped to conform to the contour of the neck at the puncture site. It was previously determined on plastic models that the 22 gauge needle is an accurate sensing devide and has a response time as rapid as that of needles of larger bore. A polyethylene tube connected the needle to a pressure transducer (Statham PM 97). The electrical signal from the transducer was amplified and recorded on one of the Visicorder channels. Preliminary calibrations were made with a water manometer.

Indirect:

Because of difficulties inherent in measuring intratracheal pressures directly except in tracheotomized subjects, intraesophageal pressures were initially recorded in the expectation that they might be valid substitutions. Van den Berg (2) and Draper (3) had reported that subglottic pressures could be reliably estimated from intraesophageal pressure. Kunze (7) concluded from a detailed study that they could not. In the present investigation intraesophageal pressures were sensed by a small latex balloon attached to the end of a polyethylene catheter passed pernasally into the esophagus. The distal end of the tube was attached to a Statham pressure transducer, converted to an electrical equivalent by amplification and recorded as a continuing graph on one of the Visicorder channels.

Regardless of the position of the balloon, the quantity of air which is contained, or the technique of sustained vocalization, the graphic pattern was always the same (Figs. 2 and 3). At the onset of a sustained phonation in which fundamental frequency and vocal loudness were held constant, intraesophageal pressure was low. As lung volume decreased, intraesophageal pressure slowly and progressively increased until, at the end of the phonatory effort, it was high. Intratracheal pressure, by contrast, since it is not dependent upon lung volume, remained constant under the same circumstances (Figs. 11, 12, 22, 23). At some one point in sustained phonation the two graphic lines intersect and intratracheal and intraesophageal pressures are equal but only momentarily. These observations corroborate those of Kunze that esophageal pressure is not a reliable indicator of subglottic pressure. Esophageal pressures were therefore not utilized in this study.

MEASUREMENT OF AIR FLOW

Air expelled during vocalization passed through the face mask and a connecting pneumotachograph, which measures the rate of flow by the drop in pressure that occurs as the air stream passes through a known mesh screen resistance. The pressure differential was converted into an electrical signal by a pressure transducer, amplified, and recorded on one channel of the Visicorder. Electrical heating of the grid prevented condensation of moisture which interferes with accuracy of the readings. A respirometer was utilized for calibration of the unit in liters per minute but was not included during experimental sessions to avoid a closed system.

MEASUREMENT OF SOUND PRESSURE LEVEL

Voice signals were picked up by a dynamic cardioid microphone (Electrovoice Model 664) placed directly in front of the face mask, at constant distance, relayed to a phono-amplifier, and recorded on one of the Visicorder channels. Attenuation in sound levels produced by presence of the mask was not considered important because measures of sound intensity were relative. As the subject vocalized, the moving spot of light on the Visicorder panel indicated the intensity of the sound in decibels. Sound pressure levels recorded on the Visicorder were calibrated with a General Radio 1559B Microphone Reciprocity Calibrator.

RESONANCE EFFECTS

The necessity of using a pneumotachograph for measuring the volume of air consumed during phonation gives rise to certain acoustical problems. The insertion of one end of the pneumotachograph cone into the mouth and clamping the nares (Isshiki) creates too artificial a situation for vocalists. A closely-fitting face mask is more satisfactory but still produces some interference with voice signals and a slight increase in subglottic pressure readings due to back pressure induced by the mask and connecting pneumotachograph. Since these effects are not great and since measurements are more relative than absolute, disadvantages of a device covering the face are acceptable.

FINDINGS

RELATION OF SOUND INTENSITY AND FUNDAMENTAL FREQUENCY TO SUBGLOTTIC PRESSURE

Greater vocal intensity at normal full voice production and at all pitch levels is accompanied by elevation of subglottic pressure (Figs. 4, 5, 6, 7). When vocal intensity is held constant and the pitch level rises, subglottic pressure also rises

(Figs. 8, 9, 10). This elevation in subglottic pressure with rise in fundamental frequency and/or intensity proved to be the most constant and reliable single experimental observation and is explained by heightened glottal resistance to transglottal air flow. Kunze concluded from similar observations in speakers that there may be a linear relationship between vocal intensity and subglottic pressure. Van den Berg believed the overall relationship between sound pressure and subglottic pressure or mean flow to be quadratic. He utilized himself as the subject, passing a small polyethylene catheter pernasally into the larynx. In the present study variability of the findings among the subjects and within a single subject precluded quantitative analysis.

RELATION OF SOUND INTENSITY AND FUNDAMENTAL FREQUENCY TO AIR FLOW

In general increasing vocal loudness and raising fundamental frequency are accompanied by greater transglottal flow of air. (Figs. 4, 5, 6).

When fundamental frequency is held constant as vocal loudness increases, air flow is variable; it usually rises but may remain unchanged (Figs. 5, 6, 7).

When sound intensity is held constant as fundamental frequency rises, air flow remains the same or falls; it does not rise (Figs. 8, 9, 10).

There is no apparent pattern of air flow, as contrasted with subglottic pressure, corroborating the observations of Kunze in speakers. It appears that intrinsic laryngeal adjustments, reflected in subglottic pressure, play a more significant role in regulating sound volume at varying pitch levels in full voice than air flow.

Isshiki concluded from observations on one non-vocalist that at very low fundamental frequency glottal resistance is dominant in controlling sound intensity, becoming less so as pitch rises, until at extremely high pitch levels intensity is controlled almost solely by the flow rate. This is contrary to findings of this study and those of Kunze, explainable perhaps by Isshiki's having assumed the falsetto and high pitch phonation to be synonymous. It has been demonstrated by high-speed photography (Bell Laboratories, Timcke et al. and Rubin) that normal (chest) registration and the falsetto are two basically different mechanisms of voice production, the latter used only infrequently in conventional singing. In the falsetto glottal resistance is provided merely by the vocal ligament whereas in head voice associated with normal registration there is the additional element of vocalis muscle action. Air flow in the falsetto to support the same sound pressure level is therefore usually greater (Figs 2, 3).

To be especially noted in air flow behavior are the lack of any consistent relationship between sound pressure levels and air flow and the frequency with which relatively low air flow supports a tone of great intensity.

AIRFLOW-SUBGLOTTIC PRESSURE INTERACTION

A revealing feature of this study is the lack of correlation between intratracheal pressure and transglottic air flow in controlled vocal situations. The reason lies in the significant influence of certain vocal parameters not recordable by the technique employed in this investigation:

(1) Laryngeal structure and technique of voice production. Aside from wide anatomical differences among individuals, intra and extra-laryngeal muscular adjustments controlling vocal pitch and relating it both to intensity and quality vary considerably. The degree of contraction of the numerous muscles employed in vocalization and their reciprocal relationships can only be surmised. Actual measurements await further advances in the application of electromyography.

(2) Harmonic composition of the vocalized sound and configuration of the vocal tract. The influence of the oscillating vocal cords and shape of the larynx, pharynx, and oral cavity acting as resonating chambers on sound pressure levels is demonstrated in Figures 13 and 14. In both test situations air flow, under control of the subject by observing a moving light beam, is held constant. In vocalizing a diatonic scale both stepwise and glissando, subglottic pressure shifts progressively and regularly with each change in fundamental frequency. Sound pressure levels, however, vary both significantly and unpredictably from one fundamental frequency to another. This is due to changes in the overtone pattern that occurs with each change in fundamental frequency. Certain overtones are reinforced and others damped, producing corresponding variations in sound volume. Although subglottic pressure mirrors the degree of glottal resistance, associated sound pressure levels do not. It follows that subglottic pressure in itself cannot be taken as an accurate indicator of sound volume, even when air flow is held constant. Fluctuations and inconsistencies in pressure-flow responses in controlled test situations occur frequently and are largely explainable by alteration both in harmonic structure and resonance amplification that takes place with change in fundamental frequency.

Additionally there is the matter of optimal voice production. In all test situations the singer vocalized to the best of his ability in so-called full voice. But what does this mean? Presumed optimal production at the moment could perhaps be improved by further training or by employing a totally different technique. Furthermore, differences among vocalists exist not only in the nature of intra-laryngeal adjustments but also in the action of abdominal, diaphragmatic, and extralaryngeal muscles so essential to providing proper breath support. The inescapable conclusion is that so-called optimal full voice may be tentative; most certainly it is highly personal, representing the sum total of many variables of which sound intensity and vocal pitch are only two. The influence of numerous unmeasured factors accounts for unexplainable and inconsistent flow-pressure responses.

VOCAL EFFICIENCY VS. VOCAL INEFFICIENCY

An artistic singing tone is one presumably physiologically and acoustically optimally produced. It contrasts with tones more frequently heard which are colored by various undesirable qualities such as breathiness, constriction, throati-ness, etc. These manifestations of what might be termed vocal inefficiency are due to deviations from a delicate balance existing in artistic vocal production between glottal tension and transglottal air flow, and they exert a marked and disturbing effect on flow-pressure relationship. Figure 15 demonstrates a vocalist shifting from full voice to very breathy production. Observe that subglottic pressure is maintained by increased air flow despite relaxation of glottal tension. The sound pressure level falls, however, because air flow alone cannot sustain it. In Figure 16 the sound volume is maintained but only by the expenditure of even more air. Vocal quality and sustaining power are poor. Inefficiency is compounded by lessening or loss on the incompletely coapted vocal folds of the normal inward sucking action of transglottal air flow (Bernoulli effect).

Normally greater loudness in full voice is accompanied by heightened intensity of glottal muscular contraction. This has been demonstrated by high-speed photography (Farnsworth, Fletcher, Timcke et al., Rubin). As vocal intensity rises, there is an increase in the ratio between the closed phase of the cycle of vocal cord oscillations and the total oscillatory cycle. In other words the louder the sound the greater is the intralaryngeal muscular resistance. Sound pressure levels can be high with relatively little increase in air flow (Figures 7 and 17) as long as glottal tension rises. This was demonstrated experimentally in dogs (Rubin). The converse, high flow-low glottal tension, does not sustain high sound pressure levels as is illustrated clinically by the voice in myasthenia laryngis and unilateral recurrent nerve paralysis (paramedian or intermediate positions). Varying degrees of breathiness often characterize the voices of beginning or poorly trained vocal students.

A form of inefficiency directly opposed to breathiness and even more common is throatiness or tightness. Here glottal and probably supraglottal tensions exceed optimal; subglottic pressure rises excessively even when sound pressure levels are constant (Figures 18b and 19b). The vocal folds are held together by greater muscularity than necessary, and air pressure is wasted forcing them apart. The disturbing effect of such inferior technique is particularly evident when graphic comparison is made with the same tone correctly produced (Figures 18a and 19a). Poor quality is manifested by a shift from regular to irregular levels of sound intensity and vibrato.

Between the extremes of breathiness and throatiness is a gamut of aberrant flow-pressure relationships presenting varying combinations which can theoretically be infinite.

Flow-pressure relationships may differ from one vocalist to another even at the same fundamental frequency and intensity (Figures 20 and 21). This is of course to be expected because of individual differences in optimal balance between glottal tension and transglottal air flow. They may even vary within a single vocalist himself. Figure 22 illustrates a single tone optimally produced by the same vocalist, presumably by the same technique, on two different occasions. The more thoroughly trained the singer the less such inconsistency is likely.

It has long been the contention of teachers of voice that controlled expiration (good breath control and ample breath support) is essential to proper tonal production. The experimental proof of this concept is graphically demonstrated in Figures 24 and 25. Each vocalist sustained a lengthy tone in full voice with air flow and fundamental frequency held constant. As long as expiration was easy and not forced, glottal tension, as measured by subglottic pressure, remained essentially unchanged. However, as air reserve decreased and extra-laryngeal muscular effort to maintain the flow of air necessary to support the tone increased, optimal flow-pressure relationships were disturbed, and glottal resistance as measured by subglottic pressure also increased. Acoustically these interfering compensatory tensions were invariably accompanied by the form of vocal inefficiency noted above as throatiness or constriction. The importance of this observation in vocal pedagogy cannot be overemphasized.

MALE VS. FEMALE VOCALISTS

Basic mechanisms of phonation appear to be identical (Figures 4, 5, 6, 7 and 11). Identification of sex cannot be made from the graphs.

WELL TRAINED VS. POORLY TRAINED VOCALIST

In comparable vocal situations the professional vocalist was able to sustain a tone of greater intensity with less air flow, suggesting greater efficiency of the vocal mechanism (Figure 26). However, this might indicate no more than greater inherent strength. Conclusions must be guarded because individual responses extend over so wide a range that a framework encompassing the qualities of a good vocalist or even relating them to those of a lesser vocalist does not emerge. It would be meaningful to study flow-pressure relationships and acoustical properties in vocal students at the start of their training and again when they had achieved a high level of skill.

CONCLUSIONS

(1) Intraesophageal pressure is not a reliable indicator of subglottic pressure.

(2) The response of subglottic pressure and air flow to changes in fundamental frequency and vocal intensity show great and unpredictable variability, due to the influence of vocal parameters additional to those measured in this study.

(3) Air flow is not the major factor in supporting a tone of increasing loudness. Glottal resistance is far more important.

(4) Subglottic pressure measurements do not necessarily reflect sound pressure levels.

(5) Vocal inefficiency in the form of constriction or breathiness exerts a markedly disturbing effect on flow-pressure measurements and relationships.

(6) Poor breath control and inadequate breath support impair vocal quality by causing secondary interfering glottal tensions.

(7) No measureable differences in production were observed between male and female vocalists.

(8) Although the human voice is being systematically reduced to its essential physical components by a variety of techniques, the best judge of its artistic quality is still the human ear.

SUMMARY

The effects of variations in fundamental frequencies (vocal pitch) and sound intensities (volume, loudness) on transglottic air flow and subglottic air pressure were studied in singers. It was observed that glottal resistance is far more important in supporting a tone of increasing loudness than air flow, that subglottic pressure measurements do not necessarily reflect sound pressure levels, that poor vocal technique exerts a markedly disturbing effect on flow-pressure relationships, that inadequate breath support impairs vocal quality by causing secondary interfering glottal tensions, and that intraesophageal pressure is not a reliable indicator of subglottic pressure.

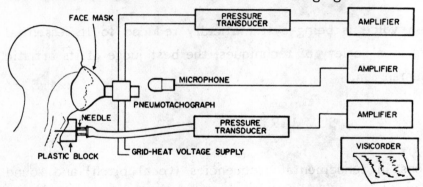

Fig. 1. Diagramatic representation of experimental arrangement.

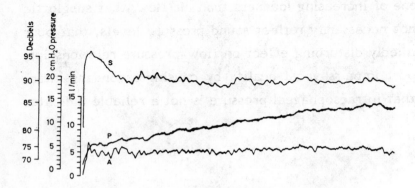

Fig. 2. Esophageal pressure is measured by a balloon passed pernasally into the esophagus. The subject sustains a single fundamental frequency in the middle vocal range at constant intensity. Esophageal pressure (P) is seen to rise slowly and progressively while air flow (A) remains the same. In contrast to esophageal pressure, subglottic pressure (S) does not vary if vocal pitch, intensity, and technique are unchanged (Figs. 11, 12, 22, 23). This graph demonstrates that esophageal pressure in phonation cannot be taken as a reliable indicator of intratracheal (subglottic) pressure.

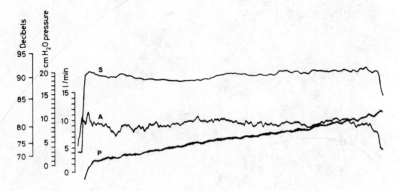

Fig. 3. This subject vocalizes on the same frequency at the same sound pressure level in the falsetto. This graph demonstrates, as in Figure 2, that unless correction is made for lung volume at any given instant, esophageal pressure cannot be taken as a measurement of subglottic pressure. The graph also demonstrates that less esophageal (intrathoracic) pressure accompanies falsetto production as compared with normal registration.

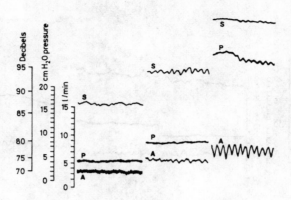

Fig. 4. Male - rise in air flow (A) and subglottic pressure (P) passing from low to middle to upper range at increasing levels of loudness (S).

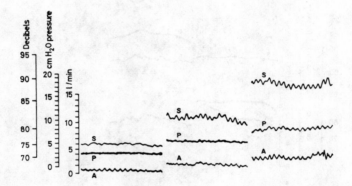

Fig. 5. Female - rise in air flow (A) and subglottic pressure (P) with increasing loudness (S) on the same fundamental frequency in her low range.

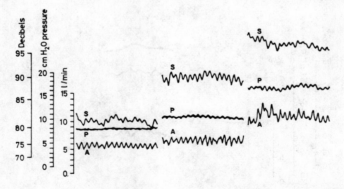

Fig. 6. Female - rise in air flow (A) and subglottic pressure (P) with increasing loudness (S) on the same fundamental frequency in her middle range. Irregular trace lines reflect a strong vibrato.

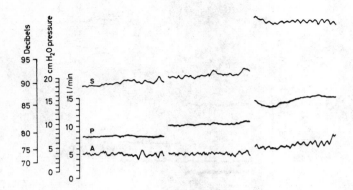

Fig. 7. Male - small rise in air flow (A) and moderate rise in subglottic pressure (P) with increasing loudness (S) on the same fundamental frequency in his upper range.

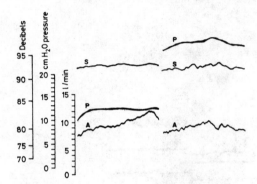

Fig 8. Vocalizing at constant sound intensity (S) professional male subject passes from middle range to tone one octave higher. Subglottic pressure (P) rises to high level, but air flow (A) falls.

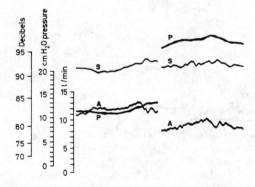

Fig. 9. Same subject as in Figure 8 vocalizes upward at constant sound intensity (S) from C to G (bass staff) in his middle range. Subglottic pressure (P) rises, but air flow (A) again falls.

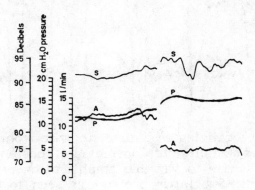

Fig. 10. Same subject as in Figure 8 vocalizes at constant sound intensity (S) from E (bass staff) in his middle range to C (Middle C) in his upper range. Subglottic pressure (P) rises greatly, but air flow (A) remains essentially the same.

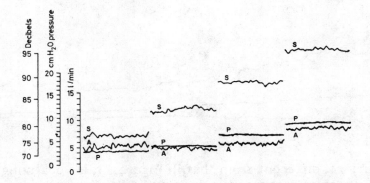

Fig. 11. Male - gradual rise in air flow (A) and subglottic pressure (P) with increasing loudness (S) on the same fundamental frequency in his middle range.

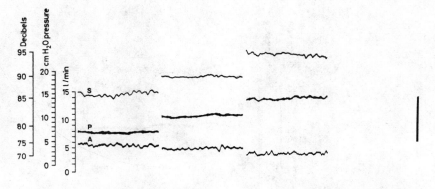

Fig. 12. Male - rise in subglottic pressure (P) and fall in air flow (A) with increasing loudness (S) on the same fundamental frequency in his middle range.

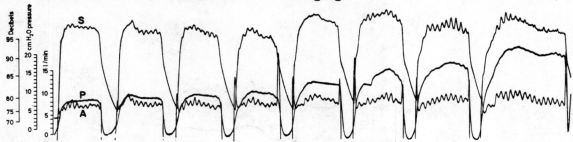

Fig. 13. The subject is vocalizing an octave stepwise from middle to upper range. Although air flow (A) and size of mouth opening are constant, sound pressure levels are not uniform. This is due to variable amplification of overtones at different fundamental frequencies. Subglottic pressure is seen to rise progressively with elevation of pitch, due entirely to heightened glottal tension. The difficulty of determining exact mathematical relationships between sound pressure levels alone and subglottic pressure (P) is obvious.

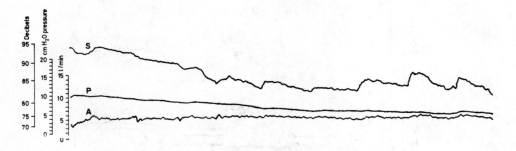

Fig. 14. The subject, different from that in Figure 13, is vocalizing downward from upper to middle range on a glissando. Air flow (A) and mouth opening are constant. The same phenomenon is again observed, i.e., sound pressure levels do not correlate with subglottic pressures because of differential amplification of resonance frequencies.

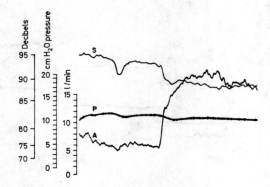

Fig. 15. Vocalist shifts from full voice to breathy type of production. Although subglottic pressure is maintained by greatly increased flow of air, sound pressure levels fall because intralaryngeal muscular tension has decreased. This demonstrates, although in a different manner from Figures 13 and 14, that subglottic pressure measurements do not necessarily reflect sound pressure levels.

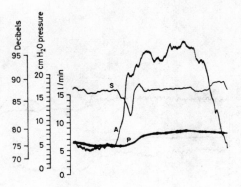

Fig. 16. Vocalist shifts from full voice to extreme breathy production. Despite decrease in glottal tension, volume velocity is so great that the sound pressure level is maintained and subglottic pressure (P) actually rises. Air wastage is considerable, and the tone can be sustained only for a short period. This graph demonstrates again the impossibility of correlating the three recorded parameters without knowing the degree of glottal tension.

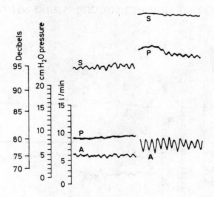

Fig. 17. Professional male vocalist produced a loud tone in the middle range and then a much louder one an octave higher. Observe the extraordinary elevation of subglottic pressure (P) with a far less impressive increase in air flow (A). This graph demonstrates that the degree of glottal contraction is more important in sustaining tones of great loudness than is the quantity of air flowing thru the larynx.

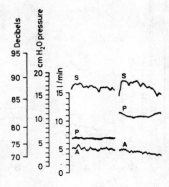

Fig. 18. The subject vocalized a tone optimally (efficiently) and then tensely (inefficiently) in middle range. Although sound levels remain constant, there is a marked alteration in flow-pressure relationships. This form of inefficiency, in contrast to that demonstrated in Figure 16, is associated with excessive glottal tension.

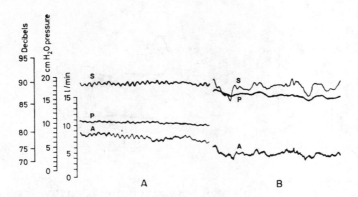

Fig. 19. The subject demonstrates, as in Figure 18, disturbance in flow-pressure relationships induced by inefficient vocalization. A depicts the pattern of an optimally produced singing tone in the upper range. In B the same tone is produced throatily with improper breath support. Sound levels are unchanged, but subglottic pressure (P) rises and air flow (A) falls. Increased glottal tension and poor breath support have produced a tone of uneven loudness and vibrato.

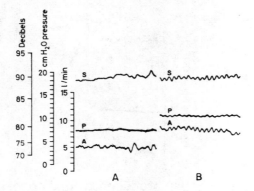

Fig. 20. Two subjects (A. well-trained, B. poorly trained) vocalized in full voice on the same fundamental frequency and at the same sound pressure level in their upper range. Flow and pressure levels are different. The graph demonstrates that factors other than vocal pitch and sound intensity affect pressure and flow levels.

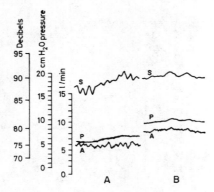

Fig. 21. Two subjects (A. well-trained, B. poorly trained) vocalized in full voice on the same fundamental frequency and at the same intensity in middle range. Flow and pressure levels are different. As in Figure 20 the trained vocalist sustains the same level of loudness with less pressure and flow.

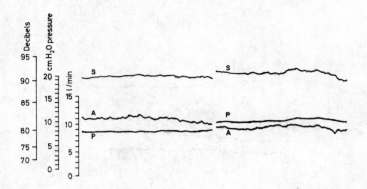

Fig. 22. The less well trained subject vocalized in full voice on the same fundamental frequency and at about the same intensity in his middle range on two different occasions. Flow-pressure levels and relationships are not the same. The graph demonstrates that unmeasured intralaryngeal adjustments significantly affect flow and pressure responses.

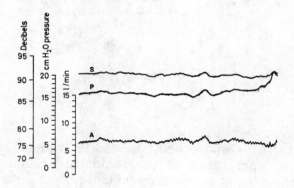

Fig. 23. This graph and Figures 24 and 25, represent the terminations of sustained vocalization on a single fundamental frequency at constant air flow. As air reserve decreases, glottal tensions increase to compensate for less effective breath support, and subglottic pressure rises. This graphically demonstrates the disturbing effect of insufficient breath support on optimal air flow-glottal tension balance.

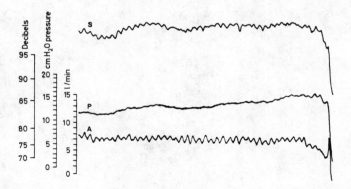

Fig. 24. See Figure 23.

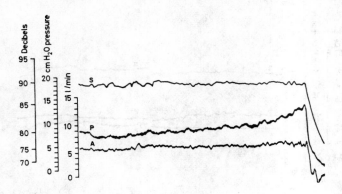

<u>Fig. 25</u>. See Figure 23.

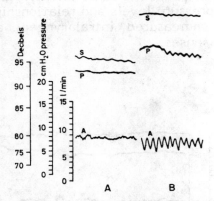

<u>Fig. 26</u>. Two vocalists (A. well-trained, B. poorly trained) sustain a tone of the same frequency in the upper range at the same rate of air flow. The trained vocalist is able to develop far greater sound volume.

REFERENCES

1. Bell Telephone Laboratories: High speed motion pictures of the vocal cords. (New York Bureau of Publication, Bell Telephone Laboratories 1937).

2. Berg, J., Van den: Direct and indirect determination of the mean subglottic pressure. Folia phoniat. 8: 1 (1956).

3. Draper, M. H.; Ladefoged, P. and Whitteridge, D.: Respiratory muscles in speech. J. Speech Res. 2: 16 (1959).

4. Farnsworth, D. W.: High speed motion pictures of the human vocal cords. Bell Laboratories Record 18: 203 (1940).

5. Fletcher, W. W.: A study of internal laryngeal activity in relation to vocal intensity. Ph. D. Dissertation, Northwestern University, 1950.

6. Isshiki, N.: Regulatory mechanism of voice intensity variation. J. Speech Res. 7: 17 (1964).

7. Kunze, L. H.: An investigation of the changes in subglottal air pressure and rate of air flow accompanying changes in fundamental frequency, intensity, vowels, and voice registers in adult male speakers. Ph. D. Dissertation, State University of Iowa 1962.

8. Rubin, H. J.: High speed sound film - Mechanism of the falsetto, 1960.

9. Rubin, H. J.: Experimental studies on vocal pitch and intensity in phonation. The Laryngoscope 73: 973 (1963).

10. Timcke, R.; Leden, H., von and Moore, P.: Laryngeal vibrations: Measurements of the glottic wave, part I. The normal vibratory cycle. Arch. Otolaryng. 68: 1 (1958).

The Effect
of Voice Training
on Lung Volumes
in Singers

and the Possible Relationship
to the Damping Factor
of Pressman

Wilbur Gould

To document the presumed relationship between vocal efficiency and respiratory efficiency in singers, and the effect of vocal training on the latter, vital capacity (VC), total lung capacity (TLC), residual volume (RV), inspiratory capacity (IC), expiratory reserve volume (ERV), and functional residual volume (FRV) were compared in professionally trained singers, students of voice, and subjects with no vocal training.

The results showed that the professional singers had a markedly reduced RV/TLC ratio -- that is, their vital capacity had apparently been expanded at the expense of the residual volume. The results also showed that those who had no vocal training had a high RV/TLC ratio -- that is, one that might be reduced with vocal training. The RV/TLC ratio of the students of voice, it was found, was intermediate between that of the professional singers and those with no vocal training, suggesting that their capacity to sing had been expanded at the expense of RV, but not so much as it might be with additional training. All of the students of voice whose RV/TLC ratio was within 2 standard deviations of the predicted value had received 5 years or less of training, while the professional singers, with

RV/TLC ratios substantially lower than predicted values, had an average of 14 years of training. Thus there seemed to be a correlation between the length of vocal training and improvement in vocal ability, as indicated by the RC/TLC ratio.

It seems clear on the basis of our results and those of others that there is a specific correlation between increased breathing capacity, as reflected in a reduction of the RV/TLC ratio in our studies, and long term vocal studies. Moreover, it would appear that the professional singer attains an increased capacity for singing by expanding the proportion of VC within TLC, thereby attaining a reduction of the RV and a concomitant increase in IC. These findings of a basically pulmonary nature may relate to the damping factor of Pressman, as will be pointed out.

Phonatory ability and efficiency depend to a large degree upon pulmonary efficiency, which may be evaluated by a variety of pulmonary or respiratory function tests. Voice researchers have long been aware of this, and have devoted considerable effort to the exploration of different aspects of pulmonary efficiency in the professional singer. We may assume, therefore, that there is a relationship between the superior vocal ability of the trained singer and a superiority in ventilatory capacity. Yet there have been surprisingly few studies to document the precise relationship between respiratory efficiency and long-term vocal training. In particular, there have been up to now few systematic analyses of the effect of voice training upon not only pulmonary potential or capacity as such, but also on the ability to use such potential in the actual production of voice.

Certain aspects of the interrelationship between vocal ability and pulmonary efficiency have been suggested by a number of earlier investigators. For example, Waldenberg (1880) reported that Wassiliew had found a larger vital capacity in singers than in non-singers. Later, Nadoleczny and Luchsinger (1934) reported a significantly larger vital capacity for the professional singer than for the untrained person. Luchsinger (1951) noted that air consumption in the well-trained singer fell as pitch rose. Similarly, Bouhuys et al. (1966) reported that in the trained singer the rate of air flow decreases with an increasing sound level, while in the inexperienced singer production of the same tone at a lower sound level requires a comparatively high rate of air flow. Proctor (1968) has pointed out that the well-trained singer is able to utilize virtually the entire vital capacity in sound production, and on this basis he has recommended that voice training concentrate on the easy and habitual use of the full vital capacity, rather than on attempts to enlarge it.

To determine whether singers do show an increase in pulmonary efficiency and whether a correlation between such efficiency and voice training exists, static lung volumes and certain other parameters generally taken to reflect various aspects of pulmonary efficiency and capacity in three different groups were analyzed. All three groups, totalling 41 people, were adults determined to be free of both pulmonary and cardiovascular disease. The first group consisted of professional singers, ranging in age from 24 to 46. Six were male and three were female, and all had from 6 to 28 years of professional singing activities. Most were operatic stars, deservedly renowned for their artistic abilities. The second group was made up of 14 students, of whom 6 were male and 8 were female. Their vocal training ranged from 2 to 5 years. The third group was comprised of 8 males and 10 females ranging in age from 19 to 33 years, none of whom had had any vocal training. The ERC, IC, and VC were measured on at least two occasions using a Collins 9-liter respirometer. The higher one was taken as the valid one in each instance and was corrected to BTPS (Body Temperature and Ambient Saturated with Water Vapor). The FRC was obtained by plethysmography, while the RV was then calculated by subtracting the ERV from the FRC; the TLC was obtained by adding the VC and the RC.

There is no need to detail the plethysmographic method, but it should be noted that changes in mouth pressure were measured by a pressure transducer (Statham PM 5). The electrical signal from this transducer was amplified (with a Honeywell Gage Control Unit) and recorded on the Y-Axis of an oscilloscope. Changes in the gaseous pressure within the plethysmograph were then converted to an electrical signal by another pressure transducer (Statham PM 97) and recorded on the X-Axis of the same oscilloscope. In this way, the FRC, which is inversely proportional to the incline made by these two pressure changes, could be easily calculated. By monitoring the curve of respiration with a Honeywell Visicorder the exact end point of a quiet respiration was obtained. Thus the FRC could be measured with great accuracy.

To minimize the influence of variations due to sex, age, and body size, each parameter that we measured was expressed as a percentage of the predicted value, using the formula of Goldman and others. The normal range of each parameter determined in the course of this study was within 2 standard deviations of the predicted value.

VITAL CAPACITY - RESIDUAL VOLUME - TOTAL

		V C	R V	T L C
PROFESSIONAL SINGERS	MEAN	122.5	72.5	107.7
	S.D.	21.9	15.8	12.7
	RANGE	104 -179	51 -98	93 -136
STUDENTS IN SINGING	MEAN	106.6	90.6	101.6
	S.D.	8.4	5.5	5.5
	RANGE	92 -122	66 -108	91 -111
CONTROLS	MEAN	99.3	100.7	98.2
	S.D.	9.4	14.4	8.5
	RANGE	83 -121	65 -130	84 -117

Table 1

RATIO OF RV TO TLC

	OBSERVED VALUES (%)			% OF THE PREDICTED		
	MEAN	S.D.	RANGE	MEAN	S.D.	RANGE
PROFESSIONAL SINGERS	20.9	5.0	12—33	69.7	13.7	37—92
STUDENTS IN SINGING	23.9	4.3	18—32	92.3	12.9	66—113
CONTROLS	27.7	3.9	18—33	105.6	14.4	75—130

Table 2

As shown in table 1, the VC of the control group (the subjects with no voice training) fell consistently within 2 standard deviations of the predicted value. Similarly, all other parameters measured in the control group regularly fell within the normal range, with the exception of the TLC, which was 79% in one of the subjects. Measurements for the students of singing similarly were uniformly within the normal or predicted range, except for a single TLC of 78% and a single VC (in another subject) of 78%.

In marked contrast to the values in these two groups, however, the professional singers showed measurements outside the normal range in every instance. Two subjects showed VCs notably higher than the normal range, at 179% and 139%, while four showed markedly lower than normal lower RVs, ranging from 27% to 59%. Moreover, there were significant statistical differences by T-Test between the VC and the RV of the professional singers and those of the other 2 study groups, with VC values markedly higher and RV levels markedly lower in the professionally trained group.

The RV/TLC ratio in controls and in the students of singing were consistently within normal limits, while the professional singers all showed an extremely low RV/TLC ratio (see table 2). In 7 of the professional singers the RV/TLC ranged from 34% to 64%. This is significantly lower than that recorded for the other 2 groups.

In the ERV, the IC, and the FRC/TLC ratio there were no striking differences in any of the parameters among the three groups studied. It may be noted that 3 of the professional singers had a relatively high IC (130 to 160% of the norm) and 2 of these also showed comparatively low FRC/TLC ratios. The ERC in 4 of the professional singers ranged from 133% to 210% above the predicted values.

If, as our results indicate, the VC of the professional singer is expanded within the TLC in large part through a reduction in the RV, it implies that the impressive singing potential of the professional rises in part from this expansion of vital capacity. Since the trained singer uses less air in producing a high tone than the untrained singer, and the untrained singer also uses a higher air flow in singing softly, the amount of pulmonary or respiratory energy required by the professional to sustain a given vocal effort is much less than that required by the untrained or little trained person. It would appear that the trained singer, as a specific result of training, benefits both from an expanded effective VC and a more efficient use of that expanded capacity. There may be other results of training as well. One may be connected with the vibratory pattern of the trained vocal folds. On the basis of studies using high-speed cinematography coupled with computer analysis of the displayed image, there may now be a means of investigating these benefits.

As seen in Figure 1, our filming system employs a high intensity, high speed strobe (model 50), developed by the E.G.& G. Company. The lamp flash rate, controllable up to 6,000 flashes/sec., is synchronized with the camera (Hycam model K2001) shutter, resulting in one flash per frame. In this way the exposure time has been reduced to less than 2.1 micro-seconds per frame. The light from the flash tube is directed onto a front surface mirror which has a one inch circular hole cut through the center for viewing. The light from the mirror is then reflected onto a laryngeal mirror, for illumination and viewing of the vocal folds. The laryngeal mirror is fixed into position and the subject must be maneuvered into proper position for optimal viewing of the vocal folds.

The data reduction system utilized for the analysis of the high speed images obtained in this manner included a projector able to project the resulting film frame by frame and a PDP-12 computer for reading and processing the visual data. The film is projected onto the face of a display scope of the computer which is programmed to simultaneously project coordinate points. The precise positions of the coordinates are adjustable by the operator, using potentiometers, and they are positioned to divide the vocal folds into 6 segments. Thus, dispensing with further technical details of the system, as the film is advanced for study, the analysis program computes the following parameters from the various coordinates as a function of time:

1. the excursion of both right and left vocal folds at all measured points, and
2. the glottal width, length, and area.

The results can either be presented visually as graphs on the display scope or typed out on teletype paper. When the magnification ratio of the vocal folds on the film is given, the absolute value of all the parameters noted above can be derived immediately.

The glottal width and area have been analyzed as relative values by previous investigators, but in the present studies it was attempted to obtain absolute values for these parameters. Essentially this was done by incorporating an objective point of reference (a metric ruler) in our filming procedure, that is, by filming a metric ruler with the same lens setting used in photographing the larynx. The scale thus obtained was then focused on the display scope and the values stored on the magnetic tape used in recording and analyzing the images of the vocal folds.

Some typical analyses obtained using this system are presented in figures 2-7. These represent a selection of film strips, taken at 3000 pictures per second, from three different subjects phonating at different frequencies and intensities. On each graph, lines A, B, C, D, E, F, and G represent the glottal width at the measured points and the curve marked "area" represents the glottal area as a function of time during one complete vibratory cycle. Here are shown vocal fold vibrations at different pitches and intensities in a single subject.

Figure 8 shows an aberrant vibratory pattern that is marked in the posterior portion of the glottis. The subject in this case had a posterior glottal chink.

As can be seen from the graphs we have shown, there are a number of advantages in displaying glottal width at a number of points in this fashion. It is readily possible, for example, to compare the amplitude at different points and thus to determine the relationship between a point of maximum amplitude and the vocal process or some other specific landmark. It also should be noted the glottal width may be measured at various superior-inferior parts of the vocal folds during a cycle. In addition, phase differences between points can be readily analyzed. Note also that our results show that the opening starts at the anterior portion and travels toward the posterior commisure (a longitudinal wave).

Figure 9 shows the relationship between the maximum vocal fold excursion and the excursion of the vocal process. The solid lines of the graph represent the glottal width at the point of maximum amplitude, while the dotted lines represent the glottal width at the vocal process as a percentage of the maximum width of the glottis. Note also that at the frequency of 400 Hz the maximum excursion of the vocal folds occurs at the A-P mid-point of the membraneous portion of the glottis, rather than at the A-P mid-point of the glottis itself.

The graph also shows the relative decrease in the excursion of the vocal process as the fundamental frequency rises. At the frequency of 400 Hz no vibrations are observed at the vocal process. This could account for shifts in the maximum excursion point.

Perhaps the most important point deriving from these studies, at least so far as this presentation is concerned, is that they have given considerable substance to what was previously just a clinical impression, namely that the action of the anterior 2/3rds of the vocal folds is separate and distinct from the posterior 1/3rd.

The anterior 2/3rds is mainly muscle and other soft tissue and it has a greater pliancy than the posterior 1/3rd, although this pliancy varied with the thickness of the fold.

The posterior portion, on the other hand, is less mobile because it contains the posterior vocal process. At low frequencies, such as 125 Hz, the anterior 2/3rds of the vocal folds separate first and only later does the posterior 1/3rd separate. This results in a blunt, more rounded, opening than that seen at higher frequencies. At 155 Hz, for example, the "V" formed by the vocal folds is notably sharper than it is at lower frequencies, and at a still higher frequency, such as 225 Hz, the cord opening is again distinctive, with only the anterior 2/3rds vibrating.

Apparently the vocal process is part of the vibratory mechanism at the lower frequencies, but it becomes increasingly fixed at higher frequencies and plays little or no direct role in the vocal mechanism. If this is the case, the tension-producing mechanism employed in vocalization may be more complex than we believed up to now.

If it can be assumed that the damping factor of Pressman is analogous to the results obtained when a stringed instrument is fingered to shorten one of the strings, thereby allowing only a portion of it to vibrate, it will be seen that the vibratory pattern observed in this paper is consistent with this. The factor, Pressman (1942) writes, "consists in the appropriate segment of one vocal cord coming into direct contact with the corresponding segment of the other." It is particularly important in the production of higher tones. In any event, Pressman's observations and those presented in this paper suggest that a damping factor is operative in the production of the higher tones.

Pressman argues that the damping effect allows the fore-shortened segment of the vocal cords to vibrate freely, so that a higher tone is produced without the need for an increase in tension of respiratory pressure. If this is the case, it may be that the trained singer is better able than the untrained singer to utilize the function of the damped vocal folds or (in the terms of these studies) the vibration of the anterior 2/3rds of the vocal cords to produce a larger range of vocalization.

In view of this, are the increased training and the increased pulmonary capacity attendant upon it related to the pressure requirements for the vibration of the fore-shortened vocal folds? What is the relationship of the larynx when held in a lower position despite production of a higher pitch as noted in the professional, and the Pressman factor? How do all of these relate to the professional's ability to change pitch without obvious audible shift of register? Is the lower position of the larynx in these instances related to the fact that the entire pulmonary system is held in a lower position, because of the increased thoracic capacity?

Finally, one must also take into account Curt von Euler's work (1966) in which he has related reflexively the opening in the larynx to the motion of the lower thoracic cage. May not this entire inter-relationship be a more effective and efficient one in the trained person?

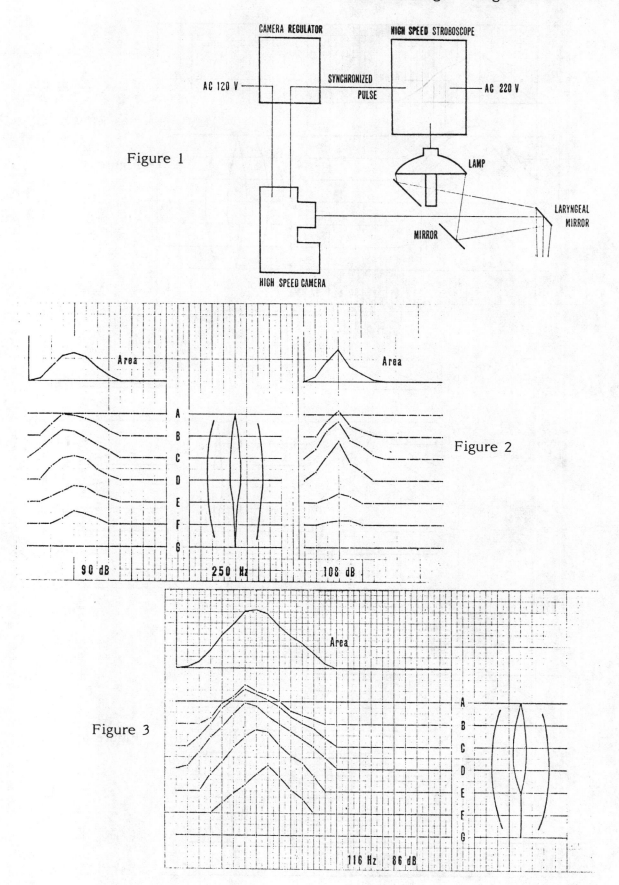

Figure 1

Figure 2

Figure 3

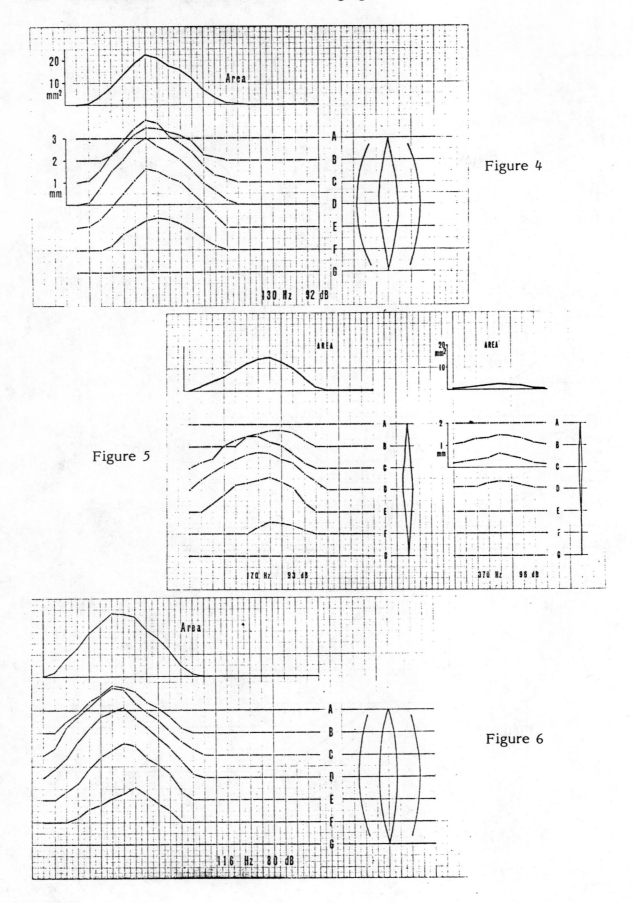

Figure 4

Figure 5

Figure 6

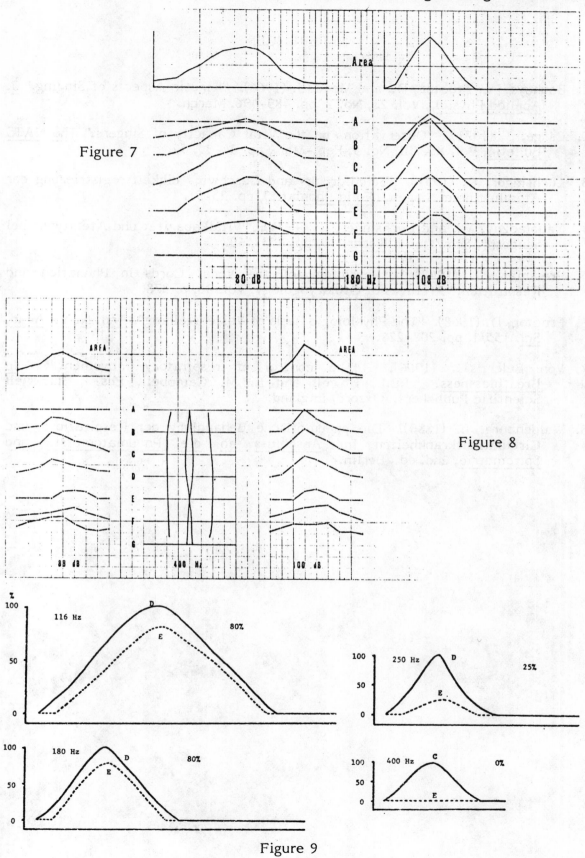

Figure 7

Figure 8

Figure 9

REFERENCES

1. Bouhuys, A., Proctor, D., and Mead, J. (1966). "Kinetic Aspects of Singing," J. Applied Physiol., Vol. 21, No. 2, pp. 483-496, March.

2. Large, J. (1971). "Observations on the Vital Capacity of Singers," The NATS Bulletin, Vol. XXVIII, No. 3, Feb.-Mar., pp. 34-35, 52.

3. Luchsinger, R. (1951). "Schalldruck- and Geschwin- digkeitsregistrierung der Atemluft beim Singen," Folia Phoniat. 3, pp. 25-51.

4. Nadoleczny, M., and Luchsinger, R. (1934). "Vitalkapazitat und Atemtypus bei Sangern", Schw. med. Wschr. 19, pp. 453-460.

5. Pressman, J. (1942). "Physiology of the Vocal Cords in Phonation and Respiration," Archives of Otolaryngology, Vol. 35, p. 378.

6. Proctor, D. (1968). "The Physiologic Basis of Voice Training", Ann. N. Y. Acad. Sci. 155/1, pp. 208-228.

7. Von Euler, C. (1966). "The control of respiratory movement." In Breathlessness. J.B.L. Howell and E.J.M. Campbell, Eds. Blackwell Scientific Publishers. Oxford, England.

8. Waldenburg, L. (1880). Die pneumotische Behandlung der Respirations- und Circulationskrankheiten im Anschluss an die Pneumatometrie und Spirometrie, 2nd. ed., Berlin.

Vocal Registers

Observations on the Human Voice

By Manuel Garcia

From Proceedings of the Royal Society of London. 1854-55
London, p. 399-410

The pages which follow are intended to describe some observations made on the interior of the larynx during the act of singing. The method which I have adopted is very simple. It consists in placing a little mirror, fixed on a long handle suitably bent, in the throat of the person experimented on against the soft palate and uvula. The party ought to turn himself towards the sun, so that the luminous rays falling on the little mirror, may be reflected on the larynx. If the observer experiments on himself, he ought, by means of a second mirror, to receive the rays of the sun, and direct them on the mirror, which is placed against the uvula. We shall now add our deductions from the observations which the image reflected by the mirror has afforded us.

OPENING OF THE GLOTTIS

At the moment when the person draws a deep breath, the epiglottis being raised, we are able to see the following series of movements: - the arytenoid cartilages become separated by a very free lateral movement; the superior ligaments are placed against the ventricles; the inferior ligaments are also drawn back, though in a less degree, into the same cavities; and the glottis, large and wide open, is exhibited so as to show in part the rings of the trachea. But unfortunately, however dexterous we may be in disposing these organs, and even when we are most successful, at least the third part of the anterior of the glottis remains concealed by the epiglottis.

MOVEMENT OF THE GLOTTIS

As soon as we prepare to produce a sound, the arytenoid cartilages approach each other, and press together by their interior surfaces, and by the anterior apophyses, without leaving any space, or inter-cartilaginous glottis; sometimes even they come in contact so closely as to cross each other by the tubercles of Santorini. To this movement of the anterior apophyses, that of the ligaments of the glottis corresponds, which detach themselves from the ventricles, come in contact with different degrees of energy, and show themselves at the bottom of the larynx under the form of an ellipse of a yellowish colour. The superior ligaments, together with the arytenoid-epiglottidean folds, assist to form the tube which surmounts the glottis; and being the lower and free extremity of that tube enframe the ellipse, the surface of which they enlarge or diminish according as they enter more or less into the ventricles. These last scarcely retain a trace of their opening. By anticipation, we might say of these cavities, that, as will afterwards appear clearly enough in these pages, they only afford to the two pair of ligaments a space in which they may easily range themselves. When the aryteno-epiglottidean folds contract, they lower the epiglottis, and make the superior orifice of the larynx considerably narrower.

The meeting of the lips of the glottis, naturally proceeding from the front towards the back, if this movement is well managed, it will allow, between the apophyses, of the formation of a triangular space, or inter-cartilaginous glottis, but one which, however, is closed as soon as the sounds are produced.

After some essays, we perceive that this internal disposition of the larynx is only visible when the epiglottis remains raised. But neither all the registers of the voice, nor all the degrees of intensity, are equally fitted for its taking this position. We soon discover that the brilliant and powerful sounds of the chest-register contract the cavity of the larynx, and close still more its orifice; and, on the contrary, that veiled notes, and notes of moderate power, open both so as to render any observation easy. The falsetto register especially possesses this prerogative, as well as the first notes of the head voice[1]. So as to render these facts more precise, we will study in the voice of the tenor the ascending progression of the chest-register, and in the soprano that of the falsetto and head registers.

EMISSION OF THE CHEST-VOICE

If we emit veiled and feeble sounds, the larynx opens at the notes do, re$_2$, mi, and we see the glottis agitated by large and loose vibrations throughout its entire extent. Its lips comprehend in their length the anterior apophyses of the arytenoid cartilages and the vocal cords; but, I repeat it, there remains no triangular space.

As the sounds ascend, the apophyses, which are slightly rounded on their internal side, by a gradual apposition commencing at the back, encroach on the length of the glottis; and as soon as we reach the sounds si, do$_3$, they finish by touching each other throughout their whole extent; but their summits are only solidly fixed one against the other at the notes do♯, re$_3$. In some organs these summits are a little vacillating when they form the posterior end of the glottis, and the two or three half-tones which are formed show a certain want of purity and strength, which is very well known to singers. From the do♯, re$_3$, the vibrations having become rounder and purer, are accomplished by the vocal ligaments alone, up to the end of the register.

The glottis at this moment presents the aspect of a line slightly swelled towards its middle, the length of which diminishes still more as the voice ascends. We also see that the cavity of the larynx has become very small, and that the superior ligaments have contracted the extent of the ellipse to less than one-half.

When instead of veiled and feeble sounds, we make use of full and vibrating ones the glottis becomes visible only at the sound mi, fa$_3$, and those above them, a limit which depends to a certain extent on the dexterity of the singer. For all the rest, the organs act as we have just said, but with a double difference:

1. The cavity of the larynx contracts itself more when the voice is intense, than when it is feeble.
2. The superior ligaments are contracted so as to reduce the small diameter of the ellipse to a width of two or three lines.

But, however powerful these contractions may be, neither the cartilages of Wrisberg, nor the superior ligaments themselves, ever close sufficiently to prevent the passage of the air, or even to render it difficult. This fact, which is verified also with regard to the falsetto and head-registers, suffices to prove that the superior ligaments do not fill a generative part in the formation of the voice. We may draw the same conclusion by considering the position occupied by the somewhat feeble muscles which correspond to these ligaments; they cover externally the extremity of the diverging fibres of the thyro-arytenoid muscles, and take part especially in the contractions of the cavity of the larynx during the formation of the high notes of the chest - and of the head-registers.

Table of the Human Voice in its Full Extent

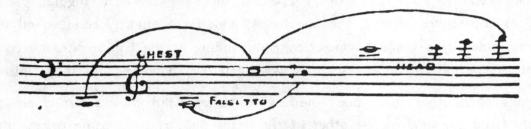

PRODUCTION OF THE FALSETTO

The low notes of the falsetto, sol, lap, la#, show the glottis infinitely better than
             2   2   2
the unisons of the chest-voice and produce vibrations more extended and more distinct. Its vibrating sides, formed by the anterior apophyses of the arytenoid cartilages, and by the ligaments, become gradually shorter as the voice ascends; at the notes la, si, the apophyses take part only at their summits; and in these notes
        3   3
there results a weakness similar to that which we have remarked in the chest notes an octave below. At the notes do#, re, the ligaments alone continue to act; then
                    4   4
begins the series of notes called head-voice. The moment in which the action of the apophyses ceases, exhibits in the female voice a very sensible difference at once to the ear and in the organ itself. Lastly, we verify, that, up to the highest sound of the register, the glottis continues to diminish in length and in width.

If we compare the two registers in these movements, we shall find some analogies in them; the sides of the glottis, formed at first by the apophyses and the ligaments, become shorter by degrees, and end by consisting only of the ligaments. The chest-register is divided into two parts, corresponding to these two states of the glottis. The register of falsetto head presents a complete similarity, and in a still more striking manner.

On other points, on the contrary, these same registers are very unlike. The length of the glottis necessary to form a falsetto note, always exceeds that which produces the unison of the chest. The movements which agitates the sides of the glottis are also augmented, and keep the vibrating orifice continually half opened, which naturally produces a great waste of air. A last difference is in the increased extent of that elliptic surface.

All these circumstances, which we shall refer to again, show in the mechanism of the falsetto, a state of relaxation, which we do not find in the same degree in the chest-register.

MANNER IN WHICH THE SOUNDS ARE FORMED

As we have just said, and what we have seen proves it, the inferior ligaments, at the bottom of the larynx, form exclusively voice, whatever may be its register or its intensity; for they alone vibrate at the bottom of the larynx[3]. But by virtue of what principle is the voice formed? It seems to me, that the answer to this question can be but this; the voice is formed in one unique manner - by the compressions and the expansions of the air, or the successive and regular explosions which it produces in passing through the glottis.

The ligaments of the glottis are situated about the mean level of the upper border of the cricoid, close the passage, and present a resistance to the air. As soon as the air has accumulated sufficiently, it parts these folds and produces an explosion. But at the same instant, by virtue of their elasticity, and the pressure from below being relieved, they meet again to give rise to a fresh explosion. A series of these compressions and expansions, or of explosions, occasioned by the expansive force of the air and the reaction of the glottis, produces the voice.

This theory, though now generally admitted for reeds, and undoubtedly evident in the liquid vein, the toothed-wheel of Savart, the syrene of the Baron Cagnard Latour, etc., has not to my knowledge, been yet applied to the glottis[4]. If we consider that the lips of this aperture, taken separately, can give no kind of sound, however we may try to make them speak, we must admit that the sounds which they give by their mutual action, are only owing to the explosions of the air produced by their stroke[5]. It is not necessary in order to obtain the explosion of sound, that the glottis should be perfectly closed each time after its opening; it suffices that it should oppose an obstacle to the air capable of developing its elasticity. In this case the rushing of the air is heard accompanying the sounds, and they take a veiled, and sometimes an extremely muffled character; an observation which we have already presented to the reader's notice in speaking of the falsetto.

CONJECTURE ON THE FORMATION OF THE DIFFERENT REGISTERS

As the entire system if vibrations arises solely from the inferior ligaments, it is evident that the cause of the different tones called registers, must be sought for in the muscles which set these ligaments in motion; and that the other parts of the larynx must be considered only as apparatus for strengthening the sounds obtained, and for modifying their quality. In our efforts to discover the more intimate processes of the vocal organs which produce the sounds, we shall recur at once to the observations already mentioned, to some anatomical remarks which we are going to make, and to the sensations which we feel in the organ itself whilst it is producing sounds.

If we detach one of the halves of the thyroid cartilage, we shall see a large muscular surface of oblique fibres, which fills all the space between the arytenoid and thyroid cartilages. At its upper end is to be seen the muscle corresponding to the superior vocal ligaments, and which sometimes extends to the notch in the thyroid. After detaching this generally frail muscle, all the fibres constituting this muscular surface seem to start from two opposite centres, viz.: the anterior surface of the arytenoid, and the re-entering angle of the thyroid. These centres, occupying the extremities of a diagonal line, send their fibres towards each other in parallel lines. Those which start from the anterior face of the arytenoid descend obliquely; the most external ones go to the cricoid, whose posterior half they cover at the side; the most internal ones descend to the vocal membrane[6], which they cover entirely. The fibres which terminate at the membrane become longer, as they become more internal. Those which start from the re-entering angle of the thyroid, re-ascend obliquely to the summit of the arytenoid, then diverge in order to form the sides of the ventricles, and then disappear in the aryteno-epiglottidean folds and even the under surface of the epiglottis. If we cut it away in successive layers, proceeding from the outside to the in, we reach a thick bundle of fibres, perfectly horizontal, which line the outer aspect of the vocal ligament, and which go from the anterior apophyses of the arytenoid to the re-entering angle of the thyroid[7].

This bundle has its posterior half covered by the lateral crico-arytenoid muscle, and its anterior half by the diverging fibres which start from the thyroid. If we cut away the horizontal bundle in successive layers, we see that the fibres are not all of the same length; the most external fibres are the longest, and the succeeding ones get gradually shorter as they become more internal; but they all originate in the anterior cavity of the arytenoid, and the muscle is inserted in the manner above explained throughout the whole length of the vocal ligaments, the thyro-arytenoid portion of it excepted. As the fibres all begin from the arytenoid, and terminate successively at more distant points of the membrane, we see that the muscle is thicker behind than before.

Thus the vocal ligament, and the membrane which depends from it, the sole sources of all vocal sounds, are under the direct action of the fibres which come from the anterior cavity of the arytenoid; the ligament under the action of the horizontal bundle, the membrane under that of the oblique fibres. The long horizontal fibres, extending from one cartilage to the other, are placed at the exterior of the short horizontal fibres, and at the interior of the oblique fibres. The diverging fibres which start from the thyroid, acting only on the superior vocal ligaments and the folds, seem to influence by their contractions only the quality and the volume of the voice.

The remarkable arrangement of the fibres which we have just examined, enables us to explain a fundamental fact - the elevation of the voice. The fibres of the horizontal bundle being placed over each other, in layers, one covering the other, and getting gradually longer and longer, as they become more external, extend their action to the more anterior parts of the edges of the glottis. This progressive action from the back to the front, encroaches gradually on the length of the vibrating portion of the ligament, and likewise increases its tension, and its faculty of accelerating its pulsations.

Another portion of the thyro-arytenoid muscle at the same time stretches and raises the vocal membrane more and more, causing a lesser depth of the ligaments to be in contact, in proportion as the sounds become higher, and thus assists by increasing the mobility of the ligaments.

We shall see in a few moments that the rotary movement, which the external fibres of the lateral crico-arytenoid muscles give to the arytenoid, by making the vocal membrane deeper, partly counteracts the above effect, and produces the chest-register.

The crico-thyroid muscle, on the contrary, is a powerful auxiliary in the elevation of the voice. This muscle, which at the same time causes the thyroid to come forwards and downwards, gives rise to a mechanical tension, not only in the vocal ligament, but even in the whole vocal membrane. The meeting of the thyroid and the cricoid cartilages, which we can feel by the touch, becomes especially marked when the inter-ligamentous glottis alone produces the sounds, which takes place as we have seen at the notes do#, re, in the chest-register, and an octave above for that of the head; with this difference, however, that for the latter a more vigorous and complete connection is necessary.

Let us now see what we may learn from the sensations we feel in the vocal organ? When we produce a chest-note, the least attention enables us to distinguish a "pinching" at the posterior part of the glottis, which becomes more vigorous as the notes ascend. This pinching seems to be formed by extension of the depth of the touching surfaces, and may become very painful; whilst the notes of falsetto, when higher than chest ones, give comparatively great relief to this part, and the surfaces in contact seem to have become thinner.

If we combine these sensations with the different remarks which have been furnished to us by the examination of the muscles, we can fix the particular mechanism of each register.

CHEST REGISTER

In fact, when the arytenoid muscles have brought in contact the arytenoid cartilages, and closed the glottis, the voice may take two very different characters; nay, more, it will be produced in pitches widely apart from one another, and will give forth the chest, or falsetto registers, according as the fibres of the thyro-arytenoid attached to the vocal membrane are active or not. By the action of these fibres, as we have seen, this muscle raises the vocal membrane, and makes it apposable part thinner; whereas the lateral crico-arytenoid gives a rotatory movement to the cartilage, which brings the apophyses into deep contact. This deep contact, which continues even after the apophyses no longer partake in the vibrations, gives a deep tension to the membranes, increases the depth of their contact[8], and, as necessary consequence, augments the resistance that we attribute the formation of the chest-register, so distinct by its particular amplitude. To it we attribute also the slowness of the beats of the glottis, and the consequent low pitch of the sounds, a pitch which, even in the highest tenor voices, is at least an octave lower than the head notes of ordinary soprano.

REGISTER OF FALSETTO

When, on the contrary, the external fibres of the lateral crico-arytenoid muscle remain inactive, we produce the falsetto. The lips of the glottis, stretched by the horizontal bundle of the thyro-arytenoid, come in contact by their edge alone, formed at once by the ligament and the apophyses, and offer little resistance to the air. Hence arises the great loss of this agent, and the general weakness of the sounds produced here.

But as soon as we reach the sound do, the beats are produced by the ligaments exclusively, and we have attained the head-register. It is certain, as we may deduce from the movement of the ligaments, that then the vocal membrane is raised by the action of the fibres of the thyro-arytenoid muscle, and its surface is diminished to an edge; but we think that the external fibres of the lateral crico-arytenoid, which would prevent this movement, remain inactive. Then also the very decided tension, which the crico-thyroid muscle effects on the vocal tendons, and which accelerates their movements, takes place.

During the chest-register, therefore, the vocal ligaments are stretched, and are in contact to an extent corresponding with the depth of the anterior apophyses of the arytenoid, whilst in the falsetto the edges alone of the ligaments are stretched and apposed; in both cases the sounds being formed, not by the actual vibrations of either the whole or part of the tendons, but by the successive explosions which they allow.

PRESSURE OF THE AIR

Until now, in our remarks on the manner in which the voice is formed, we have only referred to the rigidity of the glottis, a rigidity necessary to accomplish the 1056 vibrations in one second[9], which form the do of the chest-voice, and to accomplish the double number which produces the octave in the head-voice. There is, notwithstanding, another indispensable element for the production of vocal sounds, the pressure of the air. Pressure, as is well known, developes an elastic force in this agent, in a degree inverse to the volume which it occupies. It is by means of this power that the intensity of the sounds is obtained. The intensity of the sound can only depend on the quantity of air which goes to each sharp explosion. I say sharp explosion, as an express condition; the glottis should close itself perfectly after every vibration; for if the air found a constant passage, as in the notes of the falsetto, then the greatest movements of the glottis, and the greatest waste of air, would produce precisely the weakest notes. To reject this theory would be to attribute the intensity of the sound to the extent of the vibrations accomplished by the lips of the glottis, and to suppose that these lips, each taken separately, possess the power of producing sounds, suppositions quite contrary to the facts. The elastic force of the air arises not only from the compression of the lungs, but also from the contractions of the trachea, which adjusts its calibre to the different dimensions of the glottis. It is by means of this force that the air conquers the continually-increasing obstacle presented by the lips of the glottis when they produce sounds more and more intense.

Thus the problem of the elevation of the voice, always complicated with that of its intensity, in order to be complete, ought to show the connection which exists between the tension of the lips of the glottis, the pressure of the air, and the number and intensity of the explosions obtained. As a consequence, we may state that the greater pressure of air necessary to produce the greater intensity, would at the same time increase the number of pulsations, and so raise the tone; but to prevent this, the glottis must at the same time be lengthened, and _vice versa_, or, in other words, that the different lengths of the glottis can, under different degrees of pressure, produce the same number of shocks, but at different degrees of intensity.

OF THE QUALITIES OF THE VOICE

Various simultaneous causes modify the qualities of the voice: 1, according as the glottis partially or entirely closes the passes between the explosions, it produces veiled or brilliant sounds; 2, the tube which surmounts and surrounds it also greatly affects the quality of the voice; by its contractions it gives brilliancy to it and by its widening volume; 3, the opiglottis also plays a very important part, for every time it lowers itself, and nearly closes the orifice of the larynx, the voice gains in brilliancy; and when, on the other hand, it is drawn up, the voice immediately becomes veiled.

REFERENCES

1. Let us here observe, that three registers of voice are generally admitted: chest, falsetto, and head. The first begins lower in a man's voice than in a woman's; the second extends equally in both voices; the third reaches higher in the female voice.

2. The musical limits we establish in the course of these pages vary a little in each individual.

3. We gladly acknowledge that this most important fact has been already announced by J. Muller, although we have our objections to the theory which accompanies it. - Handbuch der Physiologic des Meachen.

4. I find that Dr. Muller hints at the possibility of the voice being thus formed, but only to attack and reject the notion. - Ibidem.

5. Many controversies have arisen respecting the sounds sometimes emitted by animals after the section of the superior and recurrent laryngeal nerves; sounds which have been perhaps occasioned by the struggling of the animal causing a swelling of the neck and a mechanical contact of the vocal ligaments. However, without doubt, after the section of these nerves, voice, as a voluntary act, can no longer take place.

6. We thus designate that part of the membrane which goes from the bottom of the vocal ligament to the edge of the cricroid.

7. Another portion of the thyro-arytenoid muscle.

8. It is then that we feel the pinching of which we have spoken.

9. Pouillet, Physique, Sixth Edition, Vol. II, page 77.

Paratasis-Gram
of the
Vocal Folds
and the Dimensions
of the Voice

Aatto Sonninen

Our knowledge of phonation is based largely on theory or on observations made under conditions differing from the normal, for example using a laryngeal mirror, or excised human larynges, etc. Few direct, objective observations have been made owing to the technical difficulties involved.

Paratasis, or stretching in the ascending scale, of the vocal folds has not yet been dealt with exhaustively (Luchsinger and Arnold, p. 62). The relationship of paratasis to the various dimensions of the voice (volume, pitch and quality) has been even less studied. Since changes in the length of the vocal folds can produce changes in tension and in mass, there is good reason to believe that changes in length essentially control the vibration patterns of the vocal folds. It is the purpose of the present work - as a pilot study - to throw light on this question on the basis of observations on a test subject. The subject was a middle-aged actress actively interested in singing; her total physiological voice range was studied in half-tone steps in different voice habits. In this way we were able to draw a series of connected curves representing the lengthening of the vocal folds. These curves will be referred to here by the term paratasisgram.

134

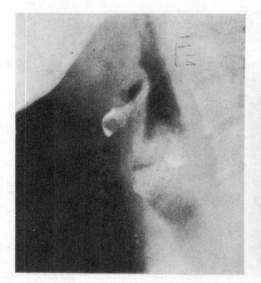
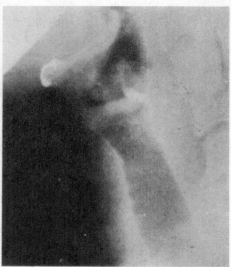
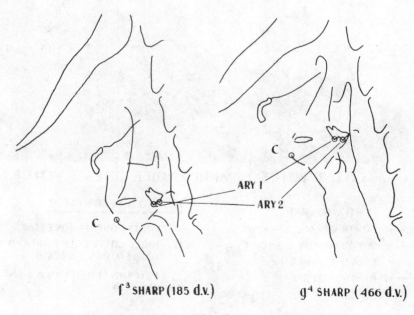

f³ SHARP (185 d.v.)   g⁴ SHARP (466 d.v.)

Fig. 1

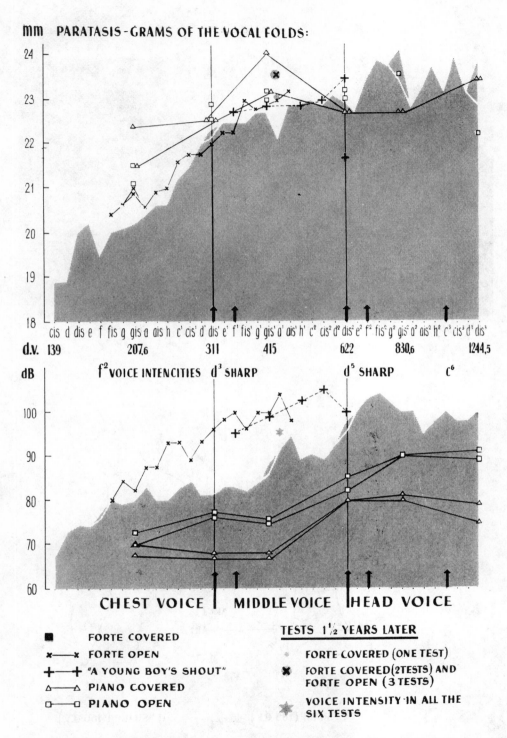

Fig. 2.   Paratasis-grams of the vocal folds (above) and voice volumes (below) obtained in X-ray studies of physiological voice range of an actress.

METHOD

Measurements of the length of the vocal folds has been performed by numerous investigators with the aid of either a laryngeal mirror (11, 12, 14, 21, 33, 38) or X-rays (7, 22, 28, 29, 37). However, to my knowledge, no studies covering the total voice range have been made so far. Roentgen examination has the advantage over the laryngeal mirror that it does not interfere with phonation. Both methods are associated with disadvantages, for example the difficulty of finding suitable points of measurement, and errors in projection. Since the year 1954 the author has utilized measurement of the calcification centres in the laryngeal cartilage, which are visible in lateral roentgenograms and become more sharply defined with increasing age (9, 24, 28, 29). The anterior point of attachment of the vocal folds, the centre of calcification in the anterior margin of the thyroid cartilage, was seen in 58 per cent of the 150 cases studied; the posterior point of attachment of the vocal folds, the calcification centres of the arytenoid cartilages, were seen in 40.6 per cent. If small holes are made in the X-ray films at the sharply defined edges of these points, it is not difficult to measure the distance between them with 0.1 mm. accuracy, using dividers adjustable with a screw. The puncturing of the holes of course presents the chief difficulty and is also most dependent on subjective factors: the points must be exactly comparable. Another difficulty arises from the fact that the calcification centres in the arytenoid cartilage may be projected one on top of the other, but this can be avoided in part by measuring separately the distance to each arytenoid cartilage and calculating the average. In Fig. 1 we can see roentgenograms taken of our subject singing at the pitches f3 sharp (185 d.v.) (at left) and g4 sharp (466 d.v.) (at right). It is easily seen from the pictures that the distance from the anterior point of attachment C to the posterior points ary 1 and ary 2 is clearly greater at higher pitch. Without attempting to calculate possible errors due to projection, I wish to state that, in a number of selected cases, the best measurement result was obtained in one in which there were eight roentgenograms of one subject taken during the same phonation period; the dispersion was 0.1 mm. The examinations for my study were carried out in November, 1959. One and a half years later a control test was made with the subject singing at the pitch a4. The measurements obtained from the six X-ray films differed at most 1.5 mm. from the corresponding previous measurements. It may be noted that the quality and intensity of the voice were not exactly similar at the two occasions of measurement, and so the difference was hardly due to measurement error alone. Though it must be admitted that, in unselected cases, the measuring technique here employed may be subject to considerable error, as claimed by Zenker and Zenker (p. 6), I would maintain that, in this selected case, the limit of accuracy is certainly reliable at least in regard to differences in length exceeding 1 mm. - perhaps even to smaller differences if the changes show a similar trend. Fig. 2 shows the paratasis-grams obtained for our test subject. Below are seen the corresponding voice intensity curves measured with the sound level instrument. We shall now hear voice samples recorded during a study session.

VOICE SAMPLE

Some of the voice samples recorded during the roentgenography were analysed with a sonograph.[1] It appeared that the open voice habit was governed by a richer partial tone spectrum reaching a higher level of frequency than the covered voice at corresponding pitch. Formants of other vowel sounds (æ, e and i) were also of greater number than with the covered voice. These differences did not seem to be essentially related to voice intensity. With a rise in pitch the number of partial tones decreased in all voice habits. The change was especially clear during the transition from the middle register to head voice. The number of partial tones was 3-5 in the head register in all voice habits, whereas the maximum in the chest register was 30.

RESULTS

Figure 2 shows the results of length measurements of the vocal folds with an accuracy of 0.1 mm. Changes exceeding 1.0 mm. may be considered absolutely reliable. It is seen that

(1) The vocal folds lengthened fairly abruptly with a rise in pitch in the chest register from f2 (174 d.v.) to d3 sharp (311 d.v.).

(2) The length of the vocal folds was approximately the same in the head voice area from d5 sharp (622 d.v.) to c6 (1046 d.v.).

(3) The lengthening of the vocal folds was considerably slower in the middle register than in the chest register. It is possible that the lengthening of this area differs in various voice habits and occurs more rapidly in open than in covered voice. This change was particularly clear in forte.

(4)   The vocal folds were longer in piano voice in the chest and middle registers than at the corresponding pitch when singing forte.

It may be mentioned, among other roentgenological findings, that in the open voice habit the Morgagni sinuses appeared distinctly smaller, the ventricular folds closer to each other, and the epiglottis more inclined backward than with the corresponding covered voice. With a rise in pitch in the chest register, the larynx ascended cranially. In the middle register, using the covered voice, the larynx moved abruptly downward to rise again in the head voice area. In the open voice habit, however, the larynx displayed throughout a steady tendency toward the cranial direction. This difference was more evident in piano voice than in forte. The distance from the larynx to the spine was smaller in open than in covered voice.

DISCUSSION

Even though our test subject coped with the difficulties of the study very well, it is clear that the singing performances are a long way from both "pure" open voice and from voice fulfilling aesthetic requirements. Here too, it seems proper that the singing performances are taken as "mainly open" or "mainly closed", as pointed out by some previous investigators. In this study it was also necessary to disregard the "dynamic features of the onset and the decay of the tone" (6, 35, 36) though these affect decisively the impression gained from the voice heard. In spite of this, the results obtained seem to provoke further thought.

It was supposed earlier that register transitions might be associated with coupling of the vocal cavities. This view is reflected in the terms "chest voice" and "head voice" still in use today. However, Trendelenburg in 1938 (34) demonstrated that this opinion is unsatisfactory (cf. 3). It has been shown that vocal cord vibrations differ according to register (5, 15, 18, 19, 25, 26, 27, 31, 32, etc.) A shift in register is due above all to a change in the mode of vibration of the vocal folds. The cause of this change is to some extent obscure. "Changes in vocal cord tension and in mass are of essential importance in this respect" (Trendelenburg p. 226).

Van den Berg (4), in his meritorious study with excised larynges, in 1960 arrived at the conclusion that longitudinal tension in the vocal muscles are the important parameters determining the response in the main registers. Six years earlier the present writer had already directed attention to the same question, and was probably the first to do so: I showed in 1954 (28) and later (29, 30), on the basis of objective observations, that the lengthening of the vocal cords is basically linked to the question of registers. The present study seems to confirm these observations and to justify agreement with Garcia who claimed, as early as 1840 (10), that there exist only two main registers and these two have a common area, "la partie commune", i.e. the middle register, which represents a transition area from one main register to the other.

Fig. 3

Vocal folds thick:	forte chest <u>open</u>		Vocal folds short:	forte chest covered
vocal folds thin:	piano head covered		Vocal folds long:	piano head <u>open</u>

In the chest register the lengthening of the vocal folds causes above all a decrease in the vibrating mass, while in the head register there is an increase in tension chiefly in the vocal ligaments, with a consequent rise in voice. Faaborg-Andersen's observation (1957) (8) concerning electrical activity of the vocalic muscle may be related to these phenomena. According to him "With phonation with increasing pitch the increase in electrical activity was considerable, as long as the increase in pitch occurred within the same register. If the increase in pitch occurred with a simultaneous shift in register, the increase in electrical activity in most instances was only slight."

It is evident that the question of open and covered singing is in some way associated with the question of register. In head voice - although the test subject did her best - her open and covered singing were practically identical, and this applies both to forte and piano. In the chest register, however, the sonagraph examination showed a distinct difference between open and covered voice. Open singing was possible both forte and piano and a shift to a higher register produced no break. It is probable that "covering" in the chest register consists chiefly in a change of the shape of the resonance cavities, the function of the vocal folds remaining practically the same as in open singing. In the middle register, however, the vocal folds showed a greater tendency to stretch in open than in covered voice. Open singing was possible only forte, and a shift to head voice was only possible by means of a break. "Covering" in the middle register seems to be a question of phonation rather than one of resonance (cf. i.e. 1, 2, 16, 17, 23).

We know from earlier studies that the vocal folds are thicker in forte than in piano voice ((20) p. 91, (27) p. 70); thicker in the chest register than in the head register (13, 20); and also thicker in open than in covered voice (20). The results of this study seem to indicate that the vocal folds are shorter in forte than in piano, shorter in the chest than the head register, but longer in open than in closed voice. Thus covered singing in the middle register would seem to resemble the head register and piano voice - apart from the fact that the vocal folds are short; open singing, again, seems to resemble forte and the chest register apart from the vocal folds being long. This may also be expressed in a diagram (Fig. 3), which may help to make the matter clearer.

The reason why open singing in the middle register is so tiring and in our experience so dangerous to the vocal folds is not yet fully known and this question requires further objective investigations. It remains a matter for the future to determine the final value of the vocal fold paratasis-gram in solving the interesting and important problem of the factors affecting voice dimensions.

SUMMARY

A middle-aged actress's vocal folds were studied by length measurements through the entire physiological voice range in half-tone steps in different voice habits. The lateral X-ray technique reported by the present author in 1954 was used. This method, utilizing the calcification centres in the larynx, gives a minimum accuracy of 1 mm. The results are shown in the form of paratasis-grams representing the changes in length of the vocal folds. The voice samples obtained in the course of the study were analysed with a sonagraph and the voice intensities measured with the sound level instrument.

The results seem to indicate that there are only two main registers: the chest and the head register, and that the middle register should be regarded as a transition area; also that a shift in register is related above all to changes in the length of the vocal folds and not to coupling of the vocal cavities. Thus key to the problem of register seems to be primarily laryngeal and not pharyngeal.

In the chest register there occurs intense stretching of the vocal folds and possibly a slight increase in longitudinal tension in the vocal ligaments. This results above all in gradual decrease of the vibrating mass. In head voice, the vocal folds apparently remain equally long, and further rise in pitch then seems to be associated above all with an increase in longitudinal tension of the vocal ligaments.

The results finally show the following points to be made:

(1)   "Dangerous" open singing in the middle register is associated with fairly thick vocal folds - thus resembling the chest register and forte voice; but this mode of singing is also associated with fairly long vocal folds - thus resembling the head register and piano voice.

(2)   "Correct" covered singing in the middle register is associated with fairly thin vocal folds - thus resembling the head register and piano voice; but also with fairly short vocal folds - thus resembling the chest register and forte.

Oto-Laryngological Hospital
University of Helsinki

BIBLIOGRAPHY

1. K. Wiik, Phonetic Labor., University of Turku.

(1) Armin, G., Die Technik der Greitspannung, pp. 45-49 (Berlin, 1931).

(2) —, Die Meisterregeln der Stimmbildungskunst, pp. 22-31 (1946).

(3) van den Berg, Jw., "Ueber die Koppelung bei der Stimmbildung", Zeitschr. f. Phonetik u. allgem. Sprachwissenschaft, 8, 281-293 (1955).

(4) —, "Vocal Ligaments versus Registers", Curr. Probl. Phoniat. Logoped, 1, 19-34 (Karger, Basel, New York, 1960).

(5) van den Berg, Jw, and Tan, T. S., "Results of Experiments with Human Larynxes," Pract. oto-rhino-laryng., 21/6, 425-450 (1959).

(6) van den Berg, Jw, and Vennard, W., "Toward an objective vocabulary for voice pedagogy", Nats Bulletin, February (1959).

(7) Curry, R., "The mechanism of pitch change in the voice", J. Physiol., 91, 254-261 (1937).

(8) Faaborg-Andersen, K., "Electromyographic Investigation of Intrinsic Laryngeal Muscles in Humans", Acta Physiol. Scandin., 41, Suppl. 140, p. 121 (Copenhagen, 1957).

(9) Fyfe, F. W. and Naylor, E., "Calcification and ossification in the cricoid cartilage of the larynx, with annotation on the mechanism of change of pitch", Proc. Canad. Otolaryng. Soc., pp. 67-79 (1958).

(10) Garcia, M., Ecole de Garcia. Traite complet de l'art du chant, p. XIV (Paris, E. Troupenas et C., 1840).

(11) Hollien, H., "Some Laryngeal Correlates of Vocal Pitch", J. Speech and Hear. Res., 3/1, 52-58 (1960).

(12) —, "Vocal Pitch Variation Related to Changes in Vocal Fold Length", J. Speech and Hear. Res., 3/2, 150-156 (1960).

(13) Hollien, H. and Curtis, J. F., "A Lamigraphic Study of Vocal Pitch", J. Speech and Hear. Res., 3/4, 361-371 (1960).

(14) Hollien, H., and Moore, G. P., "Measurements of the Vocal Folds During Changes in Pitch", J. Speech and Hear. Res., 3/2, 157-165 (1960).

(15) Kirikae, I., "Ueber den Bewegungsvorgang an den Stimmlippen und die Oeffnungs - und Verschlusszeit der Stimmritze wahrend der Phonation", Jap. Ztschr. f. Oto-Rhino-Laryng., 49, 236 (1943).

(16) Klemetti, H., Aanenkaytto puheessa ja laulussa, pp. 43-47 (WSOY. Porvoo. Helsinki. II painos. 1951).

(17) Lehman, L., Meine Gesangskunst, p. 22 (Berlin, 1909).

(18) Luchsinger, R., "Der zeitliche Ablauf der Stimmritzenveranderung bei Zeitlupen Aufnahmen der Stimmlippenbewegung", Folia phoniatr., 6, 14 (1954).

(19) —, "Falsett und Vollton der Kopfstimme (Beitrag zum Registerproblem)", Arch. Ohr.-usr. Heilk u. Z. Hals-usw. Heilk., 155, 505-519 (1949).

(20) Luchsinger, R. und Arnold, G.E., Lehrbuch der Stimm- und Sprachheilk. (Wien, 1959).

(21) Luchsinger., R. und Pfister, K., "Die Messung der Stimmlippenverlangerung beim Steigern der Tonhohe", Folia phoniat., 13, 1-12 (1961).

(22) Mitchinson, A. G. H., and Yoffey, J. M., "Changes in the vocal folds in humming low and high notes. A radiographic study," J. Anat., 82, 88 (1948).

(23) Pielke, W., "Ueber 'offen' und 'gedeckt' gesungene Vokale", Passows Beitrage, etc., 5, 215 (1912).

(24) Roncallo, P., Acta Otolaryng., 36, 110-134 (1948).

(25) Rubin, H. J., and Hirt, C. C., "The Falsetto. A High Speed Cinematographic Study", The Laryngoscope, LXX/9, 1305-1324 (1960).

(26) Smith, S., "Chest Register versus Head Register in the Membrane Cushion Model of the Vocal Cords," Folia phoniat, 9, 32 (1957).

(27) Sonesson, B., "On the Anatomy and Vibratory Pattern of the Human Vocal Folds", Acta Otolaryng., Suppl. 156 (1960).

(28) Sonninen, A., "Is the length of the vocal cords the same at all different levels of singing?", Acta Otolaryng., Suppl. 118, 219-231 (1954).

(29) —, "The Role of the External Laryngeal Muscles in Length-adjustment of the Vocal Cords in Singing", Acta Otolaryng., Suppl. 130 (1956).

(30) —, "Laryngeal Signs and Symptoms of Goitre", Folia phoniat., 12, 41-47 (1960).

(31) Timcke, E., von Leden, H., and Moore, P., "Laryngeal vibrations: Measurements of the glottic wave, I: The normal vibratory Cycle", Arch. Otolaryng., 68/1, 1-19 (1958).

(32) —, "Laryngeal Vibrations: Measurements of the Glottic Wave, II: Physiologic Variations", Arch. Otolaryng., 69/4, 438-444 (1959).

(33) Pressman, J. J., "Physiology of the vocal cords in phonation and respiration", Arch. Otolaryng., 35, 355 (1942).

(34) Trendelenburg, W., "Untersuchungen zur Kenntnis der Registerbruchstellen beim Gesang", Sitzungsber. d. Preuss. Akad. d. Wiss., Phys.-math. K1., I, 5-22 and 188-226 (1938).

(35) Winckel, F., "Physikalische Kriterien fur objektive Stimmbeurteilung", Folia phoniat., 5, 232 (1953).

(36) —, Phanomene des musikalischen Horens, p. 8 (Max Hesses Verlag, Berlin und Wunsiedel, 1960).

(37) Zenker, W., und Zenker, A., "Ueber die Regelung der Stimmlippenspannung durch von aussen eingreifende Mechanismen", Folia phoniat., 12, 6 (1960).

(38) Zimmerman, R., "Stimmlippenlangen bei Sangern und Sangerinnen", Arch. Sprach-u. Stimnheilk., 2, 103 (1938).

Vocal Ligaments
Versus Registers

Dr. Janwillem van den Berg

Dr. van den Berg is no stranger to readers of The NATS Bulletin. Two previous articles of his have appeared in these pages, and his name is often found in bibliographies of other scientific articles. He is the recipient of the William and Harriett Gould Foundation Award, given annually for distinguished laryngeal research.

This article first appeared in Current Problems in Phoniatrics and Logopedics, Vol. I, pp. 19-34 (Karger, Basel/New York, 1960). It is reprinted here with the consent of the author. The author's address: Dr. Jw. van den Berg, Physiological Laboratory, Department of Medical Physics, State University of Groningen, Bloemsingel I, Groningen, Netherlands.

The title of this paper is intentionally one-sided. There is no question, that registration involves more than the vocal ligaments. However, experiments with excised human larynges, which the author (1) performed together with T. S. Tan (2), have led to a new and simple concept of the origin of the main registers. The properties of the vocal ligaments and the conditions under which they are used are essential parameters in this concept and the title is chosen to stress this idea.

DEFINITION OF THE REGISTERS

The various vocal responses of the human larynx are most commonly divided into the three main registers: chest, head or mid, and falsetto register, and two lesser registers at the extreme low and high side: strohbass and flute or whistle register. These names are a hodge-podge arising from such divergent sources as: secondary clues (resonances in the chest with the chest voice), misconceptions (non-existing resonances in the head with the head voice), acoustical illusions (with the falsetto voice), acoustical resemblance (the rattling sound of trodden straw with the Strohbass voice), and similarity of origin, (eddies generated in a narrow opening and subsequent cavity resonance with the flute or whistle register). However, the classification is almost generally accepted and, vague as it may be, works practically without difficulty, unless experts are asked to classify tones in the region where chest, head and falsetto voices overlap each other. We then realize how subjective the judgements are, and must be, as no objective criteria are used.

It is certainly possible to objectify the classification of tones by performing an acoustical analysis, e.g. by means of a Sonagraph, taking into account the height of the pitch and the number of significant partials. One might doubt, however, whether such a theoretical approach would soon lead to a generally accepted classification of tones and voices, as the main need for such classifications arises in the artistic field.

The number of significant partials is directly related with the vibrational pattern of the vocal folds, thus with the physiological and functional behaviour of the larynx. The vibrational patterns can be studied and recorded by means of a stroboscope and delta f generator (3). It would be convenient if the number of significant partials could be determined by means of a simple Fourier analysis of the variations of the glottal area during the vocal cycle. The problem is not that easy, however, as may be demonstrated by Figure 1, which shows the vibrations of an excised larynx, photographed by means of a stroboscope and delta f generator. The sequence begins and ends with inadequate adductory forces on the vocal processes. The tone is then almost inaudible and extremely breathy and these features are not revealed by a Fourier analysis (the weakness of the sound can be explained by taking into account the persisting chink between the arytenoids and comparing this source with a loudspeaker without baffle). With adequate adductory forces a full and rich chest tone was heard and a Fourier analysis of the glottal area yields reasonable results under these circumstances.

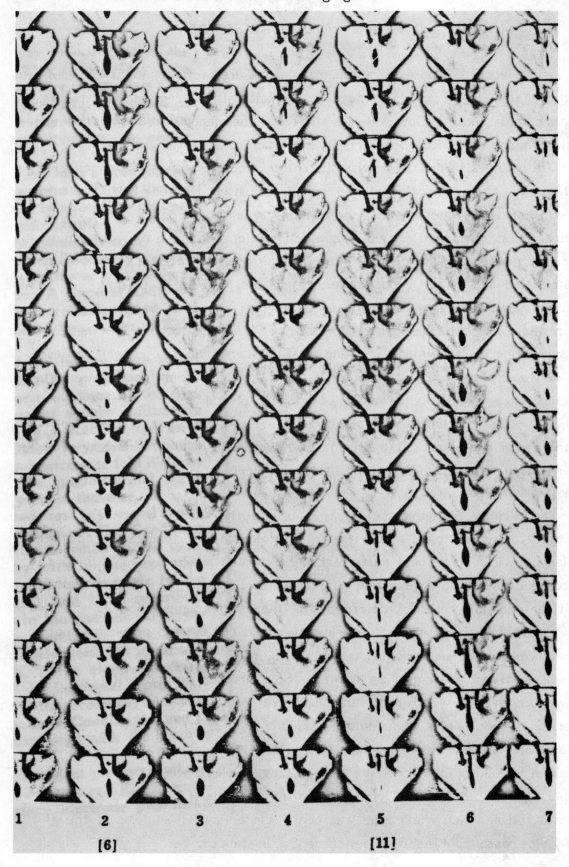

1   2   3   4   5   6   7

[6]   [11]

Figure 1. Excised Larynx

DELTA <u>f</u> MOTION PICTURES. The strips read from top to bottom in the sequence 1 to 7 across. The air flow is constant at 200 cubic centimeters per second. The angle of the thyroid is at the bottom of each frame, and a pair of tweezers can be seen at the top of each frame. The points of these tweezers are outside the vocal processes of the arytenoid cartilages, and in the vibrations pictured in the middle of the figure they exert medical compression by pressing the vocal processes together. Note that up to frame 6, strip 2, a black space appears between the vocal processes, and this space does <u>not</u> close even when the rest of the glottis <u>does</u> close (frames 10 and 11, strip ?). In this part of the sequence there was a chest tone, 70 cps, almost inaudible, extremely breathy, with a pressure below the glottis of 2 centimeters of water. In frame 6, strip 2, the tweezers close the interarytenoid space, and a vibratory sequence with adequate medial compression begins. Note that when the glottis closes, it remains closed for 7 frames (3 to 9, strip 3) and after medial compression has increased the glottis closes for 10 frames (5 to 14, strip 4). Chest tone, 85 cps, normal, powerful, subglottic pressure 8 cm of water, four times the pressure when medial compression was inadequate. In frame 11, strip 5, the tweezers open, the interarytenoid space reappears, weak tone recommences with only brief glottal closure.

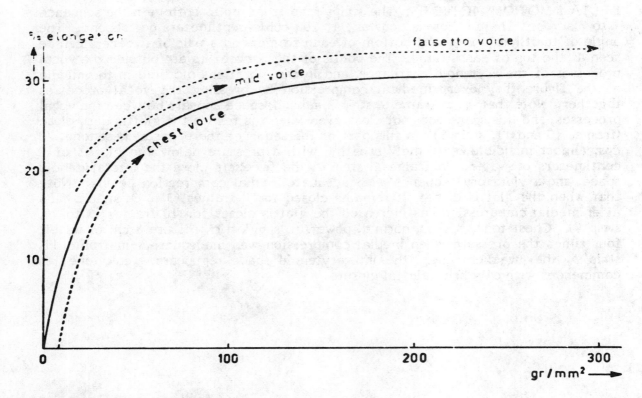

Figure 2. Excised Larynges
Elongation of the vocal ligaments versus longitudinal tension per square mm cross sectional area. The dotted lines show the elongations used in the main registers.

The overall behaviour of the larynx in the main registers, expressed in the associated vibrational patterns, depends on the properties and the adjustment of the vocal folds. The inner margins of the vocal folds have, for obvious reasons, the largest amplitudes of the vibrations. These margins contain the vocal ligaments. Properties and adjustment of the vocal ligaments must therefore be expected to be essential parameters in determining the type of vibrational pattern.

VOCAL LIGAMENTS

The properties of the vocal ligaments are elucidated by Figure 2, which gives the percentage elongation as a function of the longitudinal tension per mm^2 cross section. The curve begins with a part where the ligament is very distensible and ends with an undistensible part. This behaviour is due to the elastic and collagenous fibres composing the ligaments. At small elongations only the elastic fibres oppose the stretching force, at large elongations the collagenous fibres become stretched and allow no further elongation, as they are almost undistensible, like tendon. The whole procedure is comparable with the distension of the margin of an anklet sock. At first the margin is very distensible, only the incorporated elastic rubber strings resisting the distension, but finally the margin becomes undistensible, when the undistensible nylon fibres become stretched. In general we found, that the right vocal ligament was thicker and more distensible than the left one and that the distensibility of the ligaments decreased with increasing age.

Figure 2 may show that the vocal ligaments will allow large vibrations, i.e. a chest voice response at low pitches, at small degrees of elongation, and only very small vibrations at large degrees of elongation, i.e. a falsetto voice response at high pitches. Between these extremes there is a region of intermediate pitches with intermediate amplitudes, for which I prefer the name mid voice, to avoid the clearly wrong name of head voice. The mid voice overlaps chest and falsetto voice, but to understand this overlapping we need to discuss all factors determining pitch and vibrational pattern.

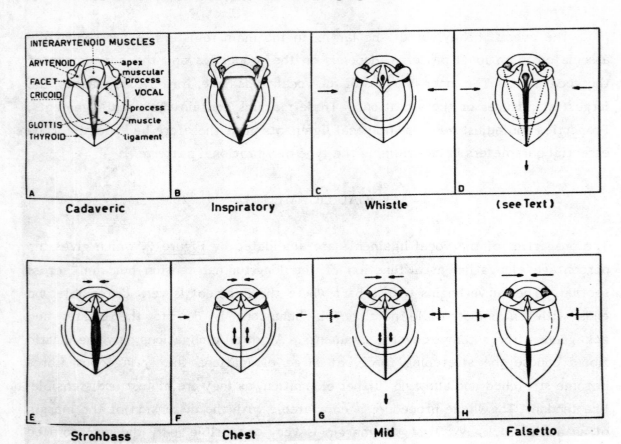

Figure 3.
Schemes of the adjustment of the larynx at zero flow.

FACTORS DETERMINING PITCH
AND VIBRATIONAL PATTERN

(1.) Adjustment of the Arytenoids

This adjustment is brought about by the contraction of the adjusting muscles: the interarytenoid muscles, particularly the transversus, the posterior and lateral cricoarytenoid muscles and the external (lateral) thyroarytenoid muscles. During phonation the posticus[1] is not active, the adjustment is then due to the activity of the interarytenoid, the lateral cricoarytenoid and the external thyroarytenoid muscles. In this respect it is essential to realize what kind of movements the arytenoids are allowed to make. The classical opinion, represented in the textbooks, is that the facets are such that gliding movements are possible and also rotations along a vertical axis from apex towards facet. The latter idea is wrong, the peculiar articulation of the arytenoid on the cricoid does not allow rotations along a vertical axis. The arytenoids can glide along the edge of the cricoid, and a contraction of the powerful transversus muscle results in a firm contact of the posterior parts of the arytenoids, but only of the upper posterior parts, at the apex, as the gliding component is very small. They can also rock on the edge of the cricoid, a contraction of the posticus results in an upward and outward movement of the vocal processes, a contraction of the lateral cricoarytenoids in an inward and slightly downward movement of the vocal processes, a contraction of the external thyroarytenoid muscles in an inward and more pronounced downward movement of the vocal processes and a forward movement of the apex. In the following schematical discussions the activity of lateral cricoarytenoids and external thyroarytenoids is put together under: activity of the laterals.

When the laterals are active but the transversus inactive, a triangular opening is seen between the arytenoids, the vocal processes contact each other, but the posterior parts at the apex do not contact each other, see Figure 3c[2]. This is true provided that the vocal folds are not stretched, as stretching of the vocal ligaments abducts the vocal processes, as the ligaments try to become orientated along the shortest line between their insertion on the thyroid and the articulation of the arytenoids on the cricoid, indicated by the dotted lines in Figure 3d. This adjustment is used for the flute or whistle register, with very high (up to 2500 c p s) and weak tones at small flows of air, up to about 75 cm^3/sec, and small subglottic pressures, up to about 3 cm water. The tone originates by the formation of eddies in the triangular opening and subsequent cavity resonance, as the author (4) proved by experiments in which gas with a higher velocity of sound than that in air was used, as the pitch was proportional to this velocity. At large flows the subglottic pressure increases to the extent that the vocal folds are thrown into vibration. TAN (2) proved, in agreement with the scheme of Figure 3c and d, that the transition to falsetto voice was difficult. This is an additional argument to prove that the very high whistle register is not an extreme of the high falsetto register, but an entirely different register, which is found in some female voices.

When the transversus is active, but the laterals inactive, the posterior parts of the arytenoids at the apex contact each other, but the vocal processes do not contact each other or the contact is very slight, see Figure 3 e. This adjustment is only suitable for the Strohbass voice, with its very low pitches, at small flows of air and with a vibrational pattern characterized by large amplitudes of the vocal folds, but no or only a short closure during the vocal cycle and, consequently, a small number of partials. At large flows of air a low pitched chest voice results, as the closure time increases progressively with increasing flow.

The main registers are produced with an active transversus and with various degrees of activity of the laterals. Our experiments showed that a gradual increase of the activity results in a gradual increase of the pitch, up to a certain level.   This can be explained by considering that an increase of the medial compression of the vocal processes results in a decrease of the effective length of the glottis, up to the moment when the vocal processes are pressed so firmly against each other that a further increase becomes meaningless. During this increase, the vibrational type remains essentially the same, i.e., the response remains in the same register. However, as the mid voice and the falsetto voice require progressively larger minimal degrees of stretching of the vocal ligaments, they require also certain minimal medial compressions of the vocal processes for the same reasons as those schematized in Figure 3d. This is schematized in Figures 3f, g and h. A complication arises when the larynx is made to respond in the regions when the main registers overlap each other. An increase of the medial compression beyond a certain limit may then result in a register transition, thus, that the response drops to the next lower register, i.e. from falsetto to mid, or from mid to chest voice. This eventual break is indicated by the vertical serpentines in Figures 3g and h.

(2) Length, Thickness and Longitudinal Tension in the Vocal Ligaments and Vocal Muscles.

As we saw in § 1 , the vocal folds are not involved in the production of the laryngeal whistle.

The Strohbass voice requires slack vocal folds, the larynx stops phonating when, at zero lateral tension, only very minute longitudinal tensions are applied. Negative longitudinal tensions are even favourable, that means pressing the thyroid backwards towards the arytenoids, as with the Gutzmann test.

The chest voice is characterized by large amplitudes of the vocal folds, and these are only possible when the vocal ligaments are slack, i.e. at small longitudinal tensions in the vocal ligaments. When the longitudinal tension in the vocal ligaments is gradually increased, the larynx will stop phonating at a very small tension, somewhere between 0 and 20 gr. This stop can be delayed and even be prevented by gradually increasing the medial compression of the vocal processes and/or the flow of air but then the larynx will change into a mid or falsetto voice response at a longitudinal tension of about 20-50 gr.

A mid voice is obtained at longitudinal tensions in the vocal ligaments somewhere between 10 and 50 gr, the stop or the break into the falsetto voice at increasing longitudinal tension again depending on the medial compression of the vocal processes and/or the flow of air, the limit being again higher the higher these values are. Right here, we should stress the point, however, that the mid voice is not a really "independent" register but a "mixture" of chest and falsetto register. In a later paragraph we shall come back to this point.

A falsetto voice originates at longitudinal tensions in the vocal ligaments larger than about 10 gr, the limit being higher, up to about 50 gr, the larger the medial compression of the vocal processes and/or the flow of air are.

Now we consider the result of a contraction of the vocal muscles. These muscles are antagonistic to those stretching the vocal folds. At the very high pitches of the falsetto voice we observe that only the margins of the vocal folds vibrate, i.e. the vocal ligaments, which are certainly connected with the vocal muscles, but this connection is brought about by elastic fibres and thus the coupling is not stiff. Therefore, we conclude, that the vocal muscles must relax in order to obtain the high pitches of the falsetto voice, so that the full effect of the muscles stretching the vocal folds can be applied to the vocal ligaments. Under these conditions of large longitudinal tension the vocal ligaments behave as almost undistensible strings and the pitch is, accordingly, almost proportional to the square root of the longitudinal tension in the vocal ligaments.

To explain the result of a longitudinal tension in the vocal muscles, caused by a contraction of these muscles, in the chest and mid voice we need to consider that the subglottic pressure tries to produce large amplitudes of the vocal folds, i.e. a wide glottal area through which the subglottal air can escape. The farther the vocal folds are thrown apart during the vocal cycle the more time it will take them to come back and the longer the vocal period will be, thus, the lower the pitch will be. Every legitimate procedure which limits the amplitudes of the vocal folds will result in an increase of the pitch. This we observe when we compress the angles of the thyroid cartilage, as it reduces the cage of the vocal folds, or when we grip the lateral parts of the vocal folds by means of a pair of tweezers. The same reduction is brought about by the contraction of the external thyroarytenoid muscles. This action we observe for example during the production of a swelling tone, the false vocal folds then come inward and downward, reducing the laryngeal ventricle, on account of the fibres surrounding these folds. The same limitation is brought about, however, when the vocal muscles contract and put themselves under longitudinal tension. The pitch increases and the glottis is relatively longer closed, i.e. the opening quotient decreases, the tone becomes louder and contains more partials. It must be stressed, however, that these arguments tacitly assumed that the vocal ligaments were kept at a constant length, i.e. under a constant longitudinal tension. Actually, an increase of the longitudinal tension in the vocal muscles, increasing the pitch, tends to produce a decrease of the longitudinal tension in the vocal ligaments, decreasing the pitch, as the vocal muscles are antagonistic to the muscles stretching the vocal folds and thus the vocal ligaments. This facilitates the production of a swelling tone at constant pitch, as an increase of the contraction of the vocal muscles has to go along with an increase of the contraction of the stretching muscles, in order to resist the antagonists, the outcome being nevertheless that the length of the vocal folds decreases slightly in order to keep the pitch constant.

Assuming that the stretching muscles keep the length of the vocal folds constant, a contraction of the vocal muscles increases the pitch in the chest and mid voice. It even appeared that more stretching of the vocal folds was allowed, in the sense that they remained in either chest or mid voice while attaining still higher pitches, when the vocal muscles contracted (and/or when more medial compression was applied to the vocal processes and/or when the flow of air was enlarged). Thus, the pitch range of chest and mid voice is enlarged in a twofold way.

We are now in a position to try to get an overall picture of the main registers. Let us do this by introducing a painter, who expresses his visions of a certain object by using various colours. His main colours are, say, red - representing the longitudinal tension in the vocal muscles - and blue - representing the longitudinal tension in the vocal ligaments. He may produce a picture in red, adding blue when necessary, corresponding with the chest voice, or a picture in blue, adding red when necessary, corresponding with the falsetto voice. He then discovers that a nice picture always asks for two additional colours, yellow - representing the adjustment of the arytenoids - and green - representing the flow of air. In this way he always produces pictures either in red or in blue, but he now decides to make pictures with intermediate hues, bridging the gap between his former expressions, by gradually changing the relative amounts of red and blue, adding convenient amounts of yellow and green. These pictures correspond with the mid voice and the symbol may illustrate why the vowel colour in the mid voice is so variable and why the classification may become rather difficult and arbitrary. It also illustrates that the human voice does not necessarily need to show a break when the pitch is gradually increased from the extreme low to the extreme high side. The painter (the experienced singer) then has a good knowledge of his gamut of expressions and starts soon to add larger amounts of blue to the red and makes s smooth transition in purple between pictures in red and blue. Evidently, however, there must come a break between the high pitched chest voice, pictures in red, and the low pitched falsetto voice, pictures in blue. See Figure 4.

The vertical dimensions (depth) of the vocal ligaments and the thickness of the vocal folds enter into the picture in the following way. The chest voice is characterized by a relatively long closure of the glottis during the vocal cycle and by large phase differences in the vertical direction, i.e. the opening of the glottis begins from underneath and progresses upward and outward, the closing begins with the contact of the lower edges of the vocal ligaments and this contact progresses downward and inward. This type of response is promoted by a large depth of the ligaments and thick vocal folds. With very deep ligaments and thick vocal folds it may even be almost impossible to get a pure falsetto response. A small depth of the ligaments and thin vocal folds promote mid and falsetto voice response. Very

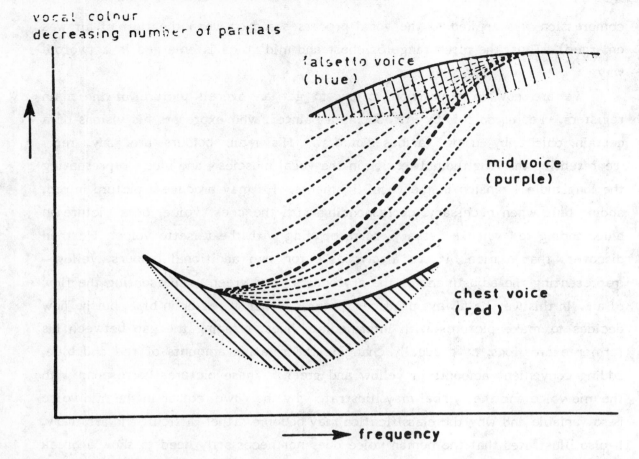

Figure 4. Scheme of the Main Registers
Chest voice - Mainly longitudinal tension in the vocal muscles, many partials (red).
Heavy line for minimal flow, diagonal lines for increasing flow. Falsetto voice -
Mainly longitudinal tension in the vocal ligaments, few partials (blue). Heavy line
for minimal flow, diagonal lines for increasing flow. Mid voice - Mixture of
longitudinal tension in vocal muscles and vocal ligaments, medium number of
partials (purple). Heavy broken line stands for a smooth transition from chest to
falsetto voice, adequate mixing of longitudinal tensions, no breaks. Thin broken
lines stand for inadequate mixing, with a final break.

high pitches of the falsetto voice can only be produced at a very large longitudinal tension/mm^2 in the vocal ligaments, i.e. when the longitudinal tension exerted by the stretching muscles is very large and/or when vocal ligaments are very thin.

The stretching muscles have been so often referred to in the above argumentation that a few remarks may be appropriate. By their way of insertion in the thyroid with respect to the articulation of the thyroid on the cricoid, the cricothyroid muscles are the stretching muscles par excellence. In recent days the combination of the thyrohyoid muscles and the cricopharyngeal muscle has been discussed to act as stretching muscles. (5, 6). This suggestion certainly needs consideration, as it is evidently true that the thyrohyoid muscles contract at the high falsetto and the cricopharyngeal sphincter does so too, as may be observed (7) by means of the pain sensations felt when a catheter has been inserted in the oesophagus via the nose. This author believes, however, that this combination of muscles has only a secondary function in this respect. In the first place, the cricopharyngeal sphincter is not really fixed at the back side, otherwise it would be impossible to move the larynx as much up and downward as we can, and one can move the larynx in the lateral directions at the high falsetto with a negligible effect on the pitch, which would be impossible in the above concept. In the second place, the component of the force exerted by the thyrohyoid muscles in the anterior direction, needed to stretch the vocal folds, is only small. The effect of so many muscles contracting at high pitches is partly due to the synergism of the entire laryngeal musculature. The secondary function of the suspending muscles is to prevent excessive vertical compression of the vocal folds, i.e. when the front part of the thyroid would come too close to the cricoid on account of the strong contraction of the cricothyroid muscles. A high position of the larynx, because of the contraction of the muscles attaching to the hyoid bone, will prevent this, as the extended trachea exerts then a considerable downward pull on the cricoid (8). This argumentation is in agreement with the fact that a very high falsetto pitch drops when the head is bent backwards (5), as an excessive vertical pull on the thyroid reduces the length of the vocal folds.

(3.) Flow of Air and Bernoulli Effect in the Glottis

An increase of the flow at constant adjustment of the larynx produces an increase of the pitch. This increase is relatively large in the chest voice and reduces to relatively small in the falsetto voice. These facts can be explained (9) by considering that the Bernoulli effect of the air escaping through the narrow glottis results in a negative air pressure in the glottis. The vocal folds are sucked towards each other by this negative pressure and this adds one more force to the forces which adduct the glottis after the previous abduction, i.e. to the elastic forces which resist the vibrational deformation of the vocal folds. These forces are relatively small in the chest voice so that the additional factor becomes relatively large then, and they are large in the falsetto voice, so that the additional factor becomes relatively small under these conditions.

In § 2 we remarked already, that an increase of the flow at constant medial compression of the vocal processes but increasing longitudinal tension in the vocal ligaments retards the transition from chest to mid and from mid to falsetto voice. The highest pitches in chest, mid and falsetto voice are obtained at maximal medial compression of the vocal processes and maximal suitable flow.

(4.) Supraglottal, Internal and Subglottal Coupling

The effects of the coupling of the supraglottal system, i.e. the vocal cavities, to the larynx have been clearly demonstrated by WEISS (10) and TRENDELENBURG (11). WEISS suggested that the register transitions might be associated with this coupling, TRENDELENBURG denied this, and the author agrees with him, on account of the fact that they were almost independent of the vowel used for the experiments. The effects of this type of coupling have been explained by the author (12) by showing that they arise in the chest voice when the first formant of the vowel is artificially lowered to the extent that it coincides with the fundamental frequency of the laryngeal vibrations.

A second type of coupling, the internal coupling in the larynx, i.e., the coupling of left and right vocal fold to each other by means of the air in the glottis, has been postulated by the author (12, 13) on theoretical grounds. The effect should be that, when both vocal folds are unequally damped, the fold with least damping leads the way and rules the vibrations of the fold with largest damping. Recently, this coupling has been experimentally verified by TAN (2) and the author. It appears especially clearly in the falsetto voice, when the vocal folds are stretched to the extent that the differences in the distensibility of the ligaments become important. In general, the fold with the smallest distensibility is then less damped and rules the vibrations.

A third type of coupling must now be added, the coupling of the subglottal system, i.e. the trachea and lungs, to the larynx. In experiments on human beings and dogs the author (14) found a pronounced resonance at about 300 c p s (and about 900 and 1500 c p s). These findings were confirmed by means of an electrical analogue of trachea, lungs and tissues. The resonance at about 300 c p s, between D and E flat above Middle C is so pronounced, that difficulties must be expected when the chest voice is pushed up towards this region. Most valuable information by Prof. W. VENNARD suggests that these arise indeed, and they may explain the necessity for a register transition in this region. At this moment it is not clear whether the fact that the lowest frequency of the first formant of all vowels is also about 300 c p s is a pure coincidence or not. It is also important to note that there comes a break at about 150 c p s, an octave below 300 c p s, when the pitch of the pure falsetto voice is decreased to this extent.

REGISTERS

Based on the above data and arguments we may now schematize the conditions and characteristics of the registers in the form of Table 1.

SUMMARY

The conditions and characteristics of the various registers are discussed in terms of properties of the vocal ligaments and vocal muscles, adjustment of the larynx, flow of air and coupling of the larynx to itself, to the supraglottal and subglottal system. It is shown that the longitudinal tension in the vocal muscles are the important parameters determining the response in the main registers.

Contraction of:	Strohblass	Chest	Mid	Falsetto	Whistle
interarytenoids	weak	weak	medium	strong	----
laterals	----	weak	medium	strong	medium
Longit. tension in:					
vocal muscles	small	large	medium	----	----
vocal ligaments	----	----	medium	large	----
Amplitude of voc. folds	large	large	medium	small	----
Closure time	small	large	medium	----	----
Number of partials	small	large	medium	small	----
Effect of increasing contr. of interaryten:					
pitch	increase	increase	increase	----	decrease
register, eventual	chest	----	----	----	chest
contr. of laterals:					
pitch	increase	increase	increase	increase	decrease
register, eventual	chest	----	chest	mid	----
Effect of increasing long.tens.voc.muscles:					
pitch	increase	increase	increase	decrease	increase
register, eventual	stop	----	chest	mid	stop
Effect of increasing long.tens.voc.ligaments:					
pitch	increase	increase	increase	increase	increase
register, eventual	stop	mid	falsetto	----	stop
Effect of increasing flow:					
pitch	increase	increase	increase	increase	decrease
register, eventual	chest	----	chest	mid	chest

Table 1.
Generalized scheme of registers.

REFERENCES

1. The posterior cricoarytenoid muscle.

2. The cooperation of Prof. W. Vennard and D. Burger, M.D., in preparing these drawings is gratefully acknowledged.

(1) VAN Den BERG, J., and TAN, T.S.: Results of experiments with human larynges. Pract. otorhino-laryng. (Basel) 21: 425-450 (1959).

(2) TAN, T.S.: Proeven over geluidsproductie in de menselijke Larynx. Thesis. Groningen (1960).

(3) VAN Den BERG, J.: A delta f generator and movie adapter unit for laryngostroboscopy. Pract. otorhino-laryng. (Basel) 21: 355-363, (1959).

(4) VAN Den BERG, J.: Myoelastic-aerodynamic theory of voice production. J. Speech Hear. Res. 1: 227-244 (1958), The NATS Bulletin, Vol. XIV, No. 4, May, 1958, and Laboratory report on experiments with hydrogen and oxygen. (1957).

(5) SONNINEN, A. A.: The role of the external laryngeal muscles in length-adjustment of the vocal cords in singing. Thesis. Helsinki (1956). Summarized in The NATS Bulletin, Vol. XV, No. 4, May, 1959.

(6) ZENKER, W., und ZENKER, A.: Uber die Regelung der Stimmlappenspannung durch von aussen eingreifende Mechanismen. Folia phoniat. 12: 1-36 (1960).

(7) VAN Den BERG, J.: Direct and indirect determination of the mean subglottic pressure. Folia phoniat. (Basel) 8: 1-24 (1956).

(8) ZENKER, W., und GLANINGER, J.: Die Starke des Trachealzuges beim lebenden Menschen und seine Bedeutung fur die Kehlkopfmechanik. Z. Biol. 11: 154-164 (1959).

(9) VAN Den BERG, J., ZANTEMA, J. F., and DOORNENBAL, Jr. P.: On the air resistance and the Bernoulli effect of the human larynx. J. Acoust. Soc. Amer. 29: 626-631, (1959).

(10) WEISS, D.: Ein Resonanzphanomen der Singstimme. Mschr. Ohrenheilk. 66: 964-967 (1932), and Zur Frage der Registerbruchstellen. Z. Hals-, Nasu. Ohrenheilk. 22: 353-358 (1932).

(11) TRENDFLENBURG, W.: Untersuchungen zur Kenntnis der Registerbruchstellen beim Gesang, S.-B. Akad. Wiss. Wien, math.-nat. Kl. 5-22 and 188-226 (1938).

(12) VAN Den BERG, J.: Uber die Koppelung bei der Stimmbildung Z. Phonetik 8: 281-293 (1954).

(13)   VAN Den BERG, J.: Sur les theories myo-elastique et neurochronaxique de la phonation. Rev. Laryng. (Bordeaux) 74: 494-512 (1954), and Ref. 4 and 12.

(14)   VAN Den BERG, J.: Ref. 4 and An electrical analogue of trachea, lungs and tissues (to be published).

Chest, Head,
and Falsetto

William Vennard, Minoru Hirano
and John Ohala

Until the time of Tosi, in the eighteenth century, only two registers were recognized. The lower and heavier was called voce di petto or voce piena. The upper and lighter was called voce di testa, voce finta, or falsetto. Tosi followed this lead, but his translators, Gailliard in English and Agricola in German, added footnotes distinguishing the head register from falsetto, (Duey, pp. 113, 116, 117). Martini also wrote of three registers (Duey, p. 122). The great nineteenth century authority, Garcia, also described three registers, and realistic students of the subject since then have not disagreed except in some cases to locate one or two additional registers, or subdivisions of registers.

At the beginning of the twentieth century many teachers, largely for phychological or pedagogical reasons, denied the existence of registers, or tried to explain them in terms of resonance. Stanley and others did not deny the importance of registration, but postulated only two extreme adjustments which overlap in compass, thereby explaining intermediate adjustments in terms of "mixing" or "coordination." Stanley (p. 58) suggested the chest voice is produced by the cricothyroid muscles, and the falsetto by the "arytenoid" muscles, and that a singer may ascend a three-octave scale by beginning with the action of his cricothyroids, reducing this while adding action of the "arytenoids," and finally emerging at the top in the use of the "arytenoids" alone.

Stanley did not have at his disposal any direct means of proving which muscle does what, such as we now have in electromyography. Katsuki is perhaps the pioneer of such study of the larynx. In 1950, he reported that in loud tones the vocalis muscle (which Stanley overlooked) is active, and in weak tones it is relatively passive. He confirmed the opinion of most voice scientists that the role of the cricothyroids is primarily that of determining pitch by stretching the vocal cords, and is therefore more active for higher pitches. Faaborg-Anderson, in his monumental electromyographic laryngeal studies (1957) reported that the vocalis muscle is active in chest voice and less active in falsetto, but until recently no researcher has been able to distinguish head voice as a separate register. The electrodes were so heavy and inflexible that such subtleties were impossible to produce under the experimental conditions (Vennard, Faaborg-Anderson and Vennard). The new technic described in the first article in this series made possible a more delicate investigation.

PROCEDURE

Each of the four subjects sang scales of various lengths throughout his entire range. The longer the scales involved more or less noticeable register transitions, but each subject was able to sing two octaves all in light register (falsetto) and two octaves in heavy register (chest), with the exception of Subject C, who sang only one octave in chest. In each case the lower octave of falsetto overlapped the upper octave of chest, with the exception again of Subject C, who had somewhat less than an octave of overlapping. Subjects R and C sang three-octave scales in keys ranging from E to C. Subject M did the same an octave lower, and Subject V sang in C and D flat. Subject R also managed four octaves several times, beginning on E_7, E_7 flat, and D_7. Over one hundred fifty scales, two octaves or more in length, ascending and descending were sung.

THE CONTROL OF PITCH

In heavy registration, or chest voice, the cricothyroids were the primary pitch agent, and each degree of the scale was marked by a corresponding amount of effort in these muscles. This effort, as is well known, stretches the vocal cords and establishes an appropriate tension for each pitch in the scale. There was parallel activity in the vocalis muscles and the laterals, but for different reasons. The vocalis (or internal thyroarytenoid) muscles form the body of the vocal cords and are thus antagonistic to the cricothyroids; that is, they resist being stretched. This not only contributes to raising the pitch, but also increases the loudness. The lateral cricoarytenoids roughly parallel the activity of the cricothyroids for a reason that is rather complicated and need not be detailed here. The vocal folds have a tendency to gap under great longitudinal tension (created by the crico-thyroids) and therefore the more the cricothyroids pull the more the laterals must work to produce what van den Berg calls "medial compression." A fuller explanation, for those who may be interested, is found in Vennard, pp. 61-63. The interarytenoids, which close the glottis by drawing the arytenoid cartilages together at the back, paralleled the activity of the other three muscles, except that even at the bottom of the scale they did not relax below a certain minimum effort without which the glottis would not remain closed.

In light registration, or falsetto, the breath was the primary pitch agent. The muscles showed greater independence and did not parallel each other as in chest. At the bottom of a two-octave falsetto range, the cricothyroids were pitch-correlated step by step, but when they neared the point of maximum stretch in the vocal cords they simply held and the changes in pitch resulted from greater breath-effort. Sometimes there were two or three points of readjustment upwards, but at the top of falsetto there was about an octave that could be sung while the cricothyroids simply held at near-maximum energy level. The vocalis muscles relaxed greatly by comparison with their chest voice effort, and this is what permitted the cricothyroids to stretch the cords for falsetto production. As the scale was ascended, however, the vocalis showed some pitch-correlation, as it did in chest voice, but it did not work as hard as in maximum chest voice effort. The laterals paralleled the cricothyroids for the same reason as before. They were pitch-correlated in low falsetto, but at the top they simply held fast. The interarytenoids behaved as in chest voice.

As can be seen in the accompanying figures, chest and falsetto can be identified in both male and female voices. Chest is at the bottom of the range and falsetto at the top in each subject. Lilli Lehmann (p. 133) was perhaps the first to state that the women's highest register is the same as a man's falsetto, a rather inconsistent position since she also denied the existence of registers!

The term "head voice" is used for an intermediate adjustment between chest and falsetto that is clearly distinguishable in most male voices. It sounds different and feels different to the singer. The term is also applied to the upper part of the female voice, which resembles falsetto in EMG. Sometimes the very top of the female voice is differentiated and the term "whistle register" is applied to it. In the lower part of the female voice, before chest is reached, a somewhat different register is recognized, called "midvoice" or "mixed registration." All four subjects sang sustained tones at various pitch levels, and on each pitch endeavored to demonstrate as many registers as he could differentiate. Some 250 such tones were sung, using the vowel (a) throughout.

On C_6 (High C) and on G_5, Subjects R and C sang several tones both loudly and softly, but designated them all the same register. On C_6 (third space, treble staff) Subject R sang in both soft and loud head voice, and also in chest, which was still louder. She repeated this on G_4 and C_4 (Middle C). On G_3 only chest was possible, which she sang at two dynamic levels.

Subject C sang only her normal registration on C_5 (a transitional tone between midvoice and head). She sang G_4 and G_3 at two volume levels, the registration of which will be discussed below.

Subject M, tenor, sang C_5 in both falsetto and head voice, but Subject V, bass, could use only falsetto there. On G_4, Subject M going from soft to loud used falsetto, two varieties of head, soft and loud, and finally chest. Subject V used only falsetto. On C_4 and G_3 both singers managed falsetto, head, and chest. On C_3 and G_2 both subjects attempted the same, but what they actually produced was three varieties of chest: breathy, soft, and loud. Subject V managed a low C_2 that was not much more than a vocal rattle or fry.

Within each register the behavior of each muscle in each subject on the different pitches was as could be expected from the study of scale passages. Activity in all the muscles was greater for higher frequencies.

On each pitch, differences in loudness (some of which could be called register differences) were reflected primarily in the vocalis and secondarily in the other muscles. In general, the heavier the registration the greater the exertion. A few interesting exceptions should be mentioned.

On G_4 and G_3, as noted above, Subject C sang with two productions. The louder of these she intended to be chest voice, but the EMG showed less vocalis than normal. Many women object to the use of "chest" voice in sopranos, and they refer to a harsh production characterized by constriction in the throat above the glottis. Subject C quite rightly shares this objection to such singing, but EMG followed by examination with laryngeal mirror showed that this is not truly heavy registration or chest voice. More will be said about this pinched production in the next article in this series. Subject C did produce chest voice as well, examples of which appear in the accompanying figures.

On G_3 Subject V thought he was differentiating head and chest, but the EMG of the vocalis showed no difference. Instead, the difference appeared in the lateral, which showed least for falsetto, more for head, and most for chest. There were more instances in other subjects where the lateral did not parallel the activity of the cricothyroid, but instead assisted the vocalis in producing greater loudness. This was especially true of the lighter, higher voices.

On C_4 and also C_4 sharp, Subject V differentiated chest, head, and falsetto, with a surprising result in the EMG. The vocalis effort was greatest for chest, less for head, and least for falsetto, as might be expected. But the cricothyroids and laterals were greater for head (as much as for falsetto an octave higher) and much less for chest and falsetto, which were about equal in amount of effort. The chest voice was always louder, but the falsetto and head were isoparametric - same vowel, same pitch, same loudness - or nearly so. Breath expenditure was measured by pneumotachograph at the Institute of Laryngology and Voice Disorders, Hans von Leden, director. It was as much as 350 cubic centimeters per second for falsetto, 200 cc/second for chest, and 150 cc/second for head. The significance of these data will be better understood in EMG of the swell-tone, or messa di voce. (See Figs. 3 and 4.)

THE CONTROL OF INTENSITY OR LOUDNESS

The sustained tones in different registers call attention to the role of registration in vocal dynamics. Each register has its characteristic loudness, and while it is possible to make head and falsetto, for example, at the same intensity level, it requires care to hold the head tone down and to bring up the falsetto to its level. In the case of falsetto and chest it is almost impossible.

The messa di voce, consisting of a long crescendo followed by a long decrescendo on a given pitch, has been used as a voice developer and a vocal ornament for centuries. Some authorities do not feel that it is done properly unless it involves a change of register along with the dynamic change. All four subjects, therefore, sang swelltones on various pitches throughout the range. Some 130 swelltones were sung.

At the extremes of the range it was difficult to get much difference in loudness, and near the middle, where the range of the light register overlaps that of the heavy, the greatest change in loudness and in laryngeal function was possible. In this part of the range EMG showed an interchange of muscular activity such as Stanley hypothesized. This can be seen in Fig. 4, middle, where Subject V sings (a) on C_4, beginning in head and swelling into chest (or full voice) and diminishing again.

Before the tone begins the cricothyroids prepare for the pitch, and at the moment of attack they are at maximum effort, more than would be exerted for falsetto an octave higher. This is because the vocalis muscles have not relaxed as they do for falsetto, but are exerting moderate effort, resisting the cricothyroids. This doubtless explains why this kind of production has been called voix mixte. It combines the cricothyroid effort of a very high falsetto with the vocalis effort of a medium chest tone.

As the singer swells the tone, the vocalis muscles increase their activity greatly. Greater breath pressure is required to overcome the vocalis muscle resistance, and this results in the greater volume. It would also raise the pitch were it not for the fact that the cricothyroids relax enough to compensate. Thus, the coordination of head and chest, in terms of the shifting of muscle function from one muscle to another, is indeed as Stanley imagined it, in spite of the fact that he guessed incorrectly when he attempted to name the muscles involved.

As before, the laterals parallel the pattern of the cricothyroids - they decrease their effort as the tone increases. The interarytenoids roughly parallel the activity of the vocalis muscles. The decrescendo reverses the action of all the muscles, of course.

The skill of producing head tones is seen to be that of reducing vocalis tension delicately but not enough to break into falsetto, and it requires great strength in the cricothyroids, even more than for high falsetto. It can be understood why exercise in falsetto develops both strength in the cricothyroids and the ability to relax the vocalis. The loudness of the voice is a function of breath pressure, which is the product of breath flow and glottal resistance. For falsetto there is small resistance but large flow, hence the possibility of considerable power, especially at the top where the cricothyroid tension is great. Chest does not use as much breath, but there is great resistance in the muscles of the glottis and great loudness. Head voice is soft in volume and less breath-consuming than either of the other two productions. Most men find it difficult, and as they crescendo the relaxation of the cricothyroids gives them a feeling of ease as they shift into chest voice. The pianissimo is far more difficult and even seems to involve more effort in the throat.

The same shift of energy from cricothyroid to vocalis with the crescendo was seen in the EMG of the other subjects. A clear example in the soprano voice is seen in the EMG of Subject C singing (a) on D_5, roughly an octave above the spot in the voice of Subject V where he got his best results. However, on pitches farther from this optimal level there were complications which can best be introduced by observing scale passages once more, with attention to differences between the subjects.

INDIVIDUAL DIFFERENCES

Up to this point the report has emphasized <u>similarities</u> in the behavior of the larynx regardless of sex or voice classification. However, there were also important <u>differences</u>. Since so few subjects were studied, it would be hazardous to attribute the variations to voice category, though of course such speculation is hard to resist.

The most noticeable difference was in the location of the break between light and heavy registration. (See Fig. 5.)

Subject R sang a four-octave scale from D_7 to D_3 and Subject C sang three octaves from E_6 to E_3. Both sopranos broke into chest voice in the neighborhood of C_4 (Middle C). That is to say, less than the lowest octave was sung in chest voice. Subject V, a bass, sang three octaves from D_5 flat to D_2 flat, with a definite break into chest at D_4 flat. The two lower octaves were in chest. All three subjects, male and female, broke at about the same pitch, but this was in the lower part of the female range and the upper part of the male.

Subject M, a lyric tenor with a very light production, sang three octaves from E_5 to E_2 with no break. The EMG shows diminishing activity in the vocalis to B_5, at which point there is a small increase followed by a gradual decrease to B_4, where it drops off again. The cricothyroid and lateral diminish smoothly from top to bottom. The ladies also sang scales in which the transitions were more smooth, and so did Subject V, but he could do so only by reducing the volume (intensity) almost to zero while making the transition from falsetto to head, after which it was easy to crescendo into chest production.

The ladies had a transition from their highest register (falsetto or whistle, or small, or head - the vocabulary varies) to another register between it and chest (head, or middle, or mixed voice) but it was very smooth and marked by a gradual increase in vocalis activity, matched moderately by cricothyroid and lateral, after which all three reduced gradually with the descending pitch until the transition into chest.

For Subject V the transition from head to chest was impercepticle, while for the female subjects the transition from falsetto to midvoice was imperceptible. The middle register was related to the upper in Subjects R and C; whereas the middle register was related to the lower in Subject V. In both sopranos the falsetto was not as loud as the transition into middle voice at the top of the treble staff. Subject R sang a scale from D_6 to D_7 in "whistle" register (Fig. 6, right), which differed from normal in that it was not only very high, but also piano. In the male voices falsetto was loud at the top, and there was a decrescendo correlated more or less with the pitch on the way down, except for the break into chest. Subject V not only had a louder high falsetto, but he used as much as 500cc of breath per second, in contrast to Subject C whose top register was softer and used no more than 350cc/second.

Only the very highest register in the women's voices appeared to be as completely aerodynamic as the male falsetto. This was shown not only in scales, but also in swelltones. In the falsetto of both Subject M and Subject V, the crescendo was accomplished by increasing expiratory pressure, rather than by an increase in the vocalis as described above. In falsetto, the vocalis diminished with the increase in power just as did the cricothyroid, the lateral, and the interarytenoid. But in Subject C, only at the top, on D_6 and E_6, did the vocalis fail to increase activity with increase in loudness.

Subject M did not achieve as much volume in his lyric (or quasifalsetto) production as did the other subjects. He has developed his tenor range from that of a baritone by learning over a period of years to blend it with falsetto, and he is now in the process of carrying more vocalis activity into the upper register without losing the smoothness of transition. In another part of the EMG investigation he sang scales from G_3 to C_5 and down again in normal, open, spread, and covered technic. These EMG will be shown in the next article, but because of their relevancy to the topic of registration they should be discussed briefly here.

In the normal scale there were several places where small readjustments were made in the vocalis, so that at no point did it become as active as would have been possible. In both open and spread production the vocalis increased on the way up to the point where it broke into falsetto. In covered production (and especially an extreme form of covering designated "depressed larynx") it increased much more than in his normal singing, but without breaking. In the year since this experiment, Subject M has practiced darkening his voice and has succeeded in making his upper voice much more robust.

DISCUSSION

In his experiments with excised larynges, van den Berg found that if air flow is increased or if the pull of any pair of muscles is simulated while the other factors remain constant, the pitch will go up and the loudness will increase. In the living larynx it is hardly possible to vary one factor at a time because usually the entire musculature is synergistic, but to the extent that there is muscular independence, van den Berg was confirmed. The cricothyroids are generally thought of as controlling pitch, but a rise in frequency also involves an intensity increase unless some other muscle compensates. The vocalis correlates with loudness and is the basic factor in register change, but in falsetto it was clearly pitch-correlated while the cricothyroid exertion remained constant. Air flow correlated with both pitch and loudness.

To the extent that there is muscular independence it may be felt as a register change to the singer, but not always. When pitch and volume change together there is no need for muscular independence, but in the messa di voce, or swelltone, volume changes while pitch is held constant, and this does require independence. In that pitch area which represents the overlap of chest and falsetto, vocalis correlated directly with loudness and cricothyroid compensated by correlating inversely. This was demonstrated on C_4 and C_4 sharp in Subject V and sensed as a change from head to chest and back to head. It was the same with Subject M on C_4 and G_4, but only when he made an extreme crescendo did he feel that he had gone into chest voice.

Below the middle range, the vocalis increased for the crescendo, but cricothyroid did not always compensate. The lateral, instead of paralleling the cricothyroid as it did in the upper voice, assisted the vocalis by increasing its activity. This was not felt as a register change by the singer. In the area above the middle in all subjects, there was interplay with air flow rather than between muscles. This again was not felt as a register change.

In the middle range of the female voice, the same interplay between cricothyroid and vocalis did not produce register change automatically, and when Subject C voluntarily extended the crescendo to the point of bringing in chest voice (Fig. 3, bottom), two things happened: all three muscles under observation increased their activity beyond the effort required for the crescendo as it was resigtered, and the cricothyroid and lateral, instead of compensating to maintain the constant pitch, jumped to a level that matched the vocalis. These extra muscular efforts did not produce comparable effects in either the pitch or the crescendo, but simply changed the quality to that of a different register. The same extra efforts were used again in the transition from chest back to midvoice.

This suggests that there is more involved than can be seen in the EMG alone. Muscular exertion may be isometric and produce no movement at all. Tension in the vocal cords could change both pitch and loudness regardless of actual change in cord length. Or muscular exertion could in other cases indicate movement. Both situations probably combine in the larynx. The undetected factor could be leverage resulting from movements of the cartilages.

For example, one might postulate a tug-of-war between cricothyroid and vocalis in which neither has an advantage, but once the approximation of the anterior parts of the cricoid and thyroid cartilages passes a certain point, the cricothyroids would have a great advantage. This would be falsetto, and to shift from it would require great extra exertion of the vocalis (and perhaps the external thyroarytenoid) and would probably involve a sudden realignment of the cartilages. Smoothness of transition would depend upon a combination of reduction of phonatory effort (including air flow) and/or extra strength in the musculature and/or added skill.

By the same logic there should be an opposite point at a lower part of the compass, where the vocalis (plus the external thyroarytenoid) would have the advantage. This would be chest. Between the two points, transition from one extreme register to the other would be easier, but the change in quality would be more difficult to identify. This area between the two critical pitches could be thought of either as a separate register or as a mixture in which the proportions of falsetto to chest could vary.

All this is only hypothetical. Another place where skeletal leverage might be significant is the cricoarytenoid articulation. This might well be a factor in damping - a still imperfectly evaluated phenomenon associated with falsetto. If so, one might look for evidence in the EMG of the lateral cricoarytenoid muscles, but the present investigation was unproductive in this respect.

However inconclusive this discussion may be, the fact remains that several interesting facts did emerge.

SUMMARY

The four subjects, two sopranos, a tenor, and a bass, sang scales, sustained tones, and swelltones in various registers over a range totalling five octaves.

Each subject has a compass of more than three octaves, and with one exception each could sing two octaves entirely in light registration and two entirely in heavy. The lower octave of light (falsetto) comprised the same pitches as the upper octave of heavy (chest).

In light registration aerodynamic factors were paramount, with the musculature active only to maintain the necessary conditions for phonation. In heavy registration myoelastic factors were paramount, with only such air flow as needed to maintain the necessary conditions.

The cricothyroid correlated with pitch, but in falsetto it was exerting itself too greatly to change with each degree of the scale. The vocalis correlated with loudness. The lateral cricoarytenoid paralleled the activity of the cricothyroid in the upper part of the vocal range, while in the lower part it correlated at least somewhat with loudness. The interarytenoid (studied in only one subject) correlated with phonatory effort but did not drop below a certain minimum needed to keep the glottis closed.

In the pitch area corresponding to low falsetto or upper chest, a distinct adjustment was recognized called "head voice" by the men and "mixed voice" by the women. Exertion of the cricothyroid was greatest for head, and about equal for chest and falsetto. Exertion of the vocalis was greatest for chest, less for head, and least for falsetto. Air flow was greatest for falsetto, less for chest, and least for head.

Swelltones were performed at intervals throughout the range of each voice. In the middle area Subject M was able to go smoothly from falsetto through head to chest and back. Subject V could go smoothly from head to chest and back, but not to falsetto. The ladies could go from light to heavier production, but not to chest without a break. When the swelltone was produced in each case vocalis increased for the crescendo and the cricothyroid decreased.

Above the middle area (nearer the top in the female subjects) the crescendo was produced by breath flow and all the muscles compensated by inverse correlation with intensity. Below the middle area the lateral sometimes assisted the vocalis in making the crescendo.

In scale passages as in swelltones, Subjects R and C found the upper register to be continuous with the middle, but broke upon entering chest. Subject V found head and chest continuous, but broke in leaving or entering falsetto. The break in both male and female voices was just above C_4 (Middle C) and was characterized by extra exertion in all the muscles. Subject M sang with smooth transitions throughout a three-octave range, by repeatedly readjusting vocalis activity to keep it from becoming excessive.

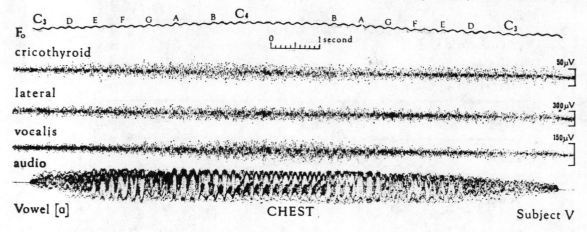

Figure 1.
Control of pitch, male chest voice. Top line shows fundamental frequency (F_o) which the ear perceives as Pitch. C_4 is middle C. Next three lines are EMG of cricothyroid, lateral cricoarytenoid, and vocalis muscles. Bottom (audio) is the microphone signal. It shows intensity, which is perceived as loudness. See discussion in text.

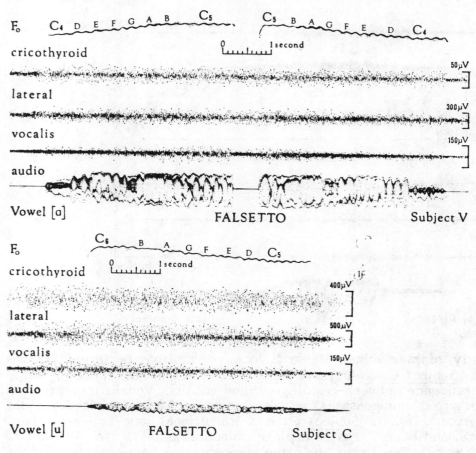

Figure 2.
Control of pitch, male and female falsetto. There is almost no readjustment of the cricothyroid for either subject. Vocalis, however, correlates with pitch. <u>Subject C</u> is performing a vocalise called "The small (u)," which she uses to induce falsetto.

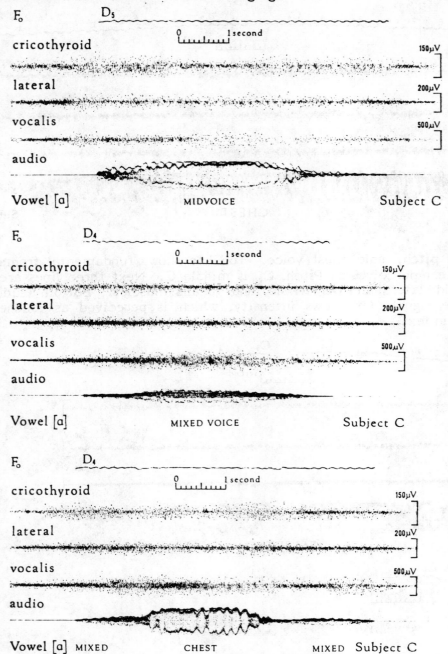

Figure 3.
Control of intensity, soprano voice. Messa di voce, or swelltone performed on two different pitches. Subject C, on D$_5$, and Subject V, on C$_4$ (Fig. 11, facing page) show typical independence between cricothyroid and vocalis. Vocalis increases for crescendo; cricothyroid compensates by decreasing. Lateral cricoarytenoid parallels cricothyroid. D$_5$, for Subject C, is a transitional tone between mixed voice, or midvoice, and head. It is in a place comparable to C$_4$ for Subject V. Middle graph, Subject C, D$_4$, shows the same compensation between cricothyroid and vocalis, but in lesser degree. Bottom graph shows a swelltone on D$_4$ with voluntary transitions to and from chest voice. Note increased energy potentials in all three muscles at both transition points. Note lack of smoothness in crescendo and decrescendo, as seen in audio.

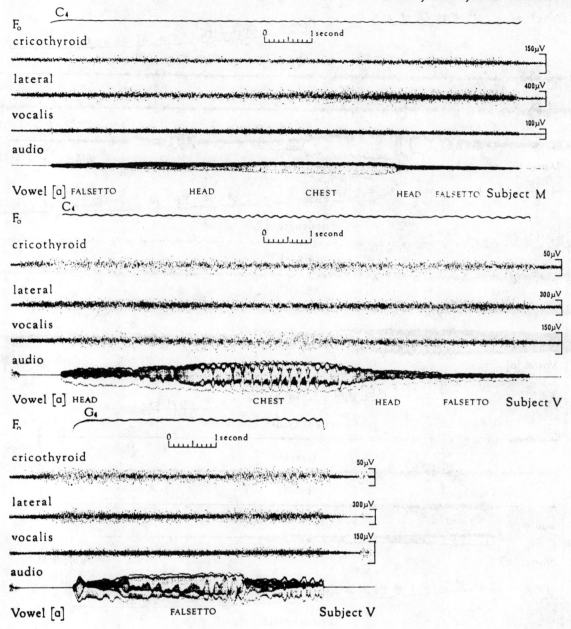

Figure 4.
Control of intensity, tenor and bass voices. Messa di voce, or swelltone, performed on different pitches. Middle graph: Typical swelltone from head to chest and back, finally going into falsetto. See discussion in text, and compare with Fig. 10 (facing page). Bottom graph in falsetto vocalis decreases for crescendo, and the swell is produced by airflow. Cricothyroid makes the same compensation as above. Lateral cricoarytenoid parallels cricothyroid. Top graph: Subject M, lyric tenor, reported that subjectively he went through three registers in making his swelltone, but vocalis shows very little readjustment, and volume (seen in audio) does not show great increase in intensity or loudness. Note that Subject M has a much more subtle vibrato than either Subject C of Subject V.

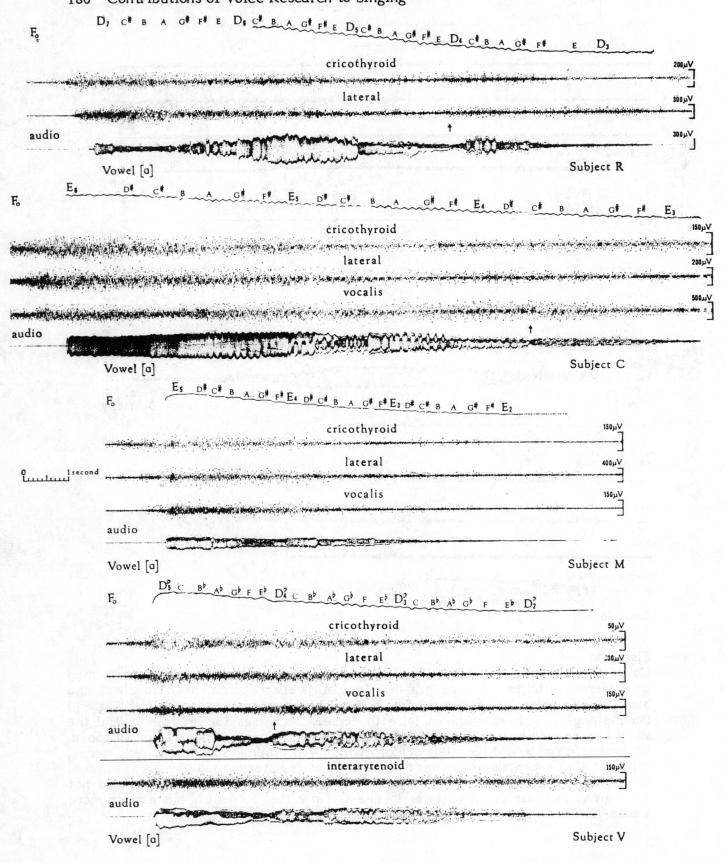

Figure 5.
Three and four-octave scales, male and female voices. Top octave in Subject R's voice was too high to register fundamental frequency (F_o). Subjects R, C and V all entered chest voice at about D_4 or C_4 sharp. The transition was not smooth, and was accompanied by extra exertion in all three muscles. Subject V was the only one whose interarytenoid was studied. The record shown at the bottom figure was of an almost identical performance, as shown by the audio which was made at the same time as the EMG of the interarytenoid. Transition to chest is also visible in the interarytenoid. Subject M sang his three octaves without noticeable breaks. The female subjects, especially Subject R, sang more softly at the very top than in the neighborhood of A_5 where they began moving from head to midvoice. The men were loudest in high falsetto and Subject V reduced volume radically in order to enter head voice.

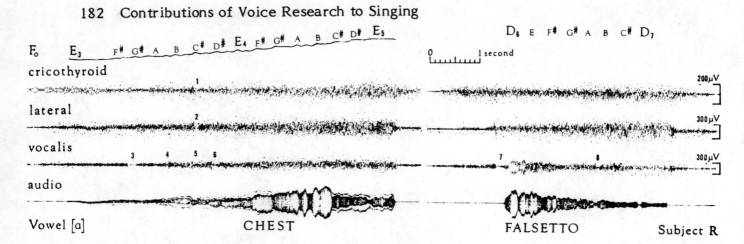

Figure 6.
Extremes of the female compass. Various blemishes in the record are marked with arabic numerals. They are artifacts of the equipment and do not represent the behavior of the muscles. Between 3 and 6 on the left, and 7 and 8 on the right, vocalis is contaminated with microphonic effects, but the EMG before and after in each case show the energy potentials in the muscle. It may be assumed that in both cases there is a steady increase throughout in the vocalis. <u>Left</u>: Subject R sings two ascending octaves in chest, to E_5, top of treble staff. <u>Right</u>: She sings an octave in high falsetto, sometimes called "whistle register." This is all above High C, too high to register on the F_o graph. Cricothyroid simply maintains maximum effort. Vocalis is pitch-correlated. Audio pattern differs from male falsetto in that it diminishes rather than swells.

REFERENCES

1. DUEY, PHILLIP A.: Bel Canto in its Golden Age. New York, King's Crown Press, 1950.

2. FAABORG-ANDERSON, KNUD: Electromyographic investigation of intrinsic laryngeal muscles in humans. Copenhagen, Acta Physiologica Scandinavica, Vol. 140, Sup. 140, 1957.

3. FAABORG-ANDERSON, KNUD, and WILLIAM VENNARD: Electromyography of extrinsic laryngeal muscles during phonation of different vowels. Annals of Otology, Rhinology and Laryngology, 75, 1, 248, 1964.

4. GARCIA, MANUEL: Hints on Singing, translated by Beata Garcia. New York, Edward Schubarth & Co., 1894.

5. KATSUKI, YASUJI: The function of the phonatory muscles. Japanese Journal of Physiology, 1, 29-36, 1950.

6. LEHMANN, LILLI: How to Sing. New York, The Macmillan Co., 1924.

7. STANLEY DOUGLAS: The Voice, Its Production and Reproduction. New York, Pittman Publishing Corp., 1933.

8. Van Den BERG, JANWILLEM, WILLIAM VENNARD, DIOMYS BERGER and CHRISTY SHERVANIAN: Voice Production - The Vibrating Larynx: Medical research film produced and distributed by Stichting Film en Wetenschap, Utrecht, 1960.

9. VENNARD, WILLIAM: Letter to the Editor. The NATS Bulletin, p. 5, Oct. 1962.

10. VENNARD, WILLIAM: Singing, the Mechanism and the Technic. New York, Carl Fischer, Inc., 1967.

This research was partially supported by the National Institutes of Health, United States Department of Health, Education, and Welfare. The electromyography was done at the University of California at Los Angeles, in the Phonetics Laboratory, presided over by Peter Ladefoged. Supporting aerodynamic studies were carried out at the Institute of Laryngology and Voice Disorders, Hans von Leden, director, affiliated with the University of Southern California.

Minoru Hirano, M.D. is now in the Department of Otolaryngology, School of Medicine, University of Kurume, Kyushu, Japan. He was in the United States on a Fulbright exchange, performing research at the Institute of Laryngology and Voice Disorders (affiliated with USC) and at the Phonetics Department, UCLA.

John Ohala, Ph.D., is now in the Department of Linguistics at the University of California at Berkeley. He was a graduate student at UCLA and assisted in the research of Dr.Hirano, after which he spent a year at the Research Institute of Logopedics and Phoniatrics, School of Medicine, University of Tokyo.

William Vennard, M.M., is a past president of NATS. He is chairman of the Voice Department of the University of Southern California and has taught summer sessions at the Meadow Brook School and the Blossom Festival School.

Studies
of the
Marchesi Model
for Female Registration

John Large and Thomas Murry

By the word register, we mean a series of succeeding sounds of equal quality a scale from low to high produced by the application of the same mechanical principle, the nature of which differs basically from another series of succeeding sounds of equal quality produced by another mechanical principle (Garcia, 1840).

Manuel Garcia (1805-1906), famous singing teacher and inventor of the laryngo-scope, write the definition of vocal register given above. A primary goal of his and other schools of Western artistic vocal pedagogy was and is the blending or equalizing of the various registers (e.g., "chest," "medium," and "head") so that no apparent line demarcation or change of timbre occurs - - giving the percept of a single register. In actuality, a skillful "even scale" singer may pass through several registers in vocalizing from one extreme of the range to the other.

It is still not definitely known how the audibly different registers normally found in a singer are produced or how they are blended. Much of the difficulty in researching vocal registers appears to stem from the existence of a number of different pedagogical models by which a voice may be trained. For example, among the several methods, the female "chest" register may be treated in different ways: (1) it may be accepted as an integral and necessary part of the vocal range, (2) it may be forbidden altogether on grounds that it constitutes vocal abuse or that it sounds too masculine, or (3) it may be merged in some way with the "medium" register to form a "mixed" or "coordinated" register.

Different pedagogical methods and models produce different kinds of singer-subjects. To control for this factor it was decided to select a pedagogical model and use as subjects for study only those singers whose training and demonstrated performance fit the model in question. Other models will be used in later investigations.

THE MARCHESI MODEL

Recently Dover Publications, Inc. issued an unabridged republication of the Theoretical and Practical Vocal Method by Mathilda Marchesi (n.d.). This model was selected for the first series of studies by virtue of its historical importance and its current availability.

Mathilda Marchesi (1821-1913) was one of the most celebrated singing teachers of the late 19th century. A pupil of Manuel Garcia, her voice training methods were praised by Rossini, well-known composer of bel canto operas. Towards the end of her career she trained such superstars as Melba, Calve, Eames, and Alda. Marchesi taught only female singers.

The essential features of the Marchesi model for female registration are as follows:

(1)   there are 3 registers: chest, medium and head;

(2)   the highest note in the chest register in all female voices - - contralto, mezzo-soprano, dramatic soprano, and light soprano - - varies between E4,330 Hz, and F4-sharp, 370Hz; the highest note in the medium register varies from F5, 698 Hz, to F5-sharp, 740 Hz;

(3)   the registers are to be blended or equalized;

(4)   with regard to the origin of the different registers, Marchesi postulated that "three Resonators, formed of different organic tissues, impart, by reason of their special physiological properties, a distinct character to each series of sounds contained within the limits of each register."

MARCHESI MODEL FOR
FEMALE REGISTRATION

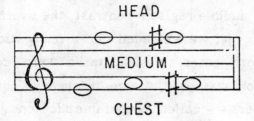

Figure 1.

Figure 2.

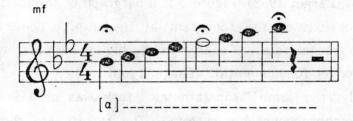

Figure 3.

METHODS

Thus far, our research into the physical nature of female registration has focused primarily on the area of major audible register contrast, the overlapping chest and medium range. Recently, howver, we extended our investigations to the upper medium-head overlap. In both cases, musical tasks were constructred, the technique of paired comaprison was used, (same frequency, equal SPL, similar vowel quality, different registers - - called "isoparametric tones"), and the pairs were studied acoustically, physiologically (airflow and laryngeal photography), and perceptually.

In figure 2, the upper scale illustrates a task designed to contain chest timbre and medium timbre and the transition between these timbres. The lower two tasks are one-timbred, minus any transition or "break".

Figure 3 illustrates the same procedure for the upper medium-head area. The complete list of instructions for the recording of these tasks is given elsewhere; see Large, 1968 and 1973.

RESULTS

Audibly different tones. In the initial series of experiments, female subjects were selected who could demonstrate an "audible timbre difference" between chest register and middle register. An example of this contrast is shown in figure 4. This is a portion of a narrow band sonogram with superimposed amplitude display of a portion of the transition tone where the register change took place. Arrows indicate points at which amplitude sections (displayed below) of the isoparametric tones were taken. (Large, 1968) Figure 5 is a bargraph of the spectra derived from the amplitude sections of the sonogram in figure 4.   The chest register is characterized by greater relative energy in the higher partials, while the medium register has a stronger fundadmental. (Large, 1968)

Subsequently, the same "isoparametric" task was used in an aerodynamic study with a pneumotachographic system. The results are shown in figure 6. Measurements of the flow of air through the glottis were made while a female singer produced chest voice and changed, without interrupting phonation, to

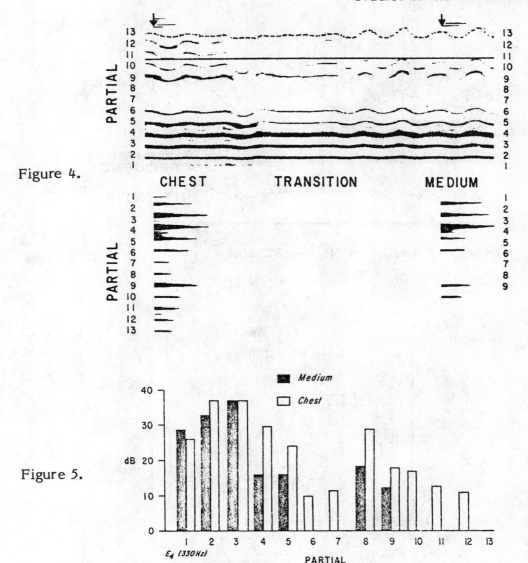

Figure 4.

Figure 5.

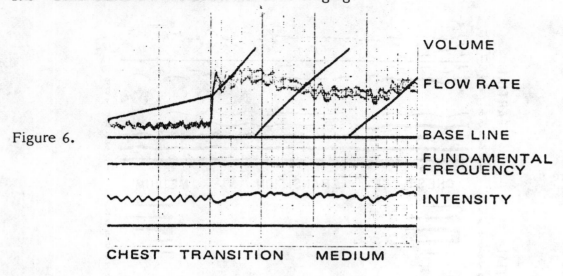

Figure 6.

VOLUME

FLOW RATE

BASE LINE

FUNDAMENTAL FREQUENCY

INTENSITY

CHEST   TRANSITION   MEDIUM

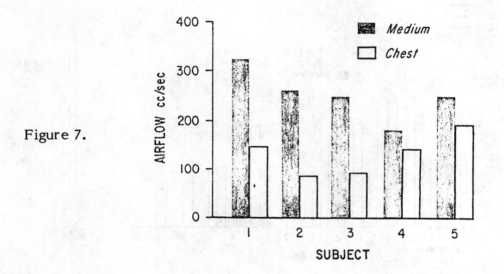

Figure 7.

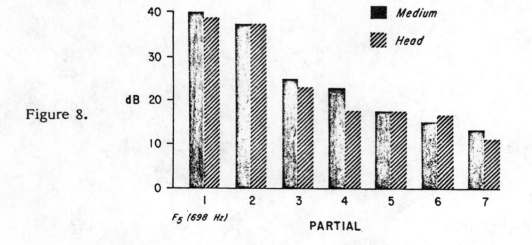

Figure 8.

medium register. This pneumotachograph illustrates a sudden transition. (Large, Iwata, and von Leden, 1970)

The mean values of the airflow rate in chest and medium registers for five subjects are presented graphically in figure 7. Although the mean values of both registers vary from subject to subject, the air flow rate in middle voice was certainly larger than that of chest voice. At this time, the investigator noticed that tone pairs exhibiting little difference in audible register timbre also tended to show little difference in airflow rate. Note the values for subjects 4 and 5. (Large, Iwata, and von Leden, 1970)

In general, the findings to this point suggested that the laryngeal wave pulse had shifted from a sharply peaked shape in chest register to a lower and broader shape in middle register. Studies in laryngeal photography confirmed this view and revealed major adjustment of the laryngeal musculature when middle register was shifted to from chest register and vice versa.

The data with regard to the contrast between medium and head resigers in female singers is less dramatic, although studies in progress reveal a marked difference between trained (equalized) and untrained (unequalized) singers. The illustrations which follow represent only one trained singer.

Figure 8 is a bargraph of the spectra from records of a soprano singing alternately in medium and head registers. Except for minor differences, the tones appear to be well-equalized.

Measurements of airflow differences between the medium register and head register are shown in figure 9. There are five takes from the same subject, three in which "equal effort" was ordered and two in which the subject matched SPL (A-weighting). The equal effort conditions all show approximately 20% greater mean airflow rate in the medium voice. The data for the equal SPL conditions would suggest that intensity alone is not the only factor controlling airflow rate. the equal effort data suggests that there is a need to examine further the hypothesis that the singer's time-varying glottal area may indeed differ from head to medium voice.

Thus far, laryngeal photography has revealed little difference in laryngeal behavior for medium-head contrasts at the same frequency. However, there is a change in the mode of vibration when frequency changes are included in the register change.

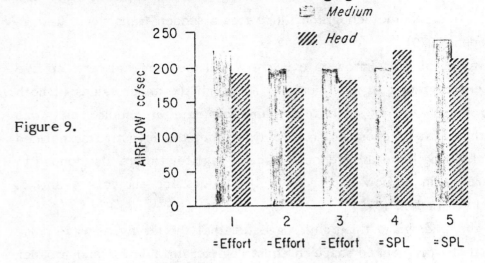

Figure 9.

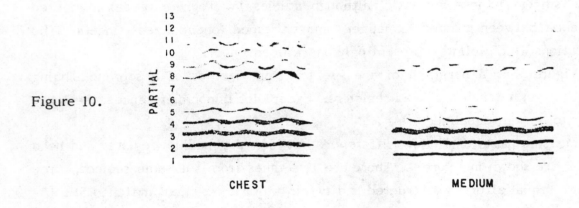

Figure 10.

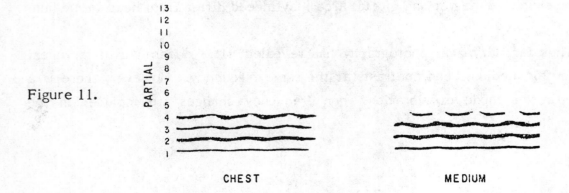

Figure 11.

Equalization studies. Additionally we have run a series of studies in which female chest-medium "isoparametric" pairs were presented to singer-judges for register identification, of the 21 samples on the test tape, 12 received unanimous scores that coincided with the singer's intention.

A follow-up study was designed to determine the relevance of several acoustic factors in the perception of these registers. As shown in figure 10, the two most obvious cues a listener might use in differentiating registers - - the inter-register transition and the prominence of high-frequency energy - - were removed. (Large and Shipp, 1969)

It was found that the judges could differentiate between registers with comparative ease when only the transition was removed. They had greater difficulty when both the transition and the high-frequency were missing. (See figure 11.) This experiment lent perceptual validation to the previous acoustic findings.

Another acoustic-perceptual study was conducted to account for register equalization. Tone pairs were recorded in which the degree of "audible register timbre difference" varied from obvious to subtle. The judgments of expert listeners produced the following results. (Large, 1973)

Figure 12 shows the mean values for tone-pairs receiving the four poorest equalization scores. The results are similar to those of the original experiment shown in figures 4 and 5.

Figure 13 shows spectra for the tone-pair judged to be the "best equalized." This comparison shows "higher" partial energy in both registers, but the 4th and 5th partials and the fundamental still appear to be differential. At this juncture it was speculated that equalization of registers might be related to the laryngeal mechanism of medial compression. (Large, 1973)

DISCUSSION AND CONCLUSIONS

Our findings with regard to the chest-medium contrast are compatible with the theory that different registers are produced by different source (laryngeal) spectra and by different laryngeal adjustments. The laryngeal adjustment theory of voice registers dates at least from Garcia (1855) and extends to van den Berg (1968) and Sonninen (1962). According to van den Berg, "longitudinal tension in the vocal ligaments and the longitudinal tension in the vocal muscles are the important parameters determing the response in the main registers." (van den Berg, 1963) Sonninen (1962) concurs, stating that "a shift in register is due above all to a change in the mode of vibration of the vocal folds."

Our date on the medium-head contrast are much less substantial, but results thus far tend to support the laryngeal adjustment determinant in that area also. Not everyone has agreed with an exclusively laryngeal-adjustment theory of vocal registers. The experiments of Weiss (1932a, 1932b, 1936), in which he used glass tubes to lengthen the vocal tract artificially, seemed to indicate that the coupling of the supra-glottal system to the larynx might account for registers. Trendelenburg (1938a, 1938b) denied this, but Nadoleczny-Millioud and Zimmerman (1938) accepted it and wrote a suitable definition, adding also the accoustic coupling of the sub-glottal system. Van den Berg (1963) records this view, i.e. that both sub- and supra-glottal couplings may affect the vibration form of the vocal folds, the former especially in the chest register (the resonant frequency of the trachea is roughly 300 Hz), and the latter when the first formant coincides with the fundamental frequency of the larynx. Oncley (1952, 1973) proposed a dual concept of voice registers comprising both physiological registers (laryngeal adjustments and acoustic registers. His research indicated that the latter would result from merely the enhancement of different harmonics as the frequency is varied while formants are held essentially constant.

Figure 14 shows transition tones from middle (medium) voice to head voice according to Ross (1959). Note that the transition frequencies vary with the vowel. Such a phenomenon suggests that the configuration of the supraglottal vocal tract must indeed be related in some way to the register problem in singing.

A review of the vowel formant information (figure 15) clearly indicates that the center resonant frequencies of the cardinal vowel F_1's are well within the range of the female middle register. Vowel modification in the female head register has been reported by Sundberg (1977).

The investigators have been testing the Marchesi model of female registration, demonstrating that her system can be illustrated with technical data. Subjects can be identified whose training or experience allow them to sing the "isoparametric" task for chest-medium and medium-head contrasts. The results of these studies thus far support a laryngeal adjustment determinant for the chest-medium contrast, and tend toward the same conclusion for the medium-head contrast.   Marchesi's speculation on the origin of the registers - - three

Figure 12.

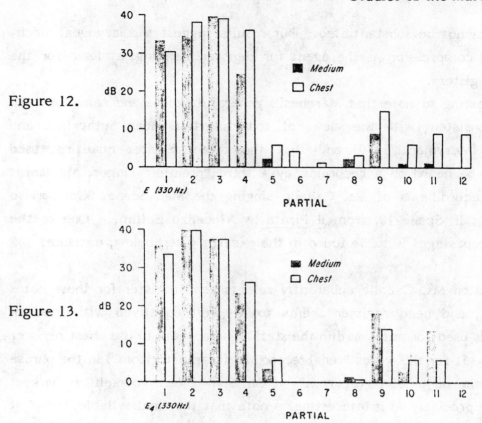

Figure 13.

Figure 14.

VOWEL	SOPRANO		ALTO		TENOR		BASS	
/i/	E	(659 Hz)	C	(523 Hz)	E	(330 Hz)	C	(262 Hz)
/u/	F	(698 Hz)	D	(554 Hz)	F	(349 Hz)	D	(277 Hz)
/e/	G	(784 Hz)	E-flat	(622 Hz)	G	(392 Hz)	E-flat	(311 Hz)
/o/	A-flat	(831 Hz)	E	(659 Hz)	A-flat	(415 Hz)	E	(330 Hz)
/a/	A	(880 Hz)	F	(698 Hz)	A	(440 Hz)	F	(349 Hz)

Figure 15.

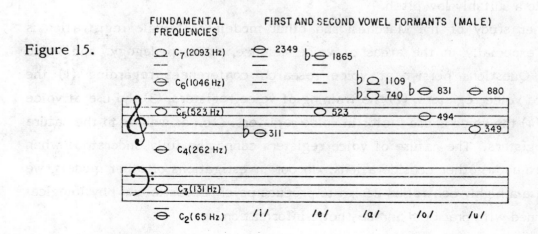

Resonators - - cannot be substantiated. Our results suggest the laryngeal mechanism of medial compression as the agent for register blending, at least for the chest-medium registers.

It is interesting to note that Marchesi's general divisions and names for the registers are consistent with the views of today's artists Joan Sutherland and Marilyn Horne (Meryman, 1970) and that the three register qualities, used artistically, can be heard on a recording by a third "premier" singer, Montserat Caballe. The recording is of Ms. Caballe singing the Mad Scene, "Col sorriso d'innocenza," Act II, Scene 10, from Il Pirata by Vincenzo Bellini.[1] One of the most illustrative passages is to be found in the excerpt given below, measures 148 to 153.

In this section Ms. Caballe apparently selects head register for those notes above the staff, and head register seems to be well equalized with medium register, which is used for notes within the staff. She appears to use chest register in measures 150-151 for the words "tenebre oscure" ("darkest gloom") in the phrase "Oh Sole! Ti vela di tenebre oscure..." ("Oh Sun!   Veil yourself in darkest gloom..."). More precisely, it is interesting to note that the final syllable, "re-," of "oscure," appears to be sung in medium register. This illustrates the vocal technique of using a "lighter" register for less emaphsis, when appropriate. The composer has contributed to this choice by turning the melodic phrase upward here. If the soprano were to remain in chest register for the final syllable on f-natural, it would probably lend too much emphasis to that syllable.

Figure 17 shows the score for an earlier excerpt from Ms. Caballe's recording of the Mad Scene from Il Pirata. Ms. Caballe uses chest register in measures 22-23 to color the word "sepolta" ("sepulchre") in the phrase "Son io nelle mie case o son sipolta?" ("Am I at home or in my sepulchre?"). The word is assigned by the composer to a suitably low pitch.

Further study of the Marchesi and other models of female registration is indicated, especially in the areas of voice science, vocal pedagogy, and voice therapy. Questions persist at voice research conferences regarding (1) the existence of voice registers, (2) the training of voice registers, (3) the use of voice registers, (4) the voice abuse factor in voice registers, etc., as well as to the nature of voice registers. The nature of voice registers cannot be fully understood when divorced from the other considerations. In our investigations of other models, we intend to use a highly controlled design to produce psychoacoustic and physiological data combined with practical and aesthetic information.

MEASURES 148 THRU 153 FROM THE 'MAD SCENE'
OF BELLINI'S IL PIRATA

Figure 16.

MEASURES 13 THRU 25 FROM THE 'MAD SCENE'
OF BELLINI'S IL PIRATA

Figure 17.

REFERENCES

1. Berg, Jw. van den (1963). "Vocal Ligaments versus Registers," The NATS Bulletin, Dec., pp. 16-21, 31.

2. Berg, Jw. van den (1968). "Sound Production in Isolated Human Larynges," Ann. N.Y. Acad. Sci. 155/1, pp. 18-26.

3. Garcia, M. (1855). "Observations on the Human Voice." The London, Edinburgh, and Dublin Philosoph. Magazine 10, July, Dec.

4. Garcia, M. (1840). Ecole de Garcia: Traite complet de l'art du chant. Paris: Troupenas et Cie.

5. Large, J. (1968). "An Acoustical Study of Isoparametric Tones in the Female Chest and Middle Registers in Singing," The NATS Bulletin, Dec., pp. 12-15.

6. Large, J. (1972). "Towards an Integrated Physiologic-Acoustic Theory of Vocal Registers," The NATS Bulletin, Feb./Mar., pp. 18-25, 30-36.

7. Large, J. (1973). "Acoustic Study of Register Equalization in Singing, "Folia Phoniatrica 25, pp. 29-61.

8. Large, J. (ed) (1973). Vocal Registers in Singing. The Hague: Mouton et Cie.

9. Large, J. and Shipp, T. (1969). "The Effect of Certain Parameters on the Perception of Vocal Registers," The NATS Bulletin, Oct., pp. 12-15.

10. Large, J., Iwata, S., and Leden, H. von (1970) "The Primary Female Register Transition in Singing: Aerodynamic Study," Folia Phoniatrica 22, pp. 385-396.

11. Marchesi, M. (n.d.) Theoretical and Practical Vocal Method. New York: Dover.

12. Meryman, R. (1970) "A Tour of Two Great Throats," Life Magazine 68, June 26, pp. 63-4 plus.

13. Nadoleczny-Millioud, M. and Zimmerman, R. (1938). "Categories et registres de la voix," Rev. fr. phoniat. 23, pp. 21-31.

14. Oncley, P. (1952). "The Acoustic Evaluation of Singing Performance," Ph.D. Dissertaion. Columbia University.

15. Oncley, P. (1973). "Dual Concept of Singing Registers," Vocal Registers in Singing. The Hague: Mouton et Cie.

16. Ross, W. (1959) Secrets of Singing. Bloomington, Ind.: published by the author.

17. Sonninen, A. (1962) "Paratasis-gram of the Vocal Cord and the Dimensions of the Voice, "Proceedings of the Fourth International Congress of Phonetic Sciences. The Hague: Mouton et Cie.

18. Sundberg, J. (1977) "Studies of the Soprano Voice," Journal of Research in Singing, I/1, pp. 25-35.

19. Trendelenburg, W. (1938a). "Untersuchungen zur Kenntnis der Register-bruchstellen beim Gesang." Mitteilung I, Sitzungsber. Preuss. Akad. Wiss., physik-math. I, pp. 5-22.

21. Trendelenburg, W. (1938b). "Untersuchungen zur Kenntnis der Register-bruchstellen beim Gesang." Mitteilung II, Sitzungsber. Preuss. Akad. XXI, pp. 188-226.

22. Weiss, D. (1932a). "Ein Resonanzphanomen der Singstimme," Mschr. Ohrenhelik. 66, pp. 964-970.

23. Weiss, D. (1932a) "Zur Frage der Registerbruchstellen beim Gesang," Z. Hals-, Nas-u. Ohrenhelik. 22 pp. 353-358.

24. Weiss, D. (1936). "Naturwissenschaftliches zum Register-problem," Mschr. Ohrenhelik. 70, p. 573.

Dr. John Large, Department of Music, University of California at San Diego, La Jolla, CA 92093.
Dr. Thomas Murry, Audiology/Speech Pathology Service, Veterans Administration Hospital, San Diego, CA 92161.

Vibrato

The Vibrato

Jacob Kwalwasser

This study was undertaken for the purpose of gathering more data on the nature of the vibrato. Such factors as training, sex, age, voice placement and vowel quality were investigated in an effort to ascertain their influence on the pitch, time and intensity fluctuation of the vibrato*.

METHOD OF PHOTOGRAPHING AND MEASURING

The photographic method was used exclusively in this study. A strip of super-speed moving picture film was fastened to the drum of the tonoscope (15) which is equipped with a synchronous motor to insure regularity in the rate of revolution. A Dorsey phonelescope, mounted on the tonoscope, was used as an optical lever. The observers sang directly into the mouthpiece of the phonelescope. Each photographic record represents a tone sustained from .50 sec. to .75 sec.

The method employed for measuring pitch in terms of wavelengths was developed and described by <u>Simon</u> (15). It consists in measuring wave-lengths either individually or in groups with the aid of a vernier microscope. The constant, 2,425 millimeters, the rate of speed per second at which the film passes the point of exposure, divided by the wave-lengths, yields the vibration rate per second. As demonstrated by <u>Simon</u> (15) the pitch and time method of recording have a high order of reliability - finer than demanded for the present purpose.

The intensity readings are less valid than the pitch and time readings. There is first the danger of one or more resonance regions in the phonelescope. The "own" resonance is at 551 d.v. This frequency was therefore avoided in all our tones of the present study. A phono-photograph of the region from 121 d.v. to 400 d.v. reveals no marked period of resonance anywhere in this scale. At the frequency of 275 d.v. which is the sub-octave of the free period, very slight change is found in the amplitude of vibration. Such factors as the length of the optical level, distance of the singer from the membrane, influence of the tube leading to the membrane, etc., were subjected to little or no experimentation. The following use of the amplitude of the wave as a distinct measure of intensity is therefore intended as merely a rough indication of the quantity for which the procedure is perhaps qualitatively adequate.

THE PARALLEL VIBRATO

The vibrato is an observable periodicity of pitch or intensity pulsations or both, falling normally within a more or less regular rate of occurrence varying from four to nine per second. The parallel vibrato is one in which the pitch and intensity pulsations are periodic, parallel, and synchronous; <u>i.e.</u>, a general tendency for the crests and troughs of pitch and intensity to be more or less coincident in time, extent and duration.

Table I shows the pitch, intensity, and time measurements of 63 tones of this type. In order to facilitate the discussion of these tones, each column will be taken up separately. Pitches to be reproduced were sounded by means of tuning forks. The observers were instructed to sing the pitch they heard, using a specific vowel or voice placement. In a few cases no standard pitches were given, but generally the pitch used was of a frequency 220 d.v. Standard pitches are listed under S.P. in Table I. The columns labeled M, show the means in time, pitch, and intensity, respectively. These columns give the true means, in each case, computed from a series of time, pitch, and intensity readings. The column labeled E.D. gives the extent, <u>i.e.</u>, the amplitude of pitch deviations in intensity and time, while those labeled M.D. represent maximum deviations.

The unit of measurement for the intensity of mean is millimeters, but the average and maximum deviations are in terms of per cent of the mean. The unit of measurement for time is in hundredths of a second. The average deviation is in terms of per cent of the mean, also.

The average extent of pitch deviations for the 63 tones of Table I is 23 percent of a tone; the maximum pitch deviations average 59 per cent of a tone. The mean and maximum intensity deviations are 11 and 50 per cent of the mean respectively. The average duration of pulsation is .16 sec., with an average deviation of 9 per cent.

Fig. 1 contains a graphic representation of 21 tones of this class. In addition to the key to these graphs given in the cut, note that pitch is denoted by d.v. (at the left) and followed by degrees of intensity denoted arbitrarily in terms of millimeters of amplitude. This measurement of amplitude of intensity or vertical displacement of the sound wave was taken directly from the original photograph. The numbers on the graphs correspond to the numbers found in the first columns of the tables.

PARALLEL VIBRATO

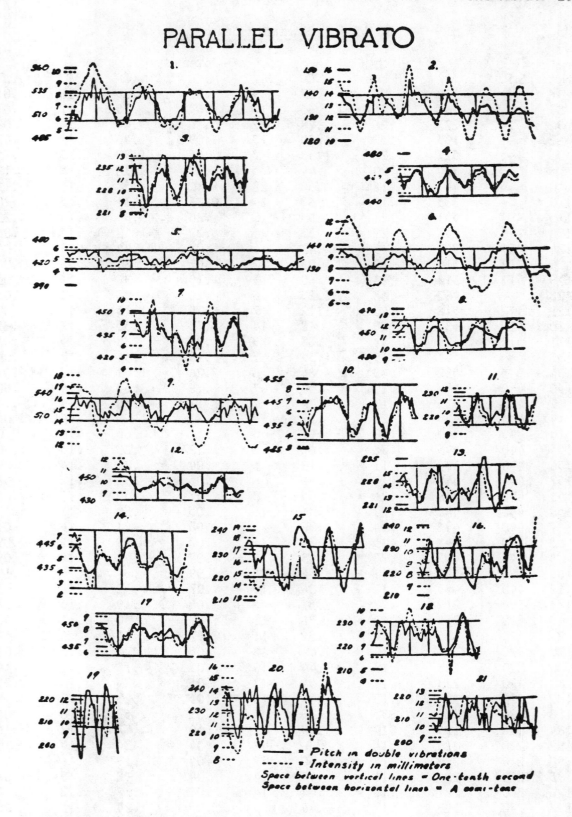

Fig. 1

Table I. Parallel vibrato

No.	S.P.	Pitch M.	Pitch E.D.	Pitch M.D.	Intensity M.	Intensity A.D.	Intensity M.D.	Time M.	Time A.D.
6		134	.27	.69	9	.21	.89	.16	.05
89		267	.25	.66	18	.07	.29	.17	.07
92		273	.26	.78	.22	.10	.44	.14	.08
2		135	.57	1.30	13	.09	.43	.11	.07
104		527	.26	1.33	7	.45	1.99	.15	.15
5		424	.20	.44	5	.07	.38	.18	.12
110		465	.18	.53	28	.12	.58	.15	.15
113		333	.19	.63	14	.08	.31	.15	.20
115		551	.21	.55	10	.20	.94	.14	.25
122	256	257	.22	.33	5	.22	1.00	.15	.05
124	256	267	.15	.43	15	.08	.44	.19	.04
1	512	519	.39	1.03	7	.07	.82	.16	.05
9	512	518	.23	.60	15	.10	.36	.16	.05
128		462	.58	1.23	8	.20	.95	.16	.05
129	512	516	.40	1.12	7	.29	1.15	.17	.09
130	512	532	.29	.68	14	.13	.50	.16	.05
131	512	525	.34	.88	9	.27	.88	.15	.05
133		541	.19	.35	7	.13	.54	.17	.04
134		532	.43	.84	6	.26	1.01	.15	.01
150	440	443	.19	.54	7	.16	.63	.14	.00
7	440	435	.13	.44	7	.17	.70	.13	.11
14	440	439	.20	.52	5	.20	1.00	.14	.05
10	440	441	.30	.62	6	.17	.68	.14	.10
155	440	445	.28	.62	6	.12	.63	.15	.00
156	440	444	.11	.18	6	.04	.21	.14	.00
157	440	448	.15	.36	6	.05	.32	.15	.06
158	440	448	.26	.72	3	.08	.52	.15	.06
159	440	441	.21	.36	6	.05	.30	.16	.10
17	440	442	.14	.36	7	.08	.41	.16	.05
8	440	448	.15	.26	11	.07	.29	.16	.09
4	440	457	.23	.43	4	.07	.41	.14	.09
165	440	449	.11	.36	15	.09	.37	.14	.10
12	440	443	.11	.26	10	.07	.32	.16	.05
171	220	219	.22	.52	8	.04	.19	.15	.06
19	220	215	.44	.76	11	.08	.30	.11	.00
21	220	215	.22	.52	11	.07	.32	.15	.12
179	220	220	.17	.44	8	.05	.20	.15	.06
180	220	226	.16	.44	10	.05	.19	.16	.14
181	220	223	.18	.44	18	.05	.25	.15	.09
182	220	224	.13	.44	16	.05	.23	.12	.14
183	320	329	.35	1.39	11	.09	.53	.16	.04
184	128	135	.10	.44	22	.10	.47	.17	.16
192	220	220	.16	.36	12	.04	.24	.14	.10
194	220	220	.18	.60	17	.04	.19	.16	.09
195	220	219	.18	.44	14	.04	.18	.19	.07
196	220	221	.16	.44	14	.03	.18	.22	.13
197	220	219	.17	.44	19	.05	.24	.15	.00
198	220	223	.13	.36	9	.04	.18	.15	.10
11	220	222	.19	.44	10	.09	.39	.15	.18
201	220	221	.26	.52	13	.05	.20	.18	.08

Table I (Continued)

No.	S.P.	M.	Pitch E.D.	M.D.	M.	Intensity A.D.	M.D.	Time M.	A.D.
205	220	221	.21	.44	6	.05	.19	.16	.12
13	220	226	.23	.59	14	.04	.22	.22	.09
210	220	226	.20	.59	16	.05	.21	.19	.05
15	220	227	.34	.74	16	.09	.39	.12	.36
20	220	229	.34	.78	12	.12	.64	.14	.07
217	220	225	.19	.52	8	.07	.36	.14	.10
16	220	224	.28	.67	9	.11	.70	.16	.16
3	220	230	.22	.59	11	.10	.49	.18	.08
18	220	223	.27	.52	8	.08	.72	.16	.11
233	220	216	.38	.76	6	.19	1.05	.14	.05
239	220	218	.20	.44	8	.07	.39	.14	.07
121	256	259	.18	.43	6	.06	.36	.19	.04
			.23	.59		.11	.50	.16	.09

For legend see text.

Table II <u>Opposite vibrato</u>

No.	S.P.	M.	Pitch E.D.	M.D.	M.	Intensity A.D.	M.D.	Time M.	A.D.
200		160	.22	.53	7	.25	.79	.20	.03
42		155	.59	1.82	16	.14	.59	.18	.16
88	320	313	.22	.80	28	.09	.33	.17	.02
43	512	528	.31	1.05	6	.16	.73	.17	.02
106		417	.22	.44	14	.13	.43	.20	.07
44	512	525	.64	.97	9	.33	1.13	.11	.07
142		187	.16	.43	4	.12	.41	.14	.15
162	880	896	.18	.54	8	.05	.27	.14	.08
174	220	219	.19	.62	11	.05	.25	.14	.08
178	220	218	.15	.36	9	.04	.18	.15	.03
185	220	222	.17	.44	18	.09	.40	.16	.03
186	220	212	.20	.52	.8	.03	.16	.16	.06
191	220	220	.17	.44	10	.04	.20	.15	.18
203	110	108	.14	.46	7	.06	.27	.14	.07
204	220	222	.10	.36	11	.10	.50	.13	.04
216	220	221	.17	.40	9	.08	.33	.13	.07
220	220	219	.20	.52	8	.04	.18	.15	.11
232	110	113	.13	.36	8	.05	.27	.13	.00
40	220	218	.17	.36	7	.09	.59	.15	.07
232	220	219	.11	.28	7	.05	.31	.15	.08
39	220	222	.38	.64	8	.19	.68	.14	.07
235	220	217	.60	1.56	6	.19	.71	.15	.05
38		329	.26	.61	6	.14	.73	.15	.03
41	220	219	.25	.72	6	.12	.64	.14	.08
			.25	.63		.11	.46	.15	.06

Table III Pitch vibrato

No.	S.P.	M.	Pitch E.D.	M.D.	M.	Intensity A.D.	M.D.	Time M.	A.D.
36	256	251	.18	.43	5	.03	.15	.16	.09
137	220	219	.12	.44	5	.04	.15	.16	.11
30	220	213	.12	.32	18	.04	.06	.15	.03
37	220	211	.16	.44	4	.06	.31	.18	.03
35	440	449	.21	.54	4	.04	.13	.15	.01
170	220	219	.22	.52	8	.04	.19	.14	.07
34	220	220	.22	.52	10	.01	.06	.15	.04
173	220	217	.18	.36	8	.02	.26	.15	.08
175	220	216	.30	.76	8	.07	.29	.13	.05
190	220	221	.22	.60	9	.02	.16	.16	.23
193	220	220	.19	.52	13	.16	.72	.25	.06
208	110	110	.18	.31	6	.03	.17	.14	.20
33	220	224	.13	.33	9	.06	.39	.16	.06
214	220	221	.18	.41	8	.05	.30	.15	.06
219	220	223	.21	.52	6	.03	.16	.16	.11
221	220	221	.17	.52	14	.04	.19	.18	.12
225	220	221	.21	.44	6	.02	.14	.18	.08
31	110	112	.28	.64	5	.04	.23	.13	.08
			.19	.48		.04	.22	.16	.08

Table IV. Intensity vibrato

No.	S.P.	M.	Pitch E.D.	M.D.	M.	Intensity A.D.	M.D.	Time M.	A.D.
45		172	.15	.45	8	.07	.51	.16	.28
46		137	.35	1.13	18	.02	.11	.14	.03
253		144	.13	.44	6	.05	.32	.20	.03
48		143	.13	.44	13	.07	.33	.10	.22
47		525	.10	.43	8	.17	.63	.19	.28
112		547	.11	.55	20	.04	.18	.17	.07
			.16	.57		.07	.35	.16	.15

Table V. No vibrato

No.		M.	Pitch E.D.	M.D.	Intensity M.	A.D.	M.D.
108		206	.21	.46	14	.04	.22
250		121	.12	.43	15	.09	.36
22		140	.14	.38	14	.02	.07
23		151	.11	.29	15	.04	.14
222		338	.17	.50	7	.04	.18
29		124	.13	.64	6	.06	.34
27		173	.16	.35	10	.02	.12
154		125	.21	.43	7	.05	.25
141		163	.72	1.26	14	.04	.24
140		125	.17	.43	6	.10	.38
252		163	.12	.26	14	.06	.23
254		134	.15	.56	10	.04	.23
172		140	.17	.69	15	.06	.20
25		140	.08	.29	12	.05	.20
28		173	1.03	2.00	13	.02	.09
51		419	.15	.38	9	.12	.60
109		351	.09	.45	9	.06	.38
120	256	266	.12	.37	4	.05	.13
125	256	251	.18	.50	4	.05	.25
139	220	207	.12	.33	4	.13	.20
26	220	207	.17	.25	19	.06	.26
24	220	205	.17	.42	11	.02	.10
207	220	193	.67	1.82	9	.04	.22
199	220	221	.17	.36	11	.05	.14
			.23	.58		.05	.23

THE OPPOSITE RELATIONSHIP VIBRATO

Twenty-four tones, representing 12 per cent of all tones possessing the vibrato, are found in Table II. In this type, the pitch crest is accompanied by an intensity trough, and the pitch trough by an intensity crest. (See Fig. 2.) While the direction of the two factors is opposite, both pitch and intensity are more or less coincident in time, extent, and duration.

The opposite vibrato is similar to the parallel vibrato, as is shown in the following figures.

OPPOSITE VIBRATO

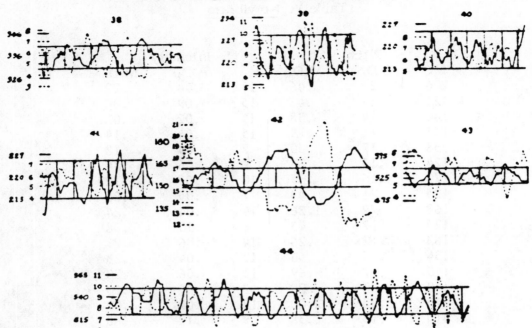

INTENSITY VIBRATO

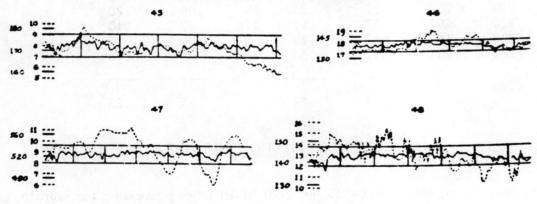

UNUSUAL VIBRATO

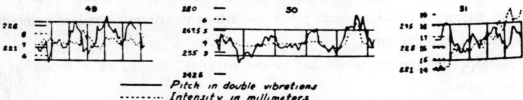

——————— Pitch in double vibrations
··············· Intensity in millimeters
Space between vertical lines - One tenth second
Space between horizontal lines - A semi-tone

Fig. 2

	Pitch		Intensity		Pitch	
	E.D.	M.D.	A.D.	M.D.	M.	A.D.
Parallel vibrato	.23	.59	.11	.50	.16	.09
Opposite vibrato	.25	.63	.11	.46	.15	.06

The only significant difference is in the relationship of pitch and intensity.

THE PITCH VIBRATO

In this vibrato the pitch factor alone reveals the periodicity. The intensity factor, which has been in either the same or opposite phase in former types, is now devoid of any cyclic characteristics, although it does fluctuate irregularly. This type of vibrato is by no means rare. Nineteen, representing 16 percent of the total number of tones, were found in this study.

The pitch fluctuations for this class are somewhat smaller than those presented before, being E.D., 19 per cent, and M.D., 48 per cent of a tone. The intensity fluctuations are smaller than those found for any of the preceding types. In respect to rate, the pitch vibrato resembles the parallel vibrato.

THE INTENSITY VIBRATO

In this type of vibrato the intensity factor alone reveals cyclic characteristics. Consult Table IV for measurements of the intensity vibrato and Fig. 2 for the graphs.

CHANGES FROM ONE TYPE OF VIBRATO TO ANOTHER

In order to facilitate the discussion of the vibrato, it has been arbitrarily divided into types or classes. An examination of Fig. 1, parallel vibrato, will reveal some cases that are parallel in regard to pitch and intensity, but are slightly out of phase. In tone No. 20 the intensity curve is "skewed" a little to the left of the pitch curve, while in the preceding tone the intensity curve is "skewed" a little to the right. No. 21 is a border-line case, for the phase relationship is almost 180 degrees. If the intensity curve were advanced a little in time, this tone would belong to the opposite vibrato type.

The last three tones of Fig. 2 are classified as unusual types of vibrato, since they change their pitch and intensity relationships from one type to another. No. 49 changes from opposite to parallel; No. 50 begins with no vibrato and ends parallel; while No. 51 resembles No. 49

TONES WHICH HAVE NO VIBRATO

In a total of 147 tones included in this study, 28 are classified as belonging to the no-vibrato group. Untrained adults contributed 87 percent of all their tones, and children 41 percent of all their tones to this class. Only 7 per cent of the tones of trained singers were of the no-vibrato type. Table V gives the measurements of these tones, and Fig. 3 contains the graphs.

The pitch fluctuations may be as large as those found in tones containing the vibrato. But mere fluctuations do not necessarily result in the vibrato. The fluctuations must be progressive and cyclic in nature in order to produce the vibrato. It is due to the lack of configuration of pitch or intensity deviations that we describe these tones as having no vibrato, even though the amount of deviation is equal to that found in tones containing the vibrato.

EFFECT OF VOICE PLACEMENT ON THE VIBRATO

In an effort to learn the effect of voice placement on the vibrato, five different types of voice placements were experimented with. Trained vocalists were asked to reproduce a tuning fork pitch of 220 d.v. in the following ways: forward, backward, nasal, throaty, and covered. The results recorded below show how placement influences the vibrato.

	Pitch		Intensity		Time	
	ED.	M.D.	A.D.	M.D.	M.	A.D.
Backward	.18	.47	.08	.38	.15	.10
Nasal.	.17	.41	.04	.21	.15	.06
Throaty.	.28	.60	.13	.62	.16	.13
Covered	.23	.56	.11	.48	.15	.07
Forward	.23	.55	.07	.38	.16	.10

Forward placement

No.	Name	M.	Pitch E.D.	M.D.	M.	Intensity A.D.	M.D.	Time M.	A.D.
170	W.E.	219	.22	.52	8	.04	.18	.14	.07
18	G.J.	223	.27	.52	8	.08	.72	.16	.11
13	H.R.	226	.23	.59	14	.04	.22	.22	.09
190	E.E.	221	.22	.60	9	.02	.16	.16	.23
150	E.C.	443	.19	.54	7	.16	.63	.14	.00
			.23	.55		.07	.38	.16	.10

Backward placement

No.	Name	M.	E.D.	M.D.	M.	A.D.	M.D.	M.	A.D.
171	W.E.	216	.22	.52	11	.06	.10	.15	.06
41	G.J.	218	.17	.36	7	.09	.59	.15	.07
210	H.R.	226	.20	.59	16	.05	.21	.19	.09
191	E.E.	220	.17	.44	10	.04	.20	.15	.18
7	E.C.	435	.13	.44	7	.17	.70	.13	.11
			.18	.47		.08	.38	.15	.10

Nasal placement

No.	Name	M.	E.D.	M.D.	M.	A.D.	M.D.	M.	A.D.
34	W.E.	220	.22	.52	10	.01	.06	.15	.04
232	G.J.	219	.11	.28	7	.05	.31	.15	.08
33	H.R.	234	.13	.33	9	.06	.39	.16	.06
192	E.E.	220	.16	.36	12	.04	.24	.14	.10
35	E.C.	449	.21	.54	4	.04	.13	.15	.01
			.17	.41		.04	.21	.15	.06

Throaty placement

No.	Name	M.	E.D.	M.D.	M.	A.D.	M.D.	M.	A.D.
173	W.E.	217	.18	.36	8	.02	.26	.15	.08
233	G.J.	216	.38	.78	6	.19	1.05	.14	.06
15	H.R.	227	.34	.74	16	.09	.39	.12	.36
193	E.E.	220	.19	.52	13	.16	.72	.25	.06
10	E.C.	441	.30	.62	6	.17	.68	.14	.10
			.28	.60		.13	.62	.16	.13

Covered placement

No.	Name	M.	E.D.	M.D.	M.	A.D.	M.D.	M.	A.D.
174	W.E.	219	.19	.62	11	.05	.25	.14	.08
39	G.J.	222	.38	.64	8	.19	.68	.14	.07
214	H.R.	221	.18	.41	8	.05	.30	.15	.06
194	E.E.	220	.18	.60	17	.04	.19	.16	.09
14	E.C.	439	.20	.52	5	.20	1.00	.14	.05
			.23	.56		.11	.48	.15	.07

NO VIBRATO

PITCH VIBRATO

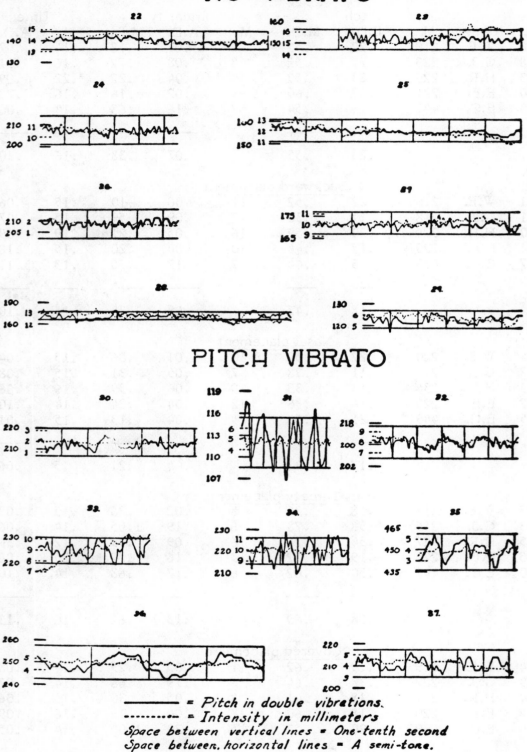

——— = Pitch in double vibrations.
- - - - - - - = Intensity in millimeters
Space between vertical lines = One-tenth second
Space between horizontal lines = A semi-tone.

Fig. 3

Since these computations are based upon five tones each, it is unwise to make unqualified statements concerning the influence of placement. Yet two tendencies are observable. The nasal placement, which produces the nasal quality, results in the smallest pitch and intensity fluctuations, the throaty placement, which results in strained and tense quality, has the greatest pitch and intensity fluctuations.

These two qualities are considered more or less objectionable by voice students, but the matter of amount of pitch and intensity deviations is not mentioned in voice literature. It is possible that this subject of extent of deviation may have a direct relationship with the pleasantness or unpleasantness of tone quality, which results from different types of placement.

THE EFFECT OF VOWEL QUALITY ON THE VIBRATO

Proceeding as before, trained singers were asked to reproduce a tuning fork pitch on the vowels a, a, e, o, and u. The results follow:

		Pitch		Intensity		Time	
		E.D.	M.D.	A.D.	M.D.	M.	A.D.
ä	. . . .	.19	.50	.09	.33	.15	.05
ā	. . . .	.21	.60	.07	.34	.15	.08
ē	. . . .	.19	.46	.07	.23	.16	.08
ō	. . . .	.21	.59	.10	.39	.16	.10
ū	. . . .	.19	.44	.07	.30	.16	.09

The differences in pitch and intensity fluctuations, due to vowel quality, is very slight.

THE EFFECT OF VOICE REGISTERS ON THE VIBRATO

Vocalists have divided the voice range into three registers, i.e., head, middle, and chest. The chest tones represent, approximately, a little more than a half-octave interval in the lowest range of the voice. The head register consists of approximately the same interval at the top of the voice range. The interval of an octave, more or less, between the head and chest registers is known as the middle register. Only the head and chest tones were experimented with at this time, since practically all other tones of this study are of the middle register type.

Greater differences were found between the head and chest tones in regard to their pitch, intensity, and time fluctuations than betweeen any other two groups of tones found in this study.

	Pitch		Intensity		Time	
	E.D.	M.D.	A.D.	M.D.	M.	A.D.
High tones	.24	.76	.08	.43	.15	.05
Low tones.	.17	.44	.05	.28	.14	.10

Before any interpretation is made of these measurements something should be said of the relationship of amplitude to pitch frequency. D. C. Miller (9) presents the formula $(nA)^2$ and a graph in discussing this subject. "The intensity or loudness of a sound is proportional to the square of the frequency, that is, to $(nA)^2$. A recording apparatus having ideal response must fulfil the following conditions: Let all tones of the musical scale, from the lowest to the highest, and all exactly of the same loudness, be sounded one after another and be separately recorded; let the amplitudes of the various responses be measured, and each amplitude be multiplied by the frequency of the tone producing it, then the squares of the products of amplitude and frequency must be constant throughout the entire series."

Miller accompanies this discussion with a graph in which he shows the actual amplitudes of sounds varying in pitch but constant in loudness. By actual measurement the amplitude of C^3 (259 d.v.) is 15 times the amplitude of C^7 (4,138 d.v.), yet the two tones are of equal loudness.

Head tones

No.	Name	M.	Pitch E.D.	M.D.	M.	Intensity A.D.	M.D.	Time M.	A.D.
222	H.R.	338	.17	.50	7	.04	.18	..	..
38	G.J.	329	.26	.61	6	.13	.73	.15	.03
183	W.E.	329	.35	1.39	11	.09	.53	.16	.04
162	E.C.	896	.18	.54	8	.05	.27	.14	.08
			.24	.76		.08	.43	.15	.05

Chest tones

No.	Name	M.	Pitch E.D.	M.D.	M.	Intensity A.D.	M.D.	Time M.	A.D.
223	H.R.	113	.13	.36	8	.05	.27	.13	.00
250	E.C.	254	.22	.44	5	.04	.28	.14	.10
184	W.E.	135	.10	.64	22	.10	.47	.17	.16
38	G.J.	112	.28	.44	5	.04	.23	.13	.08
203	E.E.	108	.14	.46	7	.06	.27	.14	.07
208	E.E.	110	.18	.31	6	.03	.17	.14	.20
			.17	.44		.05	.28	.14	.10

EFFECT OF INTENSITY CHANGES ON THE VIBRATO

Trained vocalists were asked to reproduce the pitch of a tuning fork in the three following ways: pianissimo, fortissimo, and crescendo. Head and chest tones were avoided.

	Pitch		Intensity		Time	
	E.D.	M.D.	A.D.	M.D.	M.	A.D.
Pianissimo	.20	.50	.06	.30	.16	.09
Fortissimo	.20	.47	.09	.48	.15	.07
Crescendo	.35	.94	.07	.35	.16	.07

Fortissimo

No.	Name	M.	Pitch E.D.	M.D.	M.	Intensity A.D.	M.D.	Time M.	A.D.
16	H.R.	224	.28	.67	9	.11	.70	.16	.16
4	E.C.	457	.23	.43	4	.07	.41	.14	.09
185	W.E.	222	.17	.44	18	.09	.40	.16	.03
239	G.J.	218	.20	.44	8	.07	.39	.14	.07
204	E.E.	222	.10	.36	11	.10	.50	.13	.04
			.20	.47		.09	.48	.15	.07

Pianissimo

No.	Name	M.	Pitch E.D.	M.D.	M.	Intensity A.D.	M.D.	Time M.	A.D.
225	H.R.	221	.21	.44	6	.02	.14	.18	.08
165	E.C.	449	.11	.36	16	.09	.37	.14	.10
186	W.E.	212	.20	.52	8	.03	.16	.16	.06
41	G.J.	219	.25	.72	6	.13	.64	.14	.08
205	E.E.	221	.21	.44	6	.03	.19	.16	.12
			.20	.50		.06	.30	.16	.09

Crescendo

No.	Name	M.	Pitch E.D.	M.D.	M.	Intensity A.D.	M.D.	Time M.	A.D.
207	E.E.	193	.67	1.82	9	.04	.22	.18	.08
3	H.R.	230	.22	.59	11	.10	.49	.13	.07
51	W.E.	229	.17	.41	17	.06	.35	.15	.07
			.35	.94		.07	.35	.16	.07

Since the crescendo begins pianissimo and ends fortissimo, it is not surprising to find that its intensity measurements approximate the average of the extremely soft and loud tones. The pitch measurements for the pianissimo and fortissimo are similar, but the crescendo tones are accompanied by excessive pitch fluctuations. Why the crescendo tones should not represent a compromise in pitch as in intensity is unaccountable. It is possible that the attempt to change the dynamics of a tone results in the loss of pitch control. The time measurements agree with those accompanied by a shorter pulsation rate, which means an increase in the number of pulsations per second.

THE EFFECT OF VOLUNTARY INTERFERENCE ON THE VIBRATO

In an effort to learn what could be done with the vibrato in voluntarily exaggerating and eliminating it, trained vocalists were asked, in turn, to produce tones, with and without the vibrato. In the exaggerated vibrato, the vocalists were asked to make the pulsations as obtrusive as possible, while in the inhibited vibrato they were instructed to maintain a rigid and inflexible tone. The following measurements were obtained:

	Pitch		Intensity		Time	
	ED.	M.D.	A.D.	M.D.	M.	A.D.
Exaggerated vibrato	.44	1.00	.13	.54	.14	.06
Inhibited vibrato	.20	.52	.12	.55	.15	.08

Inhibited vibrato

No.	Name	M.	Pitch		M.	Intensity		Time	
			E.D.	M.D.		A.D.	M.D.	M.	A.D.
216	H.R.	221	.17	.40	9	.08	.33	.13	.07
102	F.A.	133	.35	.69	11	.13	.47	.11	.10
104	J.W.	527	.26	1.33	7	.45	1.99	.15	.15
133	M.P.	541	.19	.35	7	.13	.54	.17	.04
156	E.C.	444	.11	.18	6	.04	.21	.14	.00
12	E.C.	443	.11	.26	10	.07	.32	.16	.05
21	W.E.	215	.22	.52	11	.07	.32	.15	.12
196	E.E.	221	.16	.44	14	.03	.18	.22	.13
			.20	.52		.12	.55	.15	.08

Exaggerated vibrato

No.	Name	M.	E.D.	M.D.	M.	A.D.	M.D.	M.	A.D.
2	F.A.	135	.57	1.30	13	.09	.43	.11	.07
42	J.K.	155	.59	1.82	16	.14	.57	.18	.16
44	M.P.	525	.64	.97	9	.33	1.13	.11	.07
155	E.C.	445	.28	.62	6	.12	.63	.15	.00
176	W.E.	216	.30	.76	8	.07	.29	.13	.05
19	W.E.	215	.44	.76	11	.08	.30	.11	.00
20	G.J.	229	.34	.78	12	.12	.63	.14	.07
195	H.R.	219	.18	.44	14	.04	.18	.19	.07
235	E.E.	217	.60	1.56	6	.19	.71	.15	.05
			.44	1.00		.13	.54	.14	.06

The exaggerated vibrato sounded like the "highly objectionable" tremolo. The pitch fluctuations produced are almost twice those of the normal vibrato. The intensity fluctuations are also exaggerated, while the attempt to make the pulsations obtrusive resulted in an increase in the number of pulsations per second.

The attempt to inhibit the vibrato was totally unsuccessful, since it was never accomplished. The pitch fluctuations for the "rigid and inflexible" tones resemble those for normal vibrato tones. The intensity readings are approximately the same as those for the exaggerated vibrato. Again, a very insignificant decrease in the pitch fluctuations, which might be interpreted as a loss of intensity control. The rate of pulsation for the inhibited vibrato is slower than that of the exaggerated vibrato, but faster than the normal rate.

It is evident that the magnitude of pitch and intensity fluctuations may be increased beyond the habitual boundaries, voluntarily, with but little effort; but the attempt to reduce the pitch and intensity fluctuations below the habitual minimum is exceedingly difficult. Complete inhibition of the vibrato fluctuations was beyond the power of the vocalists in all cases here tried.

INFLUENCE OF AGE, SEX AND TRAINING ON THE VIBRATO

1. Age. Seven children, ranging in age from eight to sixteen, with no special training in music, contributed tones for this section of the study. They were asked to sing tones which were well within their range and easy to sustain. These tones were photographed and measured. It was found that three of the eight children failed to produce any trace of the vibrato in their tones.

Children	Pitch		Intensity		Time	
	E.D.	M.D.	A.D.	M.D.	M.	A.D.
With vibrato	.17	.54	.09	.37	.17	.12
Without vibrato	.11	.42	.12	.54	. . .	. . .

The intensity fluctuations are smaller than those obtained from the tones of adult vocalists. In adult voices, however, tones devoid of the vibrato have smaller mean and maximum intensity deviations than tones containing the vibrato. The reverse of this situation is true in reference to the tones of children. Even though generalizations must be made with reservations due to the limited sampling of children's tones, it appears that the child's voice is more flexible from the standpoint of intensity and less flexible than the adult's in regard to pitch.

2. Sex. The following data give some indication of the influence of sex. They include the measurements for trained voices only:

	Pitch		Intensity		Time	
	E.D.	M.D.	A.D.	M.D.	M.	A.D.
Female	.25	.76	.30	.80	.15	.07
Male	.22	.63	.26	.42	.14	.08

Men's voices do not fluctuate as much in either pitch or intensity as do women's voices. Of the total number of tones sung by trained men, 9 per cent were without the vibrato, while only 4.5 per cent of all tones sung by women were devoid of the vibrato. It might be said, then, that the vibrato is more conspicuous in women's voices than in men's and also more frequently present.

3. Training. Proceeding as before, we find the following measurements for the trained and untrained:

	Pitch		Intensity		Time	
	E.D.	M.D.	A.D.	M.D.	M.	A.D.
Trained singers with vibrato	.23	.56	.09	.36	.16	.08
Trained singers without vibrato	.21	.55	.06	.20	...	...
Untrained singers with vibrato	.20	.62	.08	.35	.15	.12
Untrained singers without vibrato	.26	.54	.05	.21	...	...

It is evident that the vibrato appears in the tones of the untrained as well as the trained singers; but, while the above data do not indicate the frequency of appearance on the basis of training, it was found that 93 per cent of all tones produced by trained vocalists and only 27 per cent of all tones produced by untrained singers, contained the vibrato. On the basis of training alone, it is possible to predict the presence of the vibrato with a high degree of accuracy.

The above data reveal only slight differences in the pitch fluctuations for the four types. There is a definite tendency, however, for the intensity fluctuations to be greater in tones containing the vibrato than in tones devoid of the vibrato, regardless of training.

THE VIBRATO DEFINED

Prior to the study of the writer on the nature of the vibrato, two factors were isolated and measured; namely, pitch and intensity. The third factor of the vibrato, that of time, was described as relatively constant. Not only was the time factor believed to be relatively constant, but the pitch and intensity relationship was assumed to be rigidly fixed and always parallel. The six conclusions as formulated by Schoen (16) reveal what was attributed to the vibrato prior to this investigation.

(1) "The vibrato is a fundamental attribute of artistically effective singing voice in that it is a medium for the conveyance of emotion in vocal expression.

(2) "The vibrato is a manifestation of the general neuro-muscular condition that characterizes the singing organism.

(3) "The psychological effect of the vibrato is probably due to the fact that the human ear has because of the behavior of muscle under emotional stress, come to associate trembling with emotional experiences.

(4) "The voice that possesses the most constant vibrato, constant in its presence in the tones throughout the range of the singer's voice and of an amplitude and intensity not obtrusive to the ear, but of sufficient intensity to be easily audible, has the best effect on the hearer, provided the other factors that enter into artistic singing are present.

(5) "The rate of the vibrato is relatively constant, of approximately six pulsations per second.

(6) "The intensity fluctuations are synchronous with the pitch fluctuations, wave by wave for both rate and extent."

The first four conclusions as formulated by Schoen stand unimpaired by the evidence submitted in this investigation, but the last two conclusions must be modified considerably, for it has been found that the rate of pulsations is quite variable and that the pitch and intensity relationship is not always parallel or synchronous.

In defining the vibrato, it is necessary to state that the vibrato consists of an observable periodicity of either pitch or intensity pulsations, or both, in a more or less regular time sequence or relationship, varying in rate of occurrence from 4 to 9 per second. It is a phenomenon of three variables; namely, pitch, intensity, and time.

CURRENT LITERATURE ON THE VIBRATO

The vibrato has long been a subject of controversy among musicians and music critics. The literature on the subject is so confusing that it is next to impossible to glean a clear conception of the nature, causes, or desirability of the vibrato. Most of the literature available deals with the desirability of the phenomenon. some critics maintain that it is desirable when not used exesssively; others hold that even the slightest manifestation of it is objectionable.

In an effort to establish the status of the vibrato and tremolo, I shall resort to direct quotation from the works of voice critics on the subject. It must be borne in mind that these quotations are formulations of esthetic judgments and involve the desirability of the vibrato and tremolo primarily. Occasionally we find information or observations on how the vibrato is produced and what it attempts to accomplish.

In a recent work by Lehman (7) an entire chapter is devoted to the tremolo, which includes the vibrato. An attempt is made to differentiate between the tremolo and vibrato by making the amount of injury the vocalist suffers in producing them the chief criterion.

> "Big voices produced by large, strong organs through which the breath can flow in a broad, powerful stream, are easily disposed to suffer from the tremolo, because the outflow of breath against the vocal cords occurs too immediately. The breath is sent there directly from the diaphragm instead of being driven by the abdominal pressure forward against the chest, the controlling apparatus, from whence it comes, in minimal pressure and under control, is admitted to the vocal cords. Even the strongest vocal cords cannot for any length of time stand the uncontrolled pressure of breath, that is, the direct breath pressure. One must learn to tense them by means of various muscular functions.

> "The tremolo can also be produced by the false placement of the larynx which is not always fixed close enough under the nose and chin, and being disunited with e and u by means of y it wabbles around alone.

> "Even the vibrato to which full voices are prone, should be nipped in the bud, for gradually the tremolo and later something even worse, is developed from it. Life can be infused into the tone by means of vowel mixing, a way that will do no harm.

> "Vibrato is the first stage, and tremolo the second and more hopeless, which shows itself in flat singing on the upper and middle tones of the register."

The following quotation, taken from Luisa Tetrazzini's new book, (19) reveals the distinguished singer's attitude toward the tremolo:

"I am not going to attempt a catalogue of all faults which are possible, but name just a few: faulty intonation, faulty phrasing, imperfectly attacking notes, scooping up to notes, digging or arriving at a note from a semitone beneath it, singing out of tune and the tremolo. All of these faults are unforgivable, but the last two are crimes."

Thomas Edison (4) condemns the tremolo and the vibrato, too, by accusing most singers of breaking up their tones into a series of chatterings or tremolos.

"The number of waves varies from two to twelve per second. When at the latter rate, the chatterings can just be heard and are not very objectionable. If this defect could be eliminated, nothing would exceed the beauty of the human voice, but until this is done, there will only be a few singers in a century who can emit pure notes in all registers."

In discussing the beautiful voice of Jean DeRezske, Herman Klein (3) points out the following virtues: "His high notes produced with ease and always in perfect tune are magnificent in quality and as resonant as a bell. He sings without a suspicion of the tremolo," etc.

In the last few quotations it is evident that the term tremolo is used interchangeably with the term vibrato. It is unfortunate that voice critics use the two terms synonymously.

There are other voice students who might be quoted as being opposed to the vibrato, but the impression must not be conveyed that the vibrato is tabooed by all voice authorities. The vibrato is not without champions, for many able critics consider it an indispensable part of artistic singing.

"There is a desirable vibration or pulse in every tone which gives it life. This the old Italians called the vibrato; it is quite different from the tremolo. The vibrato is the natural pulse or rhythmic vibration of the tone, and in any attempt to keep the voice steady, this must not be lost; any control which presents this natural vibrato or life-pulse from entering the tone is bad."

This writer (21) has nothing more to say on the subject of the tremolo, except that it is bad. In general, critics who favor the vibrato do so because they feel that a voice without it is "cold, dead, and expressionless."

Rush (13) shows the relationship between the interval in pitch and the emotion conveyed.

> "The presence of the tremulous voice is for the purpose of emotional expression. The tremor of the second and wider intervals, expresses states of exultation, mirth, pride, haughtiness, sneer, derision and contempt. The tremor of a semitone expresses suffering, grief, tenderness and supplication."

The vibrato, however, is not the only agency for the expression of emotion, as the following quotations disclose:

> "As a general rule, pure tone should be used but there are emotions for the expression of which pure tone seems inadequate, and often inappropriate. Those emotions are more clearly suggested, more strongly impressed on the hearer by a quality more or less breathy, because the actual experiencing of these feelings induces such a quality in speech. In many passages indicative of eagerness, surprise, apprehension, dread and terror this will be found true" (6).

Finally,

> "The majority of singers neglect the arduous training which is necessary to develop the will to express. Many pupils do everything their teachers have done, but do not feel; they copy. If they thought of that which they ought to give - if they felt it, they would awaken in themselves the desired means of expressing it, and so would rise to the demands of the author and public. Nothing will assist more the development of the power of expression than a careful study of mimicry and gesture" (20).

It is needless to say that the voice critics and students are more or less puzzled and confused in their thinking on this subject. They differ as to its desirability, nature, value, causes, and appeal. Yet the vibrato appears in the tones of trained vocalists, as this and other investigations conducted at the University of Iowa show. These researchers have thrown considerable light on the nature of the vibrato, but the subject is parctically unexplored and promises to be a most profitable field for acoustical, physiological and psychological investigation.

This investigation was originally conceived with the purpose of studying the effect of the emotions on the vibrato. Unfortunately, this objective was never realized, because the question of pitch and intensity relationship presented so many problems that required intensive study. However, positive light has been thrown upon a number of art principles and practices by this study.

Every photographic record reveals the fact that a normal tone is one in which both the pitch and intensity factors fluctuate. In trained voices the fluctuations are usually both regular and cyclic, while in untrained voices they are irregular and reveal no progressive tendency. But it must be remembered that both the trained and untrained voice fluctuates. This change in pitch and intensity is normal. No observer was able to produce a tuning-fork-like tone, rigid in pitch and intensity. Yet a few critics were quoted who insisted on steady tones. Voice critics who clamor for the steady tone should analyze the tones of their favorite vocalists with the aid of voice photography to convince themselves that virtuoso vocalists are unable to produce rigid tones.

In closing this section, reference should be made to the bitter controversy which Galli-Curci's initial appearance in London occasioned. It appears that her concert was an unqualified success financially. This was probably due to the advertising campaign which antagonized the music critics and resulted in a conflict between the principal musical magazines of London. Galli-Curci's most vicious critic was Sorabji, (18) who referred to her concert as "a sorry, sordid, and ridiculous business." One of the chief faults which he points out is her vibrato, of which he speaks satirically:

> "--steadiness of tone, one of the most elementary requisites without which good singing does not even begin to exist, and as though one would have to listen to Calli-Curci to hear steadiness of tone. As who should say, 'Listen to Cortot when he plays a five-finger exercise, and see how he plays all the right notes.'"

This criticism was answered in the Musical Times (11). The writer, whose name is not revealed, comments on the artist's singing and commends her for the beauty of her "steady, clean vocal tone." Both critics heard the same voice and, yet, are unable to ascertain whether the vibrato was employed; and whether the effect was good or bad because of omission or commission. This episode shows something of the status of the vibrato and also that of musical criticism.

Turning next to the factor of intensity, we observe that this element has been ignored generally; yet it plays a coordinate part with pitch in making for beauty in singing. If a tone lacks flexibility in intensity, it is deficient in beauty. Just what can be done, in training an individual in intensity control, is a problem which has received little or no attention. Yet voice production involves more than pitch control alone.

In conclusion, it is fair to say that the art of singing is as yet based on no science of singing. The factors that constitute a tone are not clearly understood by critic or teacher. At the present time, voice teachers ignore the basic elements of time and intensity, in their desire to teach the skill required for the control of pitch. Scientific studies of the voice must be encouraged in order to reveal the true nature of the voice to the voice teacher and critic. Unfortunately, the voice teacher is unable to do this for himself, since it requires special equipment and training. Yet the voice teacher is dependent upon this information, for without it he cannot teach voice production.

SUMMARY

1. The vibrato is a periodic phenomenon of three variables; namely, pitch, time, and intensity.
2. The vibrato is produced primarily by trained vocalists, although it is found in the tones of untrained singers; the rate of occurrence being 93 per cent and 27 per cent for trained and untrained, respectively.
3. Placement affects the extent of pitch and intensity fluctuations; the nasal resulting in the smallest and throaty production the largest for both factors.
4. Vowel quality reveals only slight influence on the vibrato.
5. Low tones show a relatively smaller amplitude and a faster rate of pulsation.
6. The vibrato may be increased or diminished by voluntary effort, but it cannot be inhibited or eliminated entirely.
7. Children's voices compare favorably with adult voices in respect to intensity fluctuations, but are relatively more rigid in regard to pitch fluctuations.

BIBLIOGRAPHY

* Grateful acknowledgment is hereby made to Dean Carl E. Seashore, who directed this study. I wish to express my apreciation, also, to faculty and students of the Music School and Model School, who contributed the tones which constitute the subject matter of this thesis.

1. BROWNE and BEHNKE. Voice, Song and Speech. Putnam, 1883.

2. COOKE, J.F. Great Singers on the Art of Singing. Presser, 1921.

3. DeREZSKÉ, JEAN. Musical Times, May, 1925. Novello & Co., London.

4. EDISON, THOMAS. American Magazine, March, 1921.

5. FILLEBROWN, THOMAS. Resonance in Singing and Speaking. Boston: Ditson, 1911.

6. KIRKLAND, H.S. Expression in Singing. Boston: Badger, 1916.

7. LEHMAN, LILLI. How to Sing. New York: Macmillan, 1924.

8. MILES, W. R. Accuracy of the Voice in Simple Pitch Singing. Univ. of Iowa Stud. in Psychol., 1914, VI, pp. 13-66.

9. MILLER, DAYTON C. The Science of Musical Sounds. New York: Macmillan, 1916.

10. MACKEY, F.S. Natural Method of Voice Production. New York: Scribner & Co.

11. Musical Times. January 1, 1925, Novello & Co., London.

12. OGDEN, R.M. Hearing. Harcourt, Brace and Co., 1924.

13. RUSH, JANE. The Human Voice. Library Co., Phila., 1900.

14. SEASHORE, CARL E. The Psychology of Musical Talent. New York: Silver, Burdett & Company, 1919.

15. SEASHORE, CARL E. The Tonoscope. Univ. of Iowa Stud. in Psychol., 1914, VI, pp. 1-12.

16. SCHOEN, MAX. Pitch Factors in Artistic Singing. Univ. of Iowa Stud. in Psychol., VIII, pp. 230-259.

17. SIMON, CLARENCE. The Variability of Consecutive Wave Lengths in Vocal and Instrumental Sounds. (In this volume.)

18. SORABJI. Music News and Herald. January 10, 1925.

19.   TETRAZZINI, LUISA. How to Sing. Doran Co., 1923.

20.   WRONSKI, THADDEUS. The Singer and His Art. New York: D. Appleton and Company, 1921.

21.   ZAY, HENRY. Practical Psychology of Voice and Life. Schirmer, 1917.

The Vibrato
in Indian Music

Studies in Indian Musical Scales - II: Gamakas

B. C. Deva

Sir Cusrow Wadia Institute of Technology, Poona, India

Summary

In actual music, the frequency and amplitude of tones are never perfectly steady. The tone is always varying its frequency round a mean value; this mean value may be taken to be the scale value of the tone. The variations from the mean, when they are regular, are generally known as "vibrato". The most crucial and significant point about the vibrato is that it is not perceived consciously.

The present experiment was performed with the view to determine the nature and extent of the vibrato in the gamakas of Indian music. From the preliminary finding of this pilot experiment the very interesting result issued: there is no vibrato in Indian music. Detailed discussion is given to the effect that the lack of vibrato in Indian music may be due to the finer pitch requirements in that music; hence gamakas bear the burden of the unconscious forces and the vibrato is ruled out as unpleasant. It is possible, however, that the gamaka called kampan may be a vibrato.

1. INTRODUCTION

In the study of music in general and musical scales in particular it has been usual to assume a spurious constancy of tones and tonal relations. For instance, in physical acoustics the musical intervals are measured with reference to notes which are assumed to have definite frequencies. In physiological and psychological acoustics a similar definiteness is assumed in the terms pitch and mel.

The word "assumed" has been employed advisedly, for there is no warrant for such definiteness either from theoretical or experimental considerations. This assumption, though very convenient, is really based on the sense of sound constancy which the mind of man creates for the purposes of vocal communications - either in speech or in music.

Actually all the vibrations and modulations thereon within the limits of audibility (which again is a variable factor) must potentially be capable of being used in acoustic communication. Obviously the sound elements here are almost infinite. This is recognized in Indian music by saying that srutis (microtonal intervals) are infinite. Out of this infinite matrix of sound the limits of man's body and mind impose a choice; for without such choice communication would be an unmanageable confusion.

The chosen tones and tonal relations are clothed with a reality and constancy; for without such constancy, they cannot be "repeated" and therefore cannot be used for any ordering of elements in a system of communication. But always the unchosen sounds are there, lending a halo to the central communicative elements.

In speech such sound constancies are termed "phonemes", "allophones" and "tonemes". In music they have been called notes and scales and chords and many other names. If we examine this question of the constancy of sounds - or for that matter any perceptual constancy - it is not difficult to see that this constancy is spurious. A. Ehrenzweig has discussed this in great detail (4): here it is sufficient to point out the fact that in between the definite tones of speech and music there are many sounds of "unperceivable" fluidity which escape conscious notice. But these sounds lend a sense of richness and naturalness; without them verbal and musical sounds would lose their plasticity. The musical "reality" and "constancy" is then definitely not the reality of the physicist.

We have, then, to think of two modes of (are there more?) tonal perception on which to base our concepts of musical scales and other musical constancies.

First, the conscious, central constancies which are called the tones of music; it is from these that the various musical scales of the world are usually defined and measured. These are but the average values - the nuclei - of the sounds produced in music.

W. James has called the two modes of perception as substantive and transitive (the central and peripheral) (5).

The constancy of the musical tones as constructed by central perception has been considered a sufficient index of musical creation. The peripheral tones - which have always existed in music - had been neglected as accidental and unimportant. These accidentals - the graces - indeed give "life" to music. As a matter of fact, these "unformed" tonal cadences are the original matrix out of which definite musical constancies are bone (6). The researches of C. Seashore, to a large extent, brought out the prominence and significance of the accidental graces in Western music. His study of the vibrato in its ramifying aspects has been revolutionary (7).

The most remarkable result of these investigations was to show that much of the "beauty" in music lies to a large extent in the peripheral, consciously unperceived tonal elements. The vibrato is, according to him, a criterion of good artistic quality. It is found to a more or less extent in all kinds of music; it is also present in emotional speech.

The purpose of the present work was to investigate into the nature of such peripheral, infra-conscious processes in Indian music. These ornaments to "definite" tones are generally grouped under the title Gamaka. Gamaka is a variation of the mean tones of music for purposes of greater beauty and appeal; it comprises glides, trills, swings, glissandos, accidentals. The most widely accepted definition of the gamaka is:

> "When, in music, a tone moves from its own pitch towards another so that the second sound passes like a shadow over it, this is called a gamaka" (3).

The gamakas or graces have been described in great detail by Indian musicologists. The details of this are not of relevance in the present context. But what is of utmost importance is the fact that these graces are mostly infraconscious form principles. The conscious constancies and symbols which find expression in "definite" tones of music cannot fully convey the phantasmogoric imagery of the mind. These drives need transitive elements that have a dream-like orderlessness: for, like dreams they are channels for infraconscious drives which would otherwise be censored.

In Indian music gamakas are not all infraconscious elements. For in some Ragas[1], these form essential definitive elements of the ragas and hence are consciously sung.   But where they are not definitive, gamakas are sung as adventitious tones that carry the infraconscious emotions.

Further, the study of gamakas would lead us to a better understanding of Indian musical scales. The music of India insists so much on hair-splitting pitch differences; these can be properly defined only if the limits of tonal movements in gamakas are fully known.

2. EXPERIMENT

The first and most important condition for obtaining measureable data is that the tones whose values are to be determined should be extracted from their context. They should not be sung in isolation, independently of the rest of the music. To obtain such a condition, the musicians were required to sing a raga for about two minutes. This was first recorded on a high quality tape recorder[2].

The most serious difficulty in the experiment is this stage. For no Indian musician today will ever agree to sing withou a Tambura (1). This constant drone is an indispensable accompaniment in Indian music. However, the presence of the tones of the tambura in the records will make the further pitch analysis impossible. The hitch, hence, is that the musician must have the tambura for correct intonation; but the methods of analysis prohibit the use of such a drone. This difficulty was got over by first recording the sound of the tambura on a separate tape recorder and feeding the sound of this to the ear of the musician by means of headphones. By this expedient the musician got his drone which, however, was not recorded along with the music.

The ragas so recorded were then fed to a doublebeam cathode ray oscilloscope[3]. Either before or after recording the signal on the oscilloscope film, a tuning fork oscillator of 1000 c/s was run for a short time. This gave the average measure of the film speed, knowing which measurements of time and pitch could be made (Fig. 1).

The pitch of the tones was determined as follows: The oscillograms obtained were sampled at an average of 0.1 s. At every 0.1 s the length of film for one period of the wave was measured by means of a travelling microscope (least count 0.001 cm). Knowing the average speed of the film and the length of a period, it is easy to compute the pitch of this period of tone. (Such measurements are facilitated by the construction of a calibration graph of film length against reciprocal of pitch.)

In this preliminary study only a small duration of the music was examined - about 5 s. Tables I and II give the data from the measurements. Melody plots a and b are drawn from these (Fig. 2). The material presented therein obviously consists of the physical characteristics of the tone. They do not tell us any thing about the perceptual nature of these tones.

One raga from each of the two systems of music (North and South Indian) have been chosen. South Indian raga "Sankarabharanam" has approximately the Western just major scale (heptatonic). The North Indian raga "Bhoop" is a pentatonic mode with all just major tones except the fourth and the seventh (Fa and Si omitted). The samples examined here were both sung by well-trained singers. They possessed good voice quality according to Indian standards. These facts are mentioned here to make the following observations more significant.

Even a cursory glance at the melody plots of Indian music glaringly reveals the absence of vibrato. It is true that there are microvariations in all the tones sung by both singers. But nowhere do we find the regularity of the vibrato as in Western music. For the sake of comparison, a sample of Western music as analysed by H. Seashore is also given alongside (Fig. 3). The difference between Western and Indian music (both of good quality) is unequivocally apparent.

In the "Sankarabharanam" plot the following are observable: The tone is more steady and flat than in the "Bhoop" plot. There are two sudden dips at about 2.5 s. These are tones which touch Ga (Mi) from Ma and Pa (Fa and Sol) perceptually; there is also a swing of the voice. This kind of grace (gamaka) is called the swing (andolana). This is much slower than the vibrato and consciously clearly perceptible. The difficulty in the acoustic study of grace in this particular case is that the musician introduces glottal catches to a large extent which are characteristics of South Indian technique. This make pitch analysis difficult and the assigned pitch is not definite. These indefinite parts are shown by dotted lines in the plot.

In the "Bhoop" plot, the tones reveal slightly greater modulation. The voice is less steady than in the previous case. There are fairly regular ups and downs; but these exhibit nowhere the regularity of the vibrato.

3. DISCUSSION

From the description of the vibrato by C. Seashore, the following may be abstracted (7).

1. Vibrato is a periodic pulsation (about 6 per sec.) of the fundamental of a musical or speech tone. There are analogous modulations of intensity and formant.

2. It is not easily perceived. It may be made bold and perceivable, if the music is slowed. This shows that though vibrato is not centrally perceived, it is not too unconscious to be completely unperceived. It may be said to be a preconscious musical element.

3. It is present in all types of music: vocal, instrumental, adult, child, folk.

4. It is also present, though less than in music, in emotional speech.

5. It appears that even apparent grades in artistic quality do not influence the presence or otherwise of vibrato.

The most important and significant point about the vibrato is that it is not a fully conscious (articulate) tonal reality. On the other hand, it is a semi-conscious (inarticulate) tonal ornament. Secondly, Seashore has found it to be present in all forms of music he has examined.

When we observe the results of the present investigation, it is very clear that a similar tonal modulation is not present in Indian music. As a matter of fact, Seashore's statement that it is not easily perceived misled the present writer: for it was implicitly assumed that Seashore's inferences were universal. Hence, the first idea about vibrato in Indian music was that it was present but could not be observed, it being not conscious. A very careful auditory comparison was made of the singers of the West and Indian, even by slowing down the gramophone (following Seashore's recommendation). Whereas the pulsating tone was very clear in Western music (even without any special effort), the tone of the Indian singers was extremely flat; no amount of effort could reveal the presence of the vibrato. Acoustic measurements, as reported here, amply confirm this auditory analysis.

The important inference from such an experiment is that the <u>unconscious</u> <u>form</u> <u>principles</u> are essentially different in different kinds of music. However, it is to be noted that the vibrato itself is present in Indian music as a conscious form element in the grace called the <u>kampana</u> (Shake). This is a consciously used embellishment akin to the vibrato, trill and tremolo. There is another grace called the <u>andolana</u> (swing) which is much slower. (The acoustic details of such graces in Indian music will be reported in a forthcoming paper.) What is essential to realise here is that the vibrato is employed <u>consciously</u> and <u>infrequently</u> in Indian music; a voice or any instrument that employs the vibrato frequently is not appreciated and is called "cheap". It is used sparingly, when it partly may be an unconscious form principle, in chamber music. But in the "lighter" music of the films and "ham" singers vibrato is common.

It is quite possible, however, that a finer analysis - a period by period analysis of the acoustic stream - may reveal hidden patterns. A very similar fact was found in an Indian language, by the present writer. It was found that in speech (at least in the particular language studied), a period by period variation in pitch exists, which has a high correlation with emotion (2). It may not be a surprise that the unconscious form principles in Indian music are finer acoustical material (in pitch) than in Western music. The reason for such a difference may be sought in the sound material of various kinds of music. In modern Western music it is harmony and tone colour (which depends on the timbre) that is the articulate form; pitch variations are secondary. Hence, unconscious forms find their way into pitch characteristics where discrimination is not stringent. In Indian music, pitch discrimination is very fine (differences of a "hair-breadth" as it is called); under such circumstances pitch variations like the vibrato are too gross. They are conscious. Unconscious forms must be searched for in even finer pitch variations, in intensity and tone colour. It is very significant that in Indian music, intensity and quality of sound play a very small part in conscious expression. They do not have the importance as in Western music. This is a problem in the listening habits and auditory conditioning which deserves deeper study.

Table I

Artist: Kalyanakrishna Bhagavatar,
   Raga "Sankarabharanam"
Unless otherwise mentioned each pitch
has been measured at an average interval of 0.1 s.

No.	Pitch in c/s	Remarks:	No.	Pitch in c/s	Remarks:
1*	98.04	*At 0.02 s from	27	---	Irregular
2	181.8	the beginning.	28*	181.8	*At 0.04 s from last.
3	181.8		29	70.92	Measurements con-
4	192.3		30	156.2	tinue at 0.1s.
5	192.3		31	153.8	
6	188.7		32	158.7	
7	181.8		33	163.9	
8	188.7		34	153.8	
9	188.7		35	158.7	
10	192.3		36	163.9	
11	185.4		37	178.6	
12	204.1		38	192.3	
13	232.6		39	188.7	
14	196.1		40*	208.3	*At 0.27 s from last.
15	181.8		41	---	
16	204.1		42	---	
17	192.3		43	---	
18	188.7		44	185.2	
19	196.1		45	192.3	
20	188.7		46	192.3	
21	192.3		47	175.4	
22	188.7		48	217.4	
23	188.7		49	188.7	
24	175.4		50	172.4	
25	46.73		51	181.8	
26	200.0		52	0	

Note: Total time of music is 5.23 s. At
   At some intervals the wave is so
   irregular that no measurement
   was possible. Most probably these
   are consonatal regions or glottal
   release.

Table II

Artist: B.C. Wadikar, Raga "Bhoop"

No.	Pitch in c/s	Remarks:	No.	Pitch in c/s	Remarks:
1	168.1		23	212.8	
2	178.6		24	208.3	
3	173.0		25	215.1	
4	192.3		26	222.2	
5	172.4		27	206.2*	*Irregular.
6	180.2		28	202.0**	**Breath?
7	200.0		29	206.2	
8	181.8		30	183.8	
9	183.8		31	190.5	
10	178.6		32	188.7	
11	192.3		33	185.2	
12	192.3		34	178.6	
13	175.4		35	188.7	
14	163.9		36	192.3	
15	156.2		37	180.2	
16	188.8		38	185.2	
17	208.3		39	190.5	
18	215.1		40	180.2	
19	217.4		41	188.8	
20	232.6		42	161.3	
21	227.3		43	156.2	
22	235.3				

Note: Total time of music is 4.4 s. Sampling at 0.1 s.

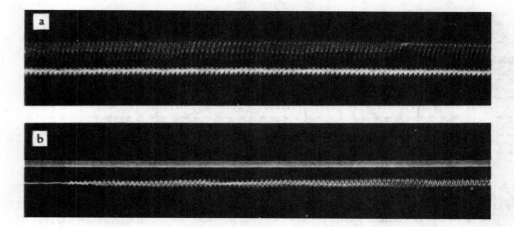

Figure 1. Sample oscillograms of the two ragas. (a) Raga "Bhoop" (upper track), (b) Raga "Sankarabharanam" (lower track). (The upper track in (b) is that of 1000-c/s oscillator used as a time base.)

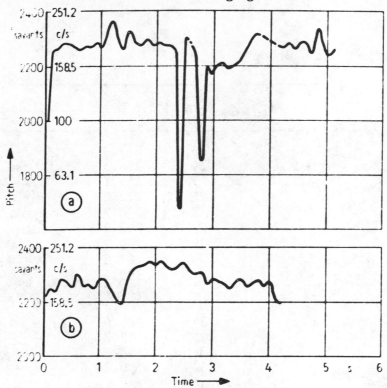

Figure 2. Melody plots of two ragas. The ordinate measures pitch or, more strictly, frequency on a logarithmic scale of savarts. Frequency in c/s is also given. Note the lack of vibrato in both cases.
(a) Raga "Sankarabharanam",
(b) Raga "Bhoop".

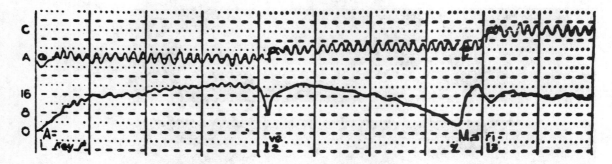

Figure 3. The Bach-Gounod "Ave Maria" as sung by H. Stark (first few bars). "Frequency (pitch) is represented by a graph for each note on a semitone staff; intensity, by the lower parallel graph in decibel scale; and duration by dots in tenths of a second. Measures are numbered at the bottom of the staff for ready reference." (From H. G. Seashore, An objective analysis of artistic singing. State University of Iowa Studies in the Psychology of Music, Vol. 4 (1936). Reproduced with kind permission of the author and the State University of Iowa.)

REFERENCES

1. <u>Raga</u> is a melodic pattern or schema. The musician singing or playing a raga does not sing a set piece or composition. He does not interpret. On the other hand, he has to create and improvise on a melodic scheme on the spot. Apart from certain traditional (sometimes parochial) rules the musician is free to create as he chooses. The virtuoso approach predominates. Some of the guiding rules are given below:

- A raga has a definite musical scale - naturals, flats and sharps.

- A raga usually has not more than 9 and not less than 5 notes.

- A raga has a prescribed form of ascent and descent.

- A raga has certain characteristic tonal combinations which have to be sung or played. Certain tones must lend emphasis.

- A raga should never omit the tonic - Sa (Do).

- A raga should have at least one of the following notes Ma (Fa), ma (Fa-Sharp), Pa (Sol).

   Apart from these major conditions each raga may have its minor characteristics which are definitive of the raga. With these arbitrarily accepted rules the musician is free to create and improvise.

2. Concertone and Ampex 600.

3. Cossor 1049.

BIBLIOGRAPHY

(1)   Deva, B. C., Tonal structure of Tambura. J. Mus. Acad., Madras 27 (1956/57), 89-112. Tambura is a four-stringed instrument used as a drone.

(2)   Deva, B. C., Psychophysics of speech-melody in Dravidian. Dissertation, Poona 1957. Summary of the experimental portions of this dissertation is being published in the Zeitschrift fur Phonetik.

(3)   Danielou, A., Northern Indian Music, Vol. I, p. 104 Christopher Johnson, London, and Visva Bharati, Calcutta 1949. He gives a good list of Indian gamakas. The present definition is adapted from his translation of the relevant verses from Sangita Samayasara a Samskrit text of the 13th century, a. D.

(4)   Ehrenzweig, A., The psycho-analysis of artistic vision and hearing. Chapter V. Routledge & Kegan Paul, London 1953.

(5)   James, W., Psychology, pp. 160-175. Abridged Edition. The Living Library, The World Publ. Co., New York 1948.

(6)   Sankaran, C. R. and Deva, B. C., Studies in Indian musical scales I: A Vedic Chant. Bull. Decca College, Poona 18 (1957), 192-204.

(7)   Seashore, C., Psychology of music, Chapter I, McGraw-Hill Book Co., New York 1938.

The Phenomenon
of Vocal Vibrato

Robert M. Mason and Willard R. Zemlin

The phenomenon of vocal vibrato may be regarded as an acoustic representation of one of the most rapid and continuous changes in pitch and intensity that the human mechanism is capable of producing. When considering the vibrato phenomenon on the pitch and intensity change continuum, the rapidity of change in these vocal parameters would place it at one end of the continuum. In that the changes in pitch and intensity occur so rapidly, one might expect vibrato to be a vocal variable employed effectively by few trained singers. The presence of vibrato, however, in the singing tones of trained singers and other subjects has been demonstrated in about 95% of their tones.[1,2] Many singers report that they find it difficult to produce one song, or indeed, even an isolated tone without the use of vibrato.[3] Vibrato is perceived as a fusion of the varied pitches and intensities employed, which in part explains why so many singers can use vibrato effectively to the enrichment of their voices.

There is a considerable literature pertaining to vocal vibrato. A majority of studies deal with the quantification of various acoustic properties of vibrato.[4,5,6] Although most teachers of singing have considerable information relating to the perceived result of vocal vibrato, there remains a dearth of knowledge regardinng vibrato physiology. To date, there are few systematic descriptions of the physiology of various structures during production of vocal vibrato. A description of vibrato physiology, in addition to localizing some of the mechanisms relating to the vibrato phenomenon, might also add to the knowledge of pitch and intensity change in voice production.

PURPOSE

The present study was designed to describe activity in the larynx and some adjacent structures concurrent with vocal vibrato production. For the purposes of this investigation, vocal vibrato was defined as a periodic modulation involving rapid changes in pitch or intensity, or combinations of them in time. The pitch modulations, the dominant feature of vibrato, average around six per second with an acceptable range of from four to eleven per second.[3]

REVIEW OF LITERATURE

The review of literature will involve two areas of interest. These are studies of the physiological nature of vocal vibrato, and methods employed to study the pitch and intensity mechanisms.

THE PHYSIOLOGICAL NATURE OF VOCAL VIBRATO

A few studies have been reported in the literature which relate to the physiological nature of vocal vibrato. In 1932, Metfessel[5] viewed the larynges of 14 subjects via a laryngoscope during their vibrato productions. On the basis of data obtained, using palpation and indirect laryngoscopy, he contended that muscle synergism in the "supralaryngeal" area could account for a frequency fluctuation in the vocal folds. In addition to oscillations observed at the level of the larynx, he also reported undulating activity on the posterior pharyngeal wall, the diaphragm, and posterior tongue.[5]

Among other studies referring to the physiological nature of vibrato, there is apparently a small consensus supporting a neurochronaxic origin for vibrato production. Schoen,[7] in one of the first investigations of the vibrato phenomenon, theorized that vibrato pitch fluctuations culminate from a tremor of the laryngeal suspensory muscle system. Schoen correlated the intensity variations in vibrato with changes in the configuration of the base of the tongue.

Stetson[8] found oscillations in the rib-cage musculature during singing which he correlated with the rate of vibrato. He speculated that the pitch changes in vibrato might occur as a function of air-pressure variations beneath the vocal folds resulting from tremors that originate in the rib-cage musculature.

Westerman[9] studied the acoustics of vibrato and made correlations between the basic rate of repetition of nerve impulses and the number of pitch and intensity fluctuations per second. His correlations, like those of Schoen and Stetson, were not based solely on information obtained from measurements during vibrato productions, but rather, from other previously established information such as the rate of repetition of nerve impulses. Subsequent studies of the pitch and intensity mechanisms have offered little support for these theoretical contentions.

The physiological nature of vocal vibrato remains somewhat unexplored. As yet, there seem to be few detailed descriptions of the mechanisms responsible for fibrato production.

METHODS TO STUDY PITCH AND INTENSITY CHANGE

Contributions to the documentation of the pitch and intensity regulatory mechanisms have been derived from a variety of sources and methods.

Many investigators have employed animal or human larynges to vary systematically specific vocal parameters.[10,11,12,13] The use of excised larynges have enabled experimenters to photograph vocal fold activity while such factors as type and consistency of air current, and vocal fold mass, elasticity, and tension are controlled. Much information pertaining to pitch and intensity regulation has been accumulated through such experimentation. Further, such study has provided additional credence for a theory of voice production.[14]

Human cadavers have been used experimentally in conjunction with clamps, needles, and other devices designed to stimulate, modify, and record changes which occur in the larynx as a result of specified performances.[15] Live human subjects have been studied during surgery, while under local anesthesia.[16] In these instances, electrodes were placed in some adjacent laryngeal structures and the effects of various stimulations on phonation were recorded. Such experiments were reviewed and analyzed in William Vennard's excellent paper.[17]

Electromyography (EMG) with needle electrodes has been accomplished with electrode placement sites in the larynx and surrounding structures.[18,19,20] Although insertion of a needle electrode into the vocal fold would apparently be quite distressing to the subject, with the possibility of tissue damage during phonation, some subjects apparently are able to tolerate this experimental approach.[21] Surface electrodes have also been employed successfully in studying some of the components of the breathing musculature as they relate to vocal attack.[22] The EMG technique utilizing surface electrodes has shown to be reliable.

High speed motion picture photography of the larynx has been a technique frequently used for studying laryngeal behavior during pitch and intensity variation.[23,24,25,26,27] This technique provides essentially a two-dimensional superior view of the vocal folds. The experimenter is thereby able to observe in slow motion many of the discrete changes in phasing, length, and vibratory sequences of vocal fold activity. Filming speeds of 4000 frames per second or greater have provided a sufficient number of frames per vocal fold vibration cycles for detailed analysis. Many of the current assumptions regarding laryngeal physiology during pitch and intensity changes were formulated on the basis of studies using high speed laryngeal photography.

The x-ray has been used to study laryngeal behavior in live subjects during phonation at varying pitches and intensities.[28,29,30,31] Frontal tomographs of the larynx have provided data plotting movements of the larynx during pitch changes. Variations in the thickness of the vocal folds are amenable to observation by frontal tomography. A relatively new technique, stroboscopic laminagraphy (STROL), provides a frontal laminagraphic view of the larynx in conjunction with cineradiography.[32] This technique, not readily available in commercial form as yet, enables the experimenter to plot more accurately the changes in mass that occur during pitch and intensity change.

This review of some of the methods used to study pitch and intensity change has demonstrated that a variety of techniques have been utilized in documenting the mechanisms relating to pitch and intensity. Many of these techniques would also seem suited for studying the physiology of vocal vibrato.

METHOD RATIONALE

Upon review of previous studies conducted on the physiological nature of vibrato and of methods applicable to the study of pitch and intensity change, it becomes apparent that in order to describe the physiology of vibrato, it would be well to study normal muscle behavior in normal human subjects producing vibrato. Specifically, we were interested in studying vibrato acoustics as well as internal laryngeal activity and the activity in the laryngeal tensor system, the laryngeal elevator system, the laryngeal depressor system, and the breathing musculature. Within the framework of the instrumentation available to us, it was decided that the simultaneous use of acoustic analysis, surface electromyography, and high speed laryngeal photography would best achieve these purposes. Acoustic analysis via high quality tape recording places no restrictions on the movements of the singer. Surface electromyography does not interfere significantly with muscle movements, and yet provides recordings of the action potentials generated by given muscles. High speed laryngeal photography, although requiring a selected posture for adequate viewing of the vocal folds, presumably does not appear to restrict appreciably the acoustic end product of phonation. The use of these techniques should provide data which can relate and compare several parameters simultaneously.

METHOD

SUBJECTS

One male and 3 female subjects, ranging in age from 20 to 24 years, were selected for study. These college students were chosen on the basis of ability to tolerate placement of a laryngeal mirror, ability to produce an acceptable vibrato having between 4 and 11 pitch modulations per second, and ability to produce vibrato while in the selected experimental positions. Two of the subjects who met these criteria were voice students (trained singers) while the two remaining subjects were highly trained for laryngeal photography (highly trained subjects). The subjects' task was to produce vocal vibrato while selected measurements were made.

APPARATUS FOR DATA GATHERING

Instrumentation employed for purposes of acoustic data gathering included a Wollensak stereo model T-1616 tape recorder and a ceramic microphone. The acoustic signals were recorded on mylar magnetic tape.

The apparatus used for indirect photography of the larynx included a Western Electric Fastax Camera, model W-163269, and a model J-410 Fastax timing device. The timing circuitry and voltage regulation enabled the camera to attain a maximum speed of 4000 frames per second. In order to eliminate most of the camera noise from the acoustic recordings, made concurrent with laryngeal photography, a booth measuring 5½ x 4½ by 8 feet enclosed the high speed camera, timing circuitry, and experimenter. Figure 1 shows a diagram of the apparatus for high speed laryngeal photography.

A four channel electromyograph designed for use with saline bridge electrodes was used to record the action potentials of four muscle groups during vibrato. The apparatus consisted of a regulated power supply and four differential preamplifiers; each producing a voltage gain of about 60 dB., with a frequency response from 8 to 3000 cps. Brass surface electrodes were used in the experiment. The muscle action potentials generated during vibrato were transferred from the EMG unit to four Wollensak stereo tape recorders, one for each of the four channels of the electromyograph. Figure 2 shows a subject during an experimental trial with some surface electrodes in place. The acoustic, laryngeal, and electromyographic recordings were synchronized by manually inserting clicks onto the taped recordings during the trials. The click source was the discharge of a 40 mfd. capacitor, which was switched by means of a circuit breaker. In those conditions in which high speed laryngeal photography was done simultaneously with the acoustic and EMG recordings, the camera circuitry impressed a click on the tapes one second prior to firing the camera. Additional clicks were generated at the instant the camera turned on and off.

All of the tape recorders used in the experiment were checked stroboscopically and it was determined that there was less than 1/10 of 1 percent time error among the recorders when checked over several one minute samples. It was therefore decided that the various recordings, made simultaneously, could be compared with reasonable accuracy.

APPARATUS FOR DATA ANALYSIS

Apparatus employed for data analysis included tape recorders, a Presto disc recording lathe, an electro-photophoneloscope, a Kay Sonograph, A General Radio direct current amplifier, an Esterline-Angus graphic recorder, a motion picture projector, and a compensating polar planimeter.

The tape recordings of the vocal samples were transferred to acetate phonograph discs made at 78 r.p.m. These phonograph records were used in the production of electro-photophonelograms. The electro-photophoneloscope, shown

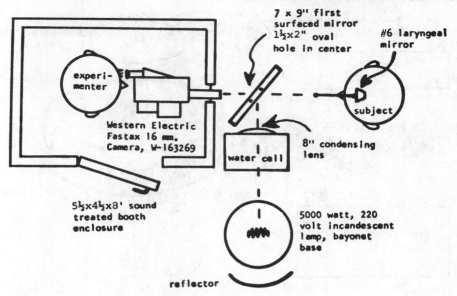

Figure 1.
Diagram of apparatus used for high speed motion picture photography of the larynx.

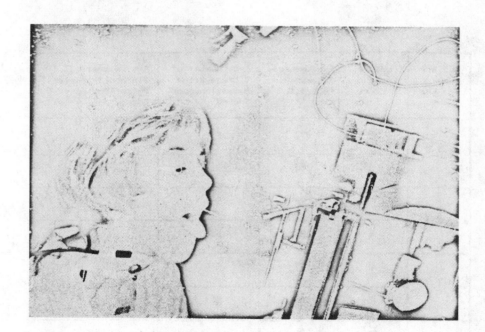

Figure 2.
Subject in position for experimental trial involving simultaneous acoustic, laryngeal, and EMG recordings during vibrato production.

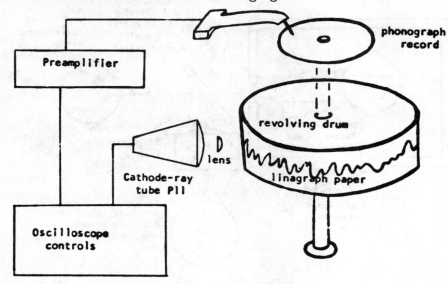

Figure 3.
Sketch of the electro-photophoneloscope, used to determine fundamental frequency of phonation and the number of pitch and intensity modulations per second.

Subject Number and Sex	Posture P=photo E=erect	Fundamental Frequency in c.p.s.	Ave. Number of Vibrato Pitch Pulsations per Second	Ave. Number of Vibrato Intensity Pulsations per Second
I ♀	P	497	5	5
	E	280	5	5
II ♀	P	290	5	5
	E	290	5	5
III ♂	P	178	5	5
	E	148	5	5
IV ♀	P	185	5	5
	E	357	5 1/2	5 1/2
IV ♀	P with tongue in	240	5	5

Table 1.
Summary of various acoustic measures on four subjects during production of vocal vibrato.

in Figure 3, is a modification of earlier models of the photophoneloscope and utilizes a cathode-ray tube in place of the more conventional galvanometers. The cathode-ray tube operates as an optical level and transducer, changing electrical current into a beam of light. The beam is focused on a piece of moving film. The cathode-ray tube modification eliminates the mechanical problems inherent in earlier models of the photophoneloscope.

Recorded vocal samples were played into a spectrograph equipped with an amplitude display accessory. It was thereby possible to display simultaneously the relationships between frequency and amplitude of the vibrato samples.

The original EMG recordings were slowed down by a factor of four by re-recording so that when they were converted into graphical form, they could be followed accurately by the pen stylus of the graphic recorder. A General Radio d-c amplifier and Esterline-Angus graphic recorder were used for the graphic conversion of the taped recordings of EMG activity.

High speed photographic films of the larynx were traced frame-by-frame. A Kodak Industrialist projector, model SFDR, was used for frame-by-frame advance of the film. Measurements of total glottal area in square millimeters were made possible with the use of a Keuffel and Esser compensating polar planimeter. Other laryngeal measures made from the films included inter-ventricular fold distance in millimeters, distance between the epiglottis and upper margin of each frame, and interarytenoid distance.

PROCEDURE. Each subject sustained an (a) vowel using vibrato during four experimental conditions. For Conditions I and II, each subject produced vibrato while in the usual posture for high speed photography with tongue protruded, neck hyperextended, and back at a 15 degree angle from a vertical position. Acoustic, laryngeal, and EMG recordings were made while the subject was in the position for laryngeal photography. EMG surface electrodes were placed over the areas of the cricothyroid, mylohyoid, 8th intercostal space, and sternothyroid muscles. These electrode placements were presumed to sample the laryngeal tensor system, the laryngeal elevator system, the breathing musculature, and laryngeal depressor system. In Conditions I and II, high speed photography was synchronized with the acoustic and EMG recordings.

For Conditions III and IV, each subject produced vibrato while sitting erect. In this posture, acoustic and EMG recordings were made. The EMG surface electrode placements were the same as in Conditions I and II.

Each subject was tested individually. He was free to choose his own comfortable pitch and intensity levels during vibrato productions so that these acoustic properties were not restricted by the experimental setting. Two postural positions (in position for photography and sitting erect) were studied in order to determine whether acoustic and muscle behavior during vibrato were altered by postural change.

DATA. The data gathered and analyzed included: tape recordings and disc phonograph recordings of vocal vibrato; electro-photophonelographic representations of frequency and intensity factors of the vocal samples; sonographic displays of frequency and amplitude relationships; graphic records of muscle activity; and high speed photographic records of laryngeal behavior. One condition from each postural situation was used in the analysis of data for each subject. The replication of each experimental condition served to establish the reliability of the data used in analysis.

RESULTS

ACOUSTIC RECORDINGS

Electro-photophonelograms made on linagraph paper were employed in determining the subjects' fundamental frequencies by counting the number of cycles in a one second sample of electro-photophonelograms. The fundamental frequencies of the subjects, shown in column 3 of Table 1, ranged from 148 to 497 cps. Because the subjects were free to choose a most comfortable phonatory level for each condition, the fundamental frequencies differed from trial to trial. There was less difference in the pitch levels used for the two trained singers (subjects II and III) than for the two highly trained subjects. Changes in fundamental frequency from trial to trial had no appreciable effect on the number of pitch and intensity fluctuations produced per second (columns 4 and 5 of Table 1). One subject (subject IV) showed an increase in the number of pitch and intensity fluctuations per second as fundamental frequency was increased. The other trials for this subject did not suggest that this was a typical pattern, however.

The number of pitch and intensity fluctuations per second were derived empirically by counting from electro-photophonelograms. In addition, a Kay Sonograph with an amplitude display accessory provided measures of amplitude fluctuations. Sonograms were also used to determine any synchrony between the fluctuations in pitch and intensity.

Pitch and intensity fluctuations per second for the group ranged from 5 to 5½ and averaged 5 per second. Sonographic analysis showed that the fluctuations of pitch and intensity were synchronous, or in phase, for each subject. Columns 4 and 5 of Table 1 show the performance averages for each subject with respect to pitch and intensity fluctuations per second during vibrato production.

The pitch fluctuations had an average extent of about one musical semi-tone, ranging from one semi-tone to almost one musical tone. The amplitude fluctuations had an average extent of 2 decibel, ranging from 1 decibel to 5 dB. These findings are within the range of acceptability for vibrato production as determined by Seashore.[3]

The extent of the pitch and intensity fluctuations during vibrato production varied somewhat as a function of posture. Subjects II, III, and IV exhibited a greater extent of pitch and intensity fluctuations in the erect sitting posture than in the posture for laryngeal photography. Sonographic analysis showed these differences to be a fraction of a musical tone in pitch and from 1 to 5 dB in intensity. Subject IV, highly trained for purposes of laryngeal photography, was able to produce vibrato while in position for laryngeal photography with her tongue either protruded or "normal." During laryngeal photography with tongue protruded or normal, the pitch and intensity extents were similar; both conditions having lesser extents than for sitting erect.

Irrespective of the amount of singing training of each subject, there were no particular performance differences between the subjects' pitch and intensity fluctuations. The vibratos of all subjects were similar in number of pulsations per second, regularity of fluctuations per second, general extents of pitch and intensity, and waveform.

LARYNGEAL RECORDINGS

At 4000 frames per second, the cycle lengths for the group ranged from 7 to 21 frames. The differences in frames per cycle between subjects and trials were attributable to changes in fundamental frequency of phonation. For example, at a camera speed of 4000 frames per second and a fundamental frequency of 100 cps, there would be 40 frames per cycle. At a camera speed of 4000 frames per second with a fundamental frequency of 200 cps, there would be 20 frames per cycle.

The opening sequence of the vocal folds, uniform for the group, progressed in a posterior to anterior sequence. This uniformity was substantiated for each condition involving laryngeal photography from the films used for purposes of establishing the reliability of such observations. The point on the open folds were maximum glottal width in millimeters was exhibited varied as a function of subject and trial. The locus of maximum average glottal width from the anterior commissure varied from subject to subject. All measurements from the vocal folds were made from the vibrating portion of the folds.

As the vocal folds passed from a period of maximum glottal width into a closing phase, the general closing pattern was a posterior to anterior sequence. The anterior segment of the vocal folds was the first segment to exhibit closure, except for subject 1. In other words, the general closing sequence of the vocal folds progressed toward midline approximation from an open position beginning from the anterior part of the folds. However, the anterior portion of the folds was last to approximate. In the instances of two subjects, complete approximation at the posterior end of the vibrating folds was never observed.

Analysis on a frame-by-frame basis was undertaken in an effort to determine the activity during vibrato of the ventricular folds, the epiglottis, and the arytenoids. The inter-ventricular fold distance remained stable throughout the vibrato cycles. The epiglottis showed antero-posterior movements ranging from 1 to 3 millimeters during vibrato. These movements were non-predictable and were considered non-essential to vibrato production. The inter-arytenoid space for each subject did not vary in size in any predictable way during vibrato. The minute changes that were measured in the inter-arytenoid space did not correspond to any particular phases of the vibrato cycles.

The individual differences found in total glottal area, maximum glottal width and length, ventricular width, locus of glottal width, inter-arytenoid distance, epiglottic movement, and phase lengths of vocal fold vibration were small, and were within the spectrum for normal variations seen in non-vibrato phonatory behavior.

ELECTROMYOGRAPHIC RECORDINGS

The laryngeal tensor mechanism was presumably sampled by recording from over the area of the cricothyroid muscle complex. In each experimental condition, the cricothyroid muscle was seen to be active in phase with increases in pitch and intensity, for each subject. The relative amount of activity of the cricothyroid muscle appeared to be dependent upon the posture in which the subjects performed

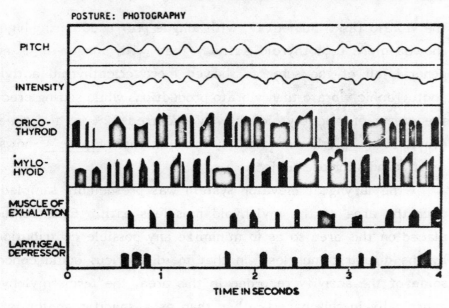

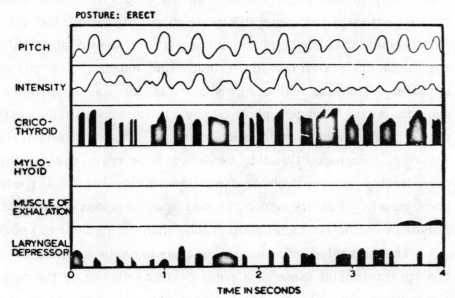

Figure 4.
Subject III producing vocal vibrato at 178 cps while in posture for high speed laryngeal photography.
(right)   Subject III producing vocal vibrato at 148 cps while in an erect sitting posture.
The reproductions of pitch and intensity are made from voice recordings of vibrato. The range of the pitch and intensity tracings is 5 cps and 5 db, respectively.
The reproductions of muscle activity during vocal vibrato are made from EMG recordings. The peaks of the curves do not necessarily represent voltage peaks, but rather, relative amounts of voltage fluctuation.
(left)   Cricothyroid muscle activity is primarily in phase with the voice signals. Mylohyoid activity is primarily out of phase with the cricothyroid. Muscle of exhalation activity is out of phase with the cricothyroid, while laryngeal depressor activity is inconsistent.
(right)   Cricothyroid muscle activity is primarily in phase with the voice signals. For this subject, no activity is recorded in the mylohyoid and muscle of exhalation areas while sitting erect. Laryngeal depressor activity bursts for this subject are more prevalent in this posture than during photography.

the vibrato task. Subject IV, with tongue protruded during high speed photography, showed more cricothyroid activity than with tongue in a normal position. In general, all of the subjects showed more cricothyroid activity during laryngeal photographic vibrato than vibrato productions while sitting erect. In both postures, the crests of cricothyroid activity occurred 82% of the time in phase with the crests of the pitch and intensity modulations. Figure 4 shows acoustic and EMG relationships for one subject.

The laryngeal elevator system was presumably sampled by recording from over the area of the mylohyoid muscle sheath. EMG surface electrodes were placed on this area so as to minimize any possible contributions to the recordings by the digastric muscles. In that m. digastricus could conceivably account for some of the activity recorded in this area, the term "mylohyoid muscle" is used generically in this paper rather than as a specific anatomical term. Mylohyoid muscle activity was generally seen to occur during the troughs of the vibrato fluctuations; that is, the maximum activity of the mylohyoid was out of phase with the maximum activity of the cricothyroid muscle. The out of phase relationship between mylohyoid and cricothyroid muscles was essentially maintained by all subjects during laryngeal photography. In the erect sitting posture two subjects, III and IV, exhibited no mylohyoid activity. This is demonstrated by subject III in Figure 4. Subjects I and II exhibited activity in the mylohyoid area that was considerably reduced from that obtained during similar activity in the posture for photography. For the group, it was apparent that mylohyoid activity was more prevalent during laryngeal photography than during an erect posture.

The breathing musculature was presumably sampled by recording from over the 8th intercostal space at a point postero-inferior to the nipple. During vibrato, this muscle area became increasingly active in time as the breathing mechanism became involved in forced exhalation. This activity was not considered essential to vibrato production and was not evident during many vibrato samples. The muscle of exhalation appeared to be involved in vibrato production only as adjustments in the breathing mechanism were required for prolonged phonation.

The laryngeal depressor system was presumably sampled by recording with electrode placements about one inch superior to the manubrium of the sternum over the sternothyroid muscuel. The extent of muscle activity during vibrato in this area varied greatly among subjects and trials. Activity, when present, occurred during both the crests and troughs of the vibrato fluctuations in both postural situations. There was no laryngeal depressor activity that appeared to correlate with vibrato production.

DISCUSSION

ACOUSTIC RECORDINGS

The vibrato samples produced by the trained singers and highly trained subjects were homogenous in many respects. The subjects all performed similarly in terms of the number of pitch and intensity fluctuations per second that were produced during vibrato. An interesting aspect of this group homogeneity was that the number of fluctuations per second did not change as a function of fundamental frequency of phonation. For example, the subjects sometimes chose a higher or lower pitch level in successive trials but the number of pitch and intensity fluctuations per second remained stable. These data suggest that the musculature responsible for the pitch and intensity fluctuations in vocal vibrato was able to function fairly independently from other mechanisms exerting controls on the larynx during phonation at various pitch levels.

From analyses of sonograms and electro-photophonelograms it is apparent that the extent of the pitch and intensity modulations used by the subjects in vibrato production varied according to the posture assumed. Generally, more muscle effort was observed during high speed photography to attain pitch and intensity extents comparable to those produced while sitting erect. In three out of four subject performances, greater pitch and intensity extents were recorded during the erect sitting posture than during high speed laryngeal photography. The posture assumed during laryngeal photography appeared to have some limiting effect on the amplitude of the acoustic recordings.

Analysis of the acoustic recordings showed that the group could not be separated in terms of the extent of their musical training. All of the subjects performed similarly with respect to the acoustics of the vibratos they produced. This homogeneity of performance between trained singers and highly trained subjects supports other research reported in the vibrato literature. A noteworthy supplement to this literature is the finding that posture sometimes tends to exert an inhibitory effect on the extents of the pitch and intensity fluctuations associated with vibrato.

LARYNGEAL RECORDINGS

At a filming speed of 4000 frames per second, the vocal fold behavior observed on moving picture film appeared to resemble vocal fold activity during non-vibrato tasks. For the four subjects being studied, there was no significant vocal fold behavior during vibrato that was correlative with the act of vibrato production. Although the resolution of the filming apparatus may have been inadequate to delineate any discrete changes that may be involved in vibrato production, such information was not apparent in cycle lengths up to 21 frames.

The cycle per second sequence of vocal fold vibration was fairly regular but was not linked to the frequency of pitch and intensity modulations. Measurements of the length of the vibrating folds, the open-closed phases of the vibratory cycles, and maximum glottal width appeared to resemble production of isolated vowels in the absence of vibrato. The variations in placement along the vocal folds where maximum glottal width occurred during vibrato appeared to be normal variants in vocal fold activity. Possibly, the two-dimensional superior view of the larynx that the high speed photographic technique provides is inadequate to record the laryngeal behavior associated with vibrato production, such as the possible changes in the mass, elasticity, and length of the vocal folds. It is feasible that the view of the larynx provided by the use of stroboscopic laminagraphy[32] would alleviate any contamination that other techniques impose on vocal fold behavior.

ELECTROMYOGRAPHIC RECORDINGS

On the basis of muscle areas sampled in this study by surface electromyography, the activity of the cricothyroid muscle was determined as the single most important factor relating to the modulations of vocal vibrato. This activity was generally in phase with the crests of the pitch and intensity modulations. The amount of voltage generated by the cricothyroid muscle during vibrato appeared to vary according to the posture in which the subjects produced vibrato. During high speed laryngeal photography, the cricothyroid exhibited more activity with less flexibility in recorded pitch and intensity, suggestive that the cricothyroid was engaged in compensatory activity imposed by the postural situation. Assuming that the erect position is a "normal" singing position, the activity exhibited by the cricothyroid during high speed photography did not appear to represent normal behavior for this muscle during rapid pitch and intensity change. The findings in the one subject who produced vibrato during photography with tongue protruded and "normal" suggest that part of the increase in cricothyroid activity during high speed photography with tongue protruded is attributable to a locking or stretching effect on the cricothyroid imposed either by posture or other muscles.

The activity of the mylohyoid muscle sheath essentially was out of phase with the cricothyroid muscle during vibrato. The activity of the mylohyoid decreased in the erect sitting posture, and in fact, in this posture two subjects showed no mylohyoid activity. This indicates that there is a tendency for mylohyoid muscle activity to diminish as cricothyroid activity is "normalized." The presence and relative absence of mylohyoid muscle activity during the photographic and erect postures, respectively, suggests that the activity sampled in this muscle area during photography does not represent normal mylohyoid activity for the vibrato task. Also, these data tend to suggest that the activity of the mylohyoid muscle during laryngeal photography disturbs the performance of the cricothyroid muscle. It appears that the importance of the mylohyoid muscle to vibrato production is minimal, except in situations where unusual demands or postural conditions are placed on the production mechanism. In those instances, through a reciprocal relationship, the mylohyoid exerts certain restraints on the cricothyroid muscle.

No causal link was revealed between the activity in the breathing musculature and laryngeal depressor mechanism, and vibrato production. Whatever activity occurred during vibrato in these systems was varied, non-predictable, and apparently not essential to vibrato production.

IMPLICATIONS OF THE STUDY

The information obtained pertaining to the activity of the cricothyroid and mylohyoid muscles during vibrato may well serve to broaden the knowledge of pitch and intensity changes in voice production. Since the pitch and intensity fluctuations during vibrato occur very rapidly, the activity observed in these muscles during vibrato was of particular interest. The fact that the cricothyroid and mylohyoid muscles acted out of phase during most of the trials served to strengthen the notion that the laryngeal tensor and elevator systems are intimately involved in the pitch and intensity regulatory process.

The consistent behavior of the cricothyroid muscle in the very rapid modulations in pitch and intensity of vocal vibrato was particularly significant. The consistent increase in mylohyoid muscle activity during postural positioning for photography suggests that the musculature which surrounds the larynx can exert some checks and balances, when needed, on laryngeal behavior. The fact that this mylohyoid activity was out of phase with the cricothyroid muscle activity would appear to add credence to this view.

The finding that the cricothyroid muscle appeared to be an important muscle for vibrato control has some implications for teaching singers to control vibrato production. It is feasible to assume that attempting to develop increased control over the cricothyroid muscle may well improve ability to use vibrato effectively. Since the cricothyroid muscle complex is palpable and amenable to external stimulation, achieving control over it would appear to be plausible with the adjunct of a moto-kinesthetic technique.

Numerous implications for further research can be derived from the outcome of this study. Although the acoustics of vibrato has been studied previously, such research has not been exhaustive. As new instrumentation is developed, closer study of the correlations between the extent of pitch and intensity fluctuations and with the physiological event of vibrato may be possible.

The importance of the cricothyroid muscle in the regulation of vibrato modulations is consistent with the findings of Rubin,[13] Faaborg-Andersen,[19] Arnold,[33] and Katsuki,[34] who demonstrated that contraction of the cricothyroid increases vocal fold tension and is associated with rising pitch. The thyroarytenoid muscle, the antagonist of the cricothyroid, was not sampled in this study. Previous studies have demonstrated that contraction of the thyroarytenoid alone raises pitch, but to a lesser degree than contraction of the cricothyroid.[13,19,33,34] According to Rubin,[13] the results of investigations of the thyroarytenoid muscles in living subjects have often been somewhat contradictory. It would be interesting, however, to determine with needle electromyography the activity of the thyroarytenoid muscles during vibrato production.

The differences in muscle behavior in performing the same task under different postural conditions, warrants a great deal of study. An example would be to study high and low pitch, high and low intensity, in an erect sitting posture and in position for laryngeal photography. It is possible that the postural requirements for laryngeal photography distort normal muscle behavior and should not be considered as being representative of normal vocal activity. The findings in this study support such a notion. The continued use of surface electromyography in conjunction with other instrumentation to study laryngeal physiology is indicated.

By measuring several parameters simultaneously, many vocal variables might be identified and controlled.

SUMMARY AND CONCLUSIONS

The purpose of this study was to describe internal laryngeal activity and the activity of contiguous laryngeal structures during the production of vocal vibrato. Four subjects, three female and one male, ranging in age from 20 to 24 years, were selected for study. Two of the subjects were trained singers and two were highly trained for laryngeal photography. They produced vocal vibrato during four experimental conditions. Two conditions involved postural positioning for laryngeal photography, and two conditions involved a sitting erect posture. Acoustic and EMG recordings were made in all conditions; in two conditions, these recordings were done simultaneously and in synchrony with laryngeal photography.

On the basis of this descriptive experimental study of the vibrato phenomenon, the following conclusions seem warranted:

(1) The extent of pitch and intensity fluctuations in vocal vibrato varies somewhat according to posture.

(2) Highly trained subjects do equally well in producing vibrato for experimental purposes in comparison to trained singers.

(3) Vocal fold activity during vocal vibrato, as seen in high speed photography, resembles non-vibrato phonatory behavior. There are apparently no characteristics of vocal fold behavior which correlate to the pitch and intensity changes in vibrato.

(4) The cricothyroid muscle appears to be a primary mechanism for regulation of modulations that occur in vibrato.

(5) During high speed laryngeal photography, the mylohyoid muscle tends to act out of phase with the cricothyroid muscle in vibrato production.

(6) The breathing musculature and laryngeal depressor mechanism do not appear to be causally linked to vibrato production.

(7) It would appear that postural positioning necessary for laryngeal photography modifies muscle activity in the larynx and adjacent structures.

(8) In teaching singers to control or modify vibrato production, it would be consistent with the findings of this study to recommend working for increased control over the cricothyroid muscle.

(9) Further research is needed in the documentation of the physiology of the vocal mechanism. The quantification of several parameters simultaneously would seem indicated. Modifications in procedure might include a standing or sitting posture to study normal muscle behavior, and a normal (non-protruded) tongue posture while recording vocal fold activity.

BIBLIOGRAPHY

1. Metfessel, M., "The vibrato in celebrated voices," Scientific Monthly, 28, 217, 1929.

2. Tiffin, J., "The role of pitch and intensity in the vocal vibrato of students and artists," University of Iowa Studies in the Psychology of Music, 1, 134, 1932.

3. Seashore, C., "Psychology of the vibrato in voice and instrument," University of Iowa Studies in the Psychology of Music, 3, 157, 1936.

4. Kwalwasser, J., "The vibrato," Psychological Monographs, 36, 84, 1926.

5. Metfessel, M., "The vibrato in artistic voices," University of Iowa Studies in the Psychology of Music, 1, 14, 1932.

6. Tiffin, J., and H. Seashore, "Summary of the established facts in experimental studies in the vibrato up to 1932," University of Iowa Studies in the Psychology of Music, 1, 344, 1932.

7. Schoen, M., "The pitch factor in artistic singing," Psychological Monographs, 31, 230, 1922.

8. Stetson, R., "The breathing movements in singing," Archives Neerlandaises de Phonetique Experimentale, 6, 115, 1931.

9. Westerman, K., "The vibrato: a specific integrational emergence upon fusure of somatic rhythms," Journal of Speech and Hearing Disorders, 6, 153, 1941.

10. Berg, J. van den, and T. Tan, "Results of experiments with human larynxes," Practica Oto-Rhino-Laryngologica, 21, #6, 425, 1959.

11. Berg, J. van den, "Vocal ligaments versus registers," NATS Bulletin, 20, #2, 16, 1963.

12. Berg, J. van den, "Modern research in experimental phonetics," Folia Phoniatrica, 14, 81, 1962.

13. Rubin, H., "Experimental studies on vocal pitch and intensity in phonation," Laryngoscope, 73, 973, 1963.

14. Berg, J. van den, "On the myoelastic-aerodynamic theory of voice production," NATS Bulletin, 14, #4, 6, 1958.

15. Schilling, R., "Der musculus sternothyreoideus und seine stimmphysiologische bedeutung," Archives fur Sprach- u. Stimmheick, 1, 65, 1937.

16. Sonninen, A., "The role of the external laryngeal muscles in length-adjustment of the vocal cords in singing," Acta-Oto-Laryngologica, Supplementum 130, 1956.

17. Vennard, W., "Some implications of the Sonninen research," NATS Bulletin, 15, #4, 8, 1959.

18. Berg, J. van den, and A. Spoor, "Microphonic effect of the larynx," Nature, 179, 625, 1957.

19. Faaborg-Andersen, K., "Electromyographic investigation of the intrinsic laryngeal muscles in humans," Acta Physiologica Scandinavica, 41, Supplement 140, 1957.

20. Faaborg-Andersen, K., and A. Sonninen, "The function of the extrinsic laryngeal muscles at different pitch," Acta Otolaryngologica, 51, 80, 1959.

21. Vennard, W., "Letter to the editor," NATS Bulletin, 19, #1, 5, 1962.

22. Hoshiko, M., and K. Berger, "Sequence of respiratory muscle activity during varied vocal attack," Speech Monographs, 32, #2, 185, 1965.

23. Timcke, R., H. von Leden, and P. Moore, "Laryngeal vibrations: measurements of the glottic wave," Archives of Otolaryngology, 68, 1, 1958.

24. Hollien, H., "Vocal pitch variation related to changes in vocal fold length," Journal of Speech and Hearing Research," 3, 150, 1960.

25. Hollien, H., and P. Moore, "Measurements of the vocal folds during changes in pitch," Journal of Speech and Hearing Research, 3, 157, 1960.

26. Fletcher, W., "A study of internal laryngeal activity in relation to vocal intensity," Unpublished Doctoral dissertation, Northwestern University, 1950.

27. Moore, P., and H. von Leden, "Larynx and voice: the function of the normal larynx," Motion picture, produced at the Voice Research Laboratory, Northwestern University Medical School, Chicago, Illinois.

28. Hollien, H., "Some laryngeal correlates of vocal pitch," Journal of Speech and Hearing Research, 3, 52, 1960.

29. Hollien, H., and J. Curtis, "Laminagraphic study of vocal pitch," Journal of Speech and Hearing Research, 3, 361, 1960.

30. Ruth, W., "The registers of the singing voice," NATS Bulletin, 19, #4, 2, 1963.

31. Rubin, H., and C. Hirt, "The falsetto. A high-speed cinematographic study," Laryngoscope, 70, 1305, 1960.

32.   Hollien, H., and J. Curtis, "Stroboscopic laminagraphy of the vocal folds," Scientific exhibit, 1964 convention of the American Speech and Hearing Association, San Francisco, California.

33.   Arnold, G., "Physiology and pathology of the cricothyroid muscle," Laryngoscope, 71, 687, 1961.

34.   Katsuki, Y., "The function of the phonatory muscles," Japanese Journal of Physiology, 1, 29, 1950.

Robert M. Mason, Ph.D., is Research Associate in Speech Science at the University of Illinois Medical Center, Chicago; Willard R. Zemlin, Ph.D., is Director of the Speech and Hearing Research Laboratories, University of Illinois, Urbana.

This study is one of many studies in laryngeal physiology underway or completed at the University of Illinois Speech and Hearing Research Laboratories, Urbana. This article is based on a doctoral dissertation in speech and theatre at the University of Illinois under the direction of Dr. Zemlin and Dr. John J. O'Neill. The study was supported in part by a neurological and sensory disease traineeship award from the public Health Service, and by a grant from the National Institutes of Health, HD DE 01153-01, U.S. Department of Health, Education, and Welfare. Interested parties should direct their correspondence to Dr. Robert M. Mason, Room 475, D.M.P. Bldg., University of Illinois, P.O. Box 6998, Chicago, Illinois, 60680.

Effect of
Threshold Reduction
on the Vibrato

J. K. Clarkson, Sheffield University, England

J. A. Deutsch, New York University

The effect of induced change in DL of pitch on the frequency and amplitude of the vibrato was measured and a correlation was sought between the amount of vibrato and DL reduction by stimulation. A strong correlation was found between vibrato amplitude and change in threshold. Though there was a large effect of DL reduction on amplitude of vibrato, there was no effect on vibrato frequency. The results suggest that there is a compensation in the rate of change of corrective movement in this skill.

In a previous publication (Deutsch & Clarkson, 1959) it was reported that the amplitude of the vibrato in singing was increased and its frequency decreased when a delay was interposed between the vocal output of an S and his auditory input. This result was taken to show that the vibrato was at least partly the result of the functioning of a control loop serving to keep the voice on a particular note. It seemed that in correcting a deviation from a target note S would overshoot the note and so produce an error in the opposite direction. A simple mechanism of this kind would therefore set up a continuous oscillation around the target note. The frequency and amplitude of such an oscillation would be determined by three separable factors. The first is the reaction time of S and is a measure of how quickly he can initiate a corrective movement.   The second factor is his differential threshold for pitch or a measure of how large a deviation from the target note must be before it is treated by S as an error signal.   The third determinant of the frequency and amplitude of oscillation is the rate of change of pitch by S or how quickly he moves away from the error zone after it has been identified and the movement initiated.   That the first of these factors operates has been shown (Deutsch & Clarkson, 1959) by the expedient of artificially lengthening the reaction time as mentioned above.   Delayed auditory feedback produced the changes of decreasing the frequency and increasing the amplitude of the vibrato.

The aim of the present experiment was to see what changes in the vibrato would occur when the second factor, the ability of S to discriminate pitch, was altered.   A means of changing frequency difference thresholds has been reported (Deutsch, 1951).   It has been shown that monaural stimulation at a given frequency for a period of 4 min. will lower the DL in the contralateral ear for notes in the region of that frequency.   The effect has been demonstrated to persist for as long as 24 hr.

METHOD

Subjects.

Thirteen male students took part.   No trained singers were used since it is probable that control over vibrato can be developed by training and it is suspected that proprioceptive cues may come to predominate.

Apparatus.

Vibrato recordings were taken through a microphone connected to an audiofrequency meter (Dawe & Deutsch, 1955). Output from the meter was fed to a pen oscillograph.   The meter itself operated without time lag and movement of the oscillograph pen was near enough linear over the range covered.   A note of frequency 180 cps was used throughout the experiment. (No special significance attaches to this particular frequency which was more or less arbitrarily chosen as well within the vocal range of male Ss and the sensitivity of the apparatus used.) The oscillograph pen was centered at this frequency.   An example of the kind of record obtained is shown in Fig. 1.

An oscillograph with finely calibrated dial was used to check the pen setting before each experimental session and to provide the auditory stimuli for measuring frequency difference thresholds. For threshold tests the circuit to S's earphones was completed through a foot pedal operated by E; dial adjustments on the oscillator were made by hand.

Experimental design.

The experiment was conducted in five stages, separated by intervals of 3 or 4 min. as follows: 1 - samples of vibrato recorded, 2 - frequency DL for 180 cps established, 3 - S binaurally stimulated by 180-cps note for 5 min., 4 - repetition of Stage 1, 5 - repetition of Stage 2.

PROCEDURE

Stage 1.

An oscillator tone of 180 cps was sounded briefly to S and he was asked to sing it. When the correct note had been produced he was instructed to sing it through the microphone three times for periods of approximately 12 sec. and his vibrato was recorded in the manner described.

Stage 2.

A difference threshold for the same oscillator tone of 180 cps was taken using the method of limits. The Ss were provided with earphones and seated facing away from apparatus and E. They were instructed that pairs of oscillator tones would be presented them separated by a short interval, and that their task was to report whether the second tone was higher than, or the same as, the first tone. Intensity level used throughout was constant at 60 db. above threshold. Each tone was presented for approximately 1 sec., and the members of each pair were separated by approximately ½ sec. Ten series, 5 ascending and 5 descending, were presented in quarter-cycle steps. At the beginning of the session two or three pairs of tones were sounded to acquaint Ss with the nature of the task.

Stage 3.

After the first DL had been determined, binaural stimulation was given through earphones with a continuous oscillator tone of 180 cps again 60 db. above threshold, for a period of 5 min. During this time Ss were permitted to read.

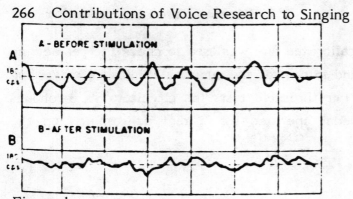

Figure 1.
Sample of an S's record, illustrating the amplitude of his frequency fluctuation before and after a reduction in his DL for pitch when he attempts to sing a steady note of 180 cps. (Each 2.5 horizontal divisions represent 1 sec.)

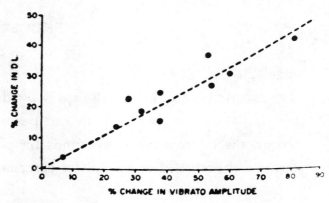

Figure 2.
Plot of the correlation between percentage of reduction in vibrato amplitude and DL for pitch.

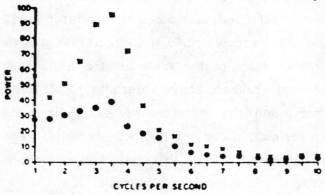

Figure 3.
Graph of the results of a power spectrum analysis of the output of a typical S. (The crosses indicate the power at various frequencies before a reduction in DL for pitch; the dots indicate the results of the same analysis after such a reduction.

Stage 4.

This was a repetition of Stage 1. Three samples of singing at 180 cps were again recorded.

Stage 5.

A further frequency difference threshold was taken, using the same procedure as in Stage 2.

RESULTS

A measure of the extent of change in amplitude of vibrato waveform after stimulation has been obtained by selecting the 20 largest point to point fluctuations from comparable sections of each record. The criterion of comparability used is occurrence in time: sections of the first and second singing periods in the two sets of vibrato records have been used for analysis. The sections are those from the first second after onset to the ninth second of singing. Choice of this particular time section was determined by the fact that from visual inspection the most stable representation of vibrato falls within these limits.

Two Ss failed to yield a measurable DL in the 10 trials given, and one S, due to a voice peculiarity not readily detectable by ear, produced a consistently "noisy" vibrato record. Results for the remaining 10 Ss are given in Tables 1 and 2. (The Mann-Whitney U test has been used for assessing the significance of vibrato amplitude change since normal distribution cannot be assumed.)

In every case a change in frequency DL has resulted in a corresponding change in vibrato amplitude. Figure 2 illustrates the relationship between proportional changes. For most Ss frequency DL measured with an electrically produced sound, is greater than vibrato amplitude. It is to be expected (Deutsch & Clarkson, 1959) that DL for a relatively unfamiliar sound will be greater than DL for S's own voice, but it cannot be assumed that the relationship between thresholds for the two sounds will be the same for all Ss. (Subject MT in the present experiment has worked on auditory thresholds and is well accustomed to sounds produced by an oscillator. His DL is very small compared with other Ss.)

Table 1

Changes in DL for a Tone of 180 cps
After 5 Min. Continuous Bianural
Stimulation at 180 cps

S	DL before Stimulation (cps)	DL after Stimulation (cps)	% Decrease	t
SM	2.514	1.181	53.0	2.562*
MS	3.153	1.265	59.9	3.678**
YR	2.208	.413	80.5	8.557***
MF	2.903	1.350	53.5	2.705*
MT	.986	.613	37.8	2.128*
FM	3.250	2.350	27.7	3.036**
NM	1.875	1.425	24.0	3.316**
JA	1.347	.917	31.9	1.679
HS	2.688	2.500	7.0	.476
QV	1.063	.656	38.3	2.332*

*p<.05.
**p<.01.
***p<.001.

Table 2

Changes in Vibrato Amplitude at 180 cps
After 5 Min. Continuous Binatural
Stimulation at 180 cps

S	Vibrato Amplitude before Stimulation (cps)	Vibrato Amplitude after Stimulation (cps)	% Decrease	U
SM	1.913	1.200	37.3	54.5***
MS	1.538	1.063	30.9	31.5***
YR	1.188	.688	42.1	12.0**
MF	2.150	1.563	27.3	59.5***
MT	2.638	1.975	25.1	75.0***
FM	2.113	1.625	23.1	57.0***
NM	1.450	1.250	13.8	138.0*
JA	1.362	1.100	19.2	106.0**
HS	1.525	1.463	4.1	179.5
QV	1.275	1.075	15.7	125.0*

*p.<.05.   **p.<.01.   ***p.<.001.

Differences between Ss in this respect may account for the lack of significant correlation between absolute changes in DL and vibrato amplitude. The percentage measure used is free from this source of variation and yields a highly significant relationship.

A further analysis of the record was undertaken to find out if there had been a change in the frequency of the vibrato after S's threshold had been reduced. We might expect that as the threshold for the detection of threshold change was lower, it would be reached sooner and that the time taken by each cycle of correction would be shorter. Accordingly a power spectrum analysis of the records was undertaken on a computer. A start was made on four records where such a change of frequency would have been probable because of the large change in the amplitude of the vibrato. As no change in frequency was detected, further records were not analyzed. For the records that were subjected to computer analysis, the pen tracings were encoded on punched cards by means of an Oscar J machine. A measurement was taken of the distance of the trace from an arbitrary base line at 1 mm. intervals. This meant that a sample was taken each 1/25 of a second. All the records for each condition were used for the analysis. The cards thus derived were then fed into a computer programmed to perform a power spectrum analysis.

The results on one S are presented in Fig. 3. These are typical of the four results. A frequency shift was either negligible or nonexistent. However the results given by the computer confirm the presence of a considerable decrease in amplitude of the vibrato which had been shown by the considerably simpler methods reported above.

DISCUSSION

The results reported above constitute a puzzle and point towards an interesting possibility. It seems that reduction in threshold for pitch leads to a decreased amplitude of corrective movement, as predicted by the hypothesis that the vibrato is the manifestation of a control loop. However, the lack of increase in frequency of the vibrato when its amplitude decreases seems at first sight inconsistent with the hypothesis that a control loop is involved, a hypothesis strongly supported by previous evidence (Deutsch & Clarkson, 1959).

An explanation which is consistent with the results of our previous experiment is that the rate of change of the corrective mechanism alters as we manipulate the sensitivity of the system to such change. It is easily seen that a corrective system with a uniform corrective rate of change has two contradictory requirements imposed upon it. The first is to return from the region of error to the target as quickly as possible. The second is to move as little into the region of error as possible. Translated into our situation, the singer must try to change from the wrong note he hears himself sing to the right note as quickly as possible. On the other hand he must attempt not to overshoot too far to the other side. Before he can initiate a corrective reaction he will have heard himself stray more than is acceptable from the target note. He therefore has to adopt some rate of change which does not leave him too long in the region of error on one hand and which does not take him too far into the region of error on the other. If the rate is reduced so that the time taken from target to first detection of error is kept the same between the normal and sensitized conditions, then the time at which the error is corrected will be the same under the two conditions as reaction time is the same. In this way the overall frequency of correction will stay the same in spite of an increase in sensitivity. The most plausible interpretation of the results, then, suggests that there is control of the rate of change during corrective movement in this form of skill.

REFERENCES

1.   Dawe, P. G. M., & Deutsch, J. A.   An audio-frequency meter for graphing frequency variations in the human voice. Electron. Engng., 1955, 27, 323.

2.   Deutsch, J. A.   A preliminary report on a new auditory after-effect. Quart, J. exp. Psychol., 1951, 3, 3-46.

3.   Deutsch, J. A., & Clarkson, J. K.   The nature of the vibrato and the control loop in singing. Nature, 1959, 183, 167-168.

This work was carried out under a Medical Research Council grant at the University of Oxford and National Institutes of Health Grant No. 10997-01 to the junior author.

The authors would like to thank R. C. Oldfield for the original inspiration of this work and for the facilities accorded to them in his laboratory; and the Biomedical Computing Laboratory at the University of California, Los Angeles.

Aerodynamic Study
of Vibrato
and Voluntary
"Straight Tone" Pairs
in Singing

J. Large[2] and S. Iwata[3]

University of Southern California and The Institute of Laryngology and

Voice Disorders, Los Angeles, Calif.

Acknowledgement. The authors wish to express their appreciation to Dr. Earl Schubert, Stanford University, for helpful suggestions in the preparation of this report.

Much work has been done in the investigation of the acoustic characteristics of vocal vibrato in singing (SCHOEN, 1922; KWALWASSER, 1926; METFESSEL, 1926, 1928; STANLEY, 1929, TIFFIN, 1931; SEASHORE, 1932, 1936; OBATA et al., 1934; LEWIS, 1936; BARTHOLOMEW, 1942; SJOSTROM, 1948; WINCKEL, 1953; GEMELLI et al., 1954; BJØRKLUND, 1961; POMMEZ, 1962). This literature is dominated by the extensive contributions of the SEASHORE group at the University of Iowa. Comparatively little information is available on vibrato physiology (SCHOEN, 1922; STETSON, 1931; METFESSEL, 1932; WESTERMAN, 1941; ZANTEMA and VAN DEN BERG, 1956; MASON and ZEMLIN, 1966; SMITH, 1970), and this literature deals almost exclusively with muscle activity. The earlier physiological studies were largely speculative; more recently electromyography has been utilized for objective specification of muscle function in vibrato.

Using surface electrodes, ZANTEMA and VAN DEN BERG (1956) obtained direct evidence, in one case, for inspiratory muscle control ('Atemstutze') of vocal vibrato, and, in another case, inferential evidence for intrinsic laryngeal muscle control. They recorded no active participation of the cricothyroid, sternothyroid, or abdominal muscles. MASON and ZEMLIN (1966) found, with surface electrodes, that the activity of the cricothyroid muscle was generally in phase with the crests of the pitch and intensity vibratos. The action of the mylohyoid sheath was essentially out of phase with the cricothyroid muscle. ZEMLIN (1968) suggested that the muscles in the mylohyoid region act to check the pitch-raising effects of the cricothyroid muscles and, further, that subglottal air pressure may account for the increases in intensity during vibrato. SMITH (1970), also utilizing surface electrodes, reported a relationship between abdominal muscular effort and the rate of vocal vibrato.

To our knowledge, no research thus far has been directed primarily towards the air flow factors in vibrato production. In a recent investigation of paired tones in adjacent registers in singing (LARGE et al., 1970), it was found that most of the samples were characterized by a synchrony between the intensity (amplitude) vibrato and the fluctuations in air flow values. The purpose of the present study was to investigate further this observation.

The vibrato[4] in Western artistic vocal music culture consists of a 'pulsation of pitch, usually accompanied with synchronous pulsations of loudness and timbre, of such extent and rate as to give a pleasing flexibility, tenderness, and richness to the tone (SEASHORE, 1936)'. According to SEASHORE, vibrato may be present in 95% of the tones produced in singing. It is also well-known that the vibrato does not appear in many untrained voices and that it can be deliberately inhibited by most accomplished singers. Such nonvibrato phonation, commonly called 'straight tone', can be described as (1) involuntary straight tone and (2) voluntary straight tone, respectively. The voluntary straight tone is often used for special expressive effects, especially in Lieder singing. The use and misuse of straight tone in solo and choral singing has been discussed by VENNARD (1967). In our study, vibrato and voluntary straight tone have been juxtaposed in a task suitable for the measurement of air flow rate at certain assigned fundamental frequencies.

PROCEDURE

Six female student singers were selected from the Voice Department of the School of Music, University of Southern California. Each subject was required to sing vowel /$\underline{a}$/ ('ah') at her most comfortable intensity at 3 fundamental frequencies: A_3 (220 Hz) in chest register, A_4 (440 Hz) in middle register, and A_5 (880 Hz) in head register. At each fundamental frequency the sung tone was sustained with normal vibrato for several seconds followed without interruption by several seconds of straight tone. Before recording, each subject was trained, using a sound level meter (General Radio No. 1551-C), to keep the intensity equal in both modes of production.

INSTRUMENTATION

The simultaneous registration of air flow rate, air volume, fundamental frequency and intensity was accomplished by a pneumotachographic system (fig. 1). A pneumotachograph of the mesh screen type with a differential pressure transducer (Sanborn No. 270) is used for measurement of the air flow rate. The electronic signal from the pressure transducer is amplified by a carrier preamplifier (Sanborn No. 350-110B) and is recorded on the 1st channel of a polybeam recorder (Sanborn No. 568-100). The air volume consumed in singing is derived by integrating the flow rate with time through an integrating preamplifier (Sanborn No. 350-3700) and is registered on the 2nd channel of the polybeam recorder. The mean air flow rate in ml/sec is obtained by dividing the air volume by the duration of time for the designated singing task. The singing voice is picked up by a condenser microphone (Bruel and Kjaer No. 4134) which is located 30 cm from the lips and recorded on one channel of a high-fidelity tape recorder. These signals are analyzed for fundamental frequency and intensity. Fundamental frequency is recorded on the 3rd channel of the polybeam recorder through a 'transpitch meter' (Frøkjaer-Jensen); intensity is recorded on the 4th channel of the polybeam recorder through the intensity meter[5]. Voice signals are recorded on the 5th channel of the polybeam recorder.

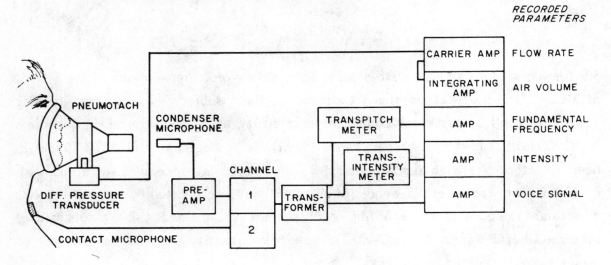

Figure 1.
Schematic drawing of equipment for aerodynamic studies.

RESULTS

The air flow rates for vibrato and for the succeeding straight tone at the same fundamental frequency and the same intensity levels with different conditions were measured for each subject. Figure 2 demonstrates the actual recordings of air flow, air volume, fundamental frequency and intensity obtained from a soprano. The upper graph shows the air flow at 220 Hz, the middle graph at 440 Hz, and the lower graph at 880 Hz; all phonations represent 'comfortable' intensity levels. The 1st part of each recording illustrates vibrato and the latter part straight tone.

In these samples amplitude vibrato is synchronous with frequency fibrato for each of the 3 conditions. The air flow pulsations seem to be correlated with the amplitude vibrato at the higher fundamental frequency levels. Air flow rates for this singer were as follows: 80 ml/sec for vibrato and 70 ml/sec for straight tone at 220 Hz; 210 ml/sec for vibrato and 170 ml/sec for straight tone at 440 Hz; and 340 ml/sec for vibrato and 270 ml/sec for straight tone at 880 Hz. It is clear that the air flow rate for vibrato tends to be greater than that for straight tone.

The air flow rates for vibrato and straight tone for the 3 conditions are summarized in table I.

Condition 1.

220 Hz phonation in chest register. Various values of air flow rates were obtained for vibrato and straight tone among the subjects. The data for all subjects showed that air flow fluctuations were correlated with the amplitude vibrato and that air flow rates for vibrato were slightly higher than those for straight tone. The differences between these values ranged from 5 ml/sec to 40 ml/sec, with a mean value of 21.7 ml/sec.

Condition 2.

440 Hz phonation in middle register. Air flow rates in middle register were higher than those in chest register. The synchronous frequency, amplitude and air flow fluctuations for vibrato are more obvious in middle register than in chest register. As shown in table I, the air flow rates for vibrato were slightly higher than those for straight tone in this register. The difference between these values ranged from 10 ml/sec to 45 ml/sec with a mean value of 20.8 ml/sec.

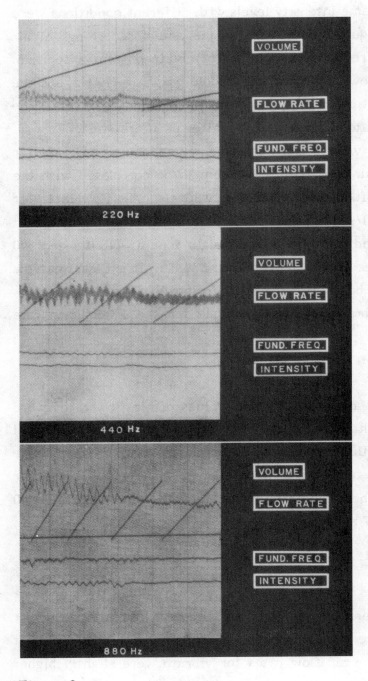

Figure 2.
Pneumotachograms of vibrato and straight tone in chest (220 Hz), middle (440 Hz), and head (880 Hz) registers obtained from a soprano subject (recording speed, 2.5 cm/sec).

Condition 3.

880 Hz phonation in head register. Air flow rates for vibrato were also higher than those for straight tone in this register, except for one subject. The difference between these values ranged from 0 ml/sec to 60 ml/sec with a mean value of 25.8 ml/sec. The mean value of air flow difference was certainly higher than that for the other registers, but this difference would seem to be non-- essential for the different registers.

Table I. Air flow rates (ml/sec) for vibrato and straight tone

Subjects	220 Hz (chest register)		440 Hz (middle register)		880 Hz (head register)	
	Vibrato	Straight tone	Vibrato	Straight tone	Vibrato	Straight tone
1	60	55	200	180	200	185
2	70	65	125	110	120	120
3	50	35	140	130	115	100
4	110	80	210	190	270	210
5	220	180	200	155	335	315
6	280	245	305	320	265	220

Air flow in vibrato consists of alternating fluctuations of air flow (AC factor) and constant air flow (DC factor), as demonstrated in figure 2. The magnitude of fluctuations of air flow was very large and clearly correlated with the amplitude vibrato as demonstrated in figure 3. The magnitude of fluctuations of air flow accompanying the amplitude vibrato seems to increase with increasing fundamental frequency levels. This correlation seems to be more characteristic of head register than of the middle and the chest registers. The magnitude and phase of air flow fluctuations were not always constant. The air volume and duration of each period of air flow vibrato were measured. The mean values and the standard deviations of these measurements are presented in table II.

The mean values of air volume in each vibrato cycle at 220 Hz ranged from 13.0-70 ml, and the lengths of the periods ranged from 0.17-0.24 sec; these air volumes and periods between successive vibrato cycles slightly fluctuated within subjects. At 440 Hz, the mean air volume and the mean lengths of the periods ranged from 26.0-55.0 ml/sec, and 0.19-0.23 sec respectively. The fluctuations of

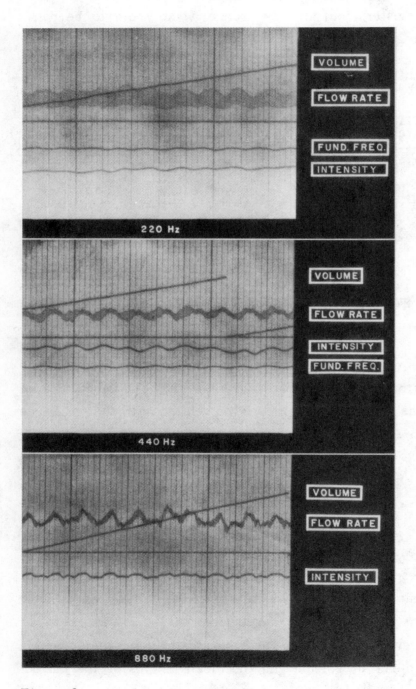

Figure 3.
Simultaneous recordings of air flow, amplitude and frequency vibrato in 3 registers (recording speed, 10 cm/sec).

air volume and periods between vibrato cycles were more irregular in middle register than those in chest register. At 880 Hz, the mean values of the air volume and lengths of the periods ranged from 18.0-67.0 ml, and 0.19-0.24 sec respectively. In head register, air volume and phase periods between vibrato cycles within subjects seemed more stable than in chest and middle registers.

Table II. Mean values and standard deviations of air volumes and length of periods in vibrato cycles for different conditions

	Mean values of Air volume		Mean values of length of periods	
	(ml)	SD	(sec)	SD
220 Hz				
1	70.0	8.9	0.24	0.024
2	17.0	2.5	0.18	0.020
3	13.0	2.5	0.21	0.024
4	22.0	2.5	0.17	0.012
5	41.0	6.6	0.21	0.012
6	16.0	2.0	0.24	0.024
440 Hz				
1	55.0	11.4	0.19	0.028
2	26.0	5.6	0.19	0.020
3	29.0	3.7	0.20	0.016
4	27.0	3.2	0.18	0.008
5	38.0	5.1	0.18	0.032
6	31.0	3.7	0.23	0.020
880 Hz				
1	51.0	6.6	0.23	0.008
2	18.4	2.9	0.19	0.008
3	37.0	2.4	0.16	0.036
4	37.0	5.0	0.18	0.028
5	67.0	5.1	0.20	0.012
6	30.0	4.8	0.24	0.028

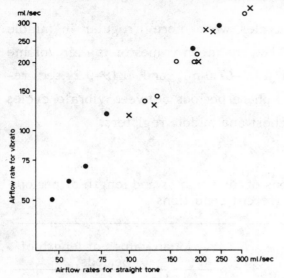

Figure 4.
The relationship of air flow rates between vibrato and straight tone. ● = chest register (220 Hz);   ○ = middle register (440 Hz);   x   = head register (880 Hz).

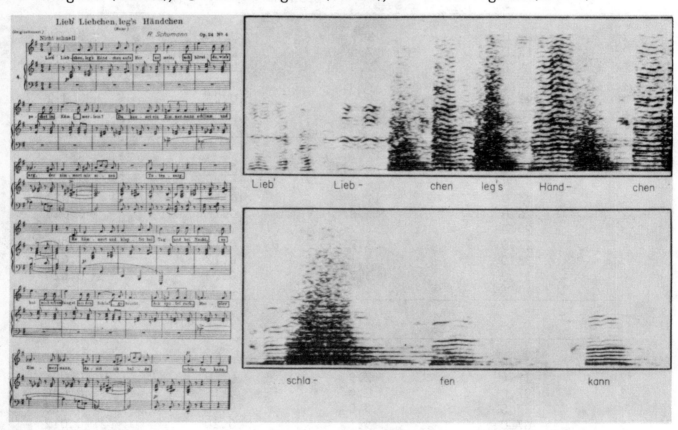

Figure 5.
Musical score and sonograms of song No. 4 from R. Schumann's Liederkreis, op. 24. The sections of the text enclosed by thin lines were sung by D. FISCHER-DIESKAU with straight tone.   The second 'Lieb-' in the upper sonogram illustrates the characteristic use of vibrato; the 'kann' in the lower sonogram illustrates straight tone.

The relationship of air flow rates between vibrato and straight tone are displayed in figure 4. The air flow rates in vibrato are linearly proportional to the air flow rates in straight tone for the 3 registers. This relationship between vibrato and straight tone can be expressed in the following formula, with a 95% confidence limit of 0.97:

$$AFR_{(v)} = 1.11 \times AFR_{(st)} + 7.1 \text{ ml/sec}$$

where

$AFR_{(v)}$ is air flow rate in vibrato,

$AFR_{(st)}$ is air flow rate in straight tone phonation at the same intensity and fundamental frequency.

In general, this formula demonstrates the finding that the air flow rate is approximately 10% higher in vibrato than in straight tone in all registers.

DISCUSSION

Vibrato is said to make the singing tone 'warmer' and more 'exciting'; voluntary straight tone can be used to bring 'coldness' and 'monotony' into the voice. Straight tone is effective in portraying moods of mystery, terror, or wonderment. Another related usage is found in the technique of the 'vibrato crescendo' (VENNARD, 1967), in which a tone is first sustained without vibrato, then a small amount of vibrato added and the extent gradually increased. Characteristic of much of the singing of Wagnerian vocal music, this type of production, somewhat modified, is now also employed extensively in some 'pop' styles. A distinction must be made between deliberate, expressive straight tone (voluntary), as used tastefully by such artists as Dietrich Fischer-Dieskau, and the vibratoless tones (involuntary) of undeveloped voices.

The singing of DIETRICH FISCHER-DIESKAU of Robert Schumann's Liederkreis, Opus 24 (1840) was perceptually studied by 3 musicians to determine the percentage of straight tone used by this particular artist for a particular performance (Deutsche Grammophon Gesellschaft, 139 109 Stereo). The results are tabulated in table III.

Table III. Straight tone in performance practice
(As used by DIETRICH FISCHER-DIESKAU, Deutsche Grammophon Gesellschaft, 139 109 Stereo)

Liederkreis, op. 24		R. Schumann
Song No.	Song title	Percentage of S. tone
1	Morgens steh' ich auf	44%
2	Es treibt mich hin	59%
3	Ich wandelte unter den Baumen	21%
4	Lieb' Liebchen, leg's Handchen	70%
5	Schone Wiege meiner Leiden	25%
6	Warte, warte, wilder Schiffman	47%
7	Berg' und Burgen schau'n herunter	21%
8	Anfangs wollt' ich fast verzagen	24%
9	Mit Myrten und Rosen	48%
	Total song cycle average	40%

The Lied having the highest percentage of straight tone usage (70%) was No. 4, 'Lieb' Liebchen, Leg's Handchen'. As indicated in figure 5, the artist employs a straight tone throughout the phrase:

'Da hauset ein Zimmermann schlimm und arg,

There dwells a carpenter, evil and bad,

der zimmert mir einen Totensarg.'

who is making me a coffin.

Straight tone, however, does not appear to be limited exclusively to expressive effect. It is found in many instances where the note values are quite short, and it seems to be used occasionally merely for contrast with vibrato. It would appear that FISCHER-DIESKAU avoids the use of straight tone on the higher tones, probably because they would tend to sound strained. Note that all 4 E-naturals (330 Hz) assigned to the syllables 'horst', 'po-', 'hat', and 'langst', are sung with vibrato.

The sonograms accompanying the musical score in figure 5 give a visual portrayal of the beginning and ending tones of the song, several of which were unaccompanied. Note the characteristic appearance of vibrato especially in the second 'Lieb-' and the relatively straight lines of straight tone on 'kann'. The total cycle average of 40% straight tone certainly raises a question with regard to SEASHORE'S claim that vibrato is found in 95% of all artistically sung tones. FISCHER-DIESKAU (1970) has stated that straight tone should be reserved mainly for compositions in which the text predominates, and then it should be used only by singers who possess a good vocal technique.

SEASHORE (1932) measured the rate of the vibrato and found 5-8 pulsations/sec aesthetically acceptable. In our study, vibrato rate ranged from 4.8-6.7/sec with no significant difference among the various registers. SEASHORE reported various phase relationships between the frequency and amplitude vibrati ('parallel vibrato', 'opposite', etc.). Our samples, figure 3, show only 'parallel vibrato', i.e., the frequency vibrato is always synchronous with the amplitude vibrato. This synchrony was observed in all three registers. SJOSTROM (1948) and WINCKEL (1953) observed that the duration of the intensity vibrato cycles were not constant. As shown in figure 3, our subjects demonstrated slight irregularities in both amplitude and frequency vibrato.

The aerodynamic correlates of vibrato have not been studied to any extent. SCHILLING (1925) speculated that vocal vibrato depended primarily upon the oscillation of subglottic air pressure. ZEMLIN (1968) suggested, more specifically, that the subglottal air pressure fluctuations may account for the amplitude vibrato. The results of our study support the latter view. Our data show that fluctuations of air flow in vibrato are synchronous with the amplitude vibrato (fig. 3). The frequency rate of these fluctuations remains approximately the same in the various registers. These fluctuations become more obvious at the higher levels of fundamental frequency (440 Hz and 880 Hz).

The relationship of air flow rates to different fundamental frequencies and intensity levels in sustained speech phonation has been studied by many researchers (LUCHSINGER, 1951; VAN DEN BERG, 1956; ISSHIKI, 1964, 1965; RUBIN et al., 1969; HIRANO et al., 1969). The results of these investigations indicate that air flow during phonation has a close relation to fundamental frequency and intensity levels. ISSHIKI (1965) reported that in lower pitch levels, the vocal intensity is increased primarily by increasing the glottal resistance rather than by increasing the flow rate; however, at high pitch phonation, air flow rate was directly proportional to intensity. ISSHIKI emphasized the importance of the role of glottal resistance at low pitch and of air flow rate at high pitch to the control of intensity. YANAGIHARA and VON LEDEN (1966) found that the electrical activity in the cricothyroid muscle is closely correlated with glottal resistance and also that the glottal resistance increases and decreases proportionally with the rise and fall of vocal pitch when the intensity of the voice is maintained within a limited range. The acoustic properties of vibrato are obviously interdependent with aerodynamic events and muscle activities related to phonation.

The magnitude of air flow fluctuations in vibrato increases from chest (220 Hz) to head (880 Hz), as shown in figure 3. As explained above, the lesser magnitude of air flow fluctuation in chest register is probably due to greater glottal resistance; the greater magnitude of air flow fluctuations in middle and head registers is directly related to the amplitude fluctuations of the vibrato and probably to the subglottic pressure fluctuations as a function of intensity. Additionally, as shown in table II, the air volume in each vibrato cycle tended to increase from the lower register to the higher ones. These air volumes varied slightly from cycle to cycle. The phase also shifted similarly in all registers for successive vibrato cycles.

In comparing the air flow rates of vibrato and straight tone, two observations are possible: (1) the air flow rate for vibrato is usually higher than that for straight tone in each of the three registers, and (2) the air flow rates for vibrato are linearly proportional to the values for straight tone. The air flow rate for vibrato is on the average 10% greater. When a singer uses straight tone during long phrases, e.g. for Baroque melismas, he may be demonstrating, in part, the practical application of this finding.

The singers used as subjects in our experiment produce straight tone by inhibiting the vibrato. According to HARTLIEB (1953), the vibrato is a modulation of frequency and amplitude resulting from the pendulum-like movements of the intrinsic laryngeal musculature and the respiratory musculature. These movements are said to prevent fatigue at the laryngeal level. In other words, the musculature is alternately working and resting in vibrato. In the production of straight tone the musculature is constantly working. Such a condition promotes greater average glottal resistance than is found in vibrato and could account for the 10% difference in air flow rate. These findings are confirmed by similar results obtained when our task was reversed, i.e., when the subject sang straight tone to vibrato rather than vibrato to straight tone.

SUMMARY

Vibrato and voluntary straight tone were juxtaposed in a task in which fundamental frequency and intensity were kept constant. The vowel /a/ was sung by advanced student female singers in 3 different registers: chest register at 220 Hz, middle register at 440 Hz, and head register at 880 Hz. Air flow was recorded by a pneumotachographic system. It was found that fluctuations of air flow in vibrato were synchronous with the amplitude vibrato. These fluctuations were more obvious in middle and head registers than in chest register, probably due to changes in glottal resistance. The air flow rate for vibrato is usually 10% higher than that for straight tone in all registers. This relationship may be expressed in the formula:

$$AFR_{(v)} = 1.11 \times AFR_{(st)} + 7.1 \text{ ml/sec}$$

Such a result can be explained on the basis of the greater average glottal resistance resulting from the constantly working musculature necessary to inhibit the vibrato. The acoustic properties of vibrato are obviously interdependent with aerodynamic events and muscle activities related to phonation. The results of this study suggest that the physiological control of vocal vibrato is a combined laryngeal and respiratory mechanism, with the laryngeal factor predominating.

REFERENCES

BARTHOLOMEW, W.: Acoustics of music (Prentice-Hall, Englewood Cliffs 1942).

BJØRKLUND, A.: Analyses of soprano voices, J. acoust. Soc. Amer. 33: 575-582 (1961).

FISCHER-DIESKAU, D.: Personal commun. (1970.

GEMELLI, A.; SACERDOTE, G., e BELLUSSI, G.: Analisi elettroacustica della voce cantata. Boll. Soc. Ital. Fonet. Sperim. 4: 3-8 (1954).

HARTLIEB, K.: Schadigungen der ausseren Kehlkopfmuskeln als Ursachen fur Storungen der Sangerstimme. Folia phoniat. 5: 146-166 (1953).

HIRANO, M.; OHALA, J., and VENNARD, W.: The function of laryngeal muscles in regulating fundamental frequency and intensity of phonation. J. Speech Res. 12: 616-628 (1969).

ISSHIKI, N.: Regulatory mechanism of voice intensity variation. J. Speech Res. 7: 17-29 (1964).

ISSHIKI, N.: Vocal intensity and air flow rate. Folia phoniat. 17: 92-104 (1965).

KWALWASSER, J.: The vibrato. Psychol. Monogr. 36: 84-108 (1926).

LARGE, J.; IWATA, S., and LEDEN, H., VON: The primary female register transition in singing: Aerodynamic study. Folia phoniat. 22: 385-396 (1970).

LEWIS, E.: Vocal resonance. J. acoust. Soc. Amer. 8: 91-99 (1936).

LUCHSINGER, R.: Schalldruck- und Geschwindigkeitsregistrierung der Atemluft beim Singen. Folia phoniat. 3: 25-51 (1951).

MASON, R. and ZEMLIN, W.: The phenomenon of vocal vibrato. NATS Bull. 22: 12-77 (1966).

METFESSEL, M.: Sonance as a form of tonal fusion. Psychol. Rev. 33: 459-466 (1926).

METFESSEL, M.: What is the voice vibrato? Psychol. Monogr. 31: 126-134 (1928).

METFESSEL, M.: The vibrato in artistic voices; in SEASHORE The vibrato. University of Iowa studies in the psychology of music, vol. 1, pp. 14-117 (University Press, Iowa City 1932).

OBATA, J.; HIROSE, M., and TESIMA, T.: On the physical nature of the characteristic trill in the Utai, a Japanese recitative chant. Proc. imp. Acad. 10: 326-329 (1934).

POMMEZ, J.: Etude acoustique du vibrato de la voix chantée. Rev. Laryng., Bordeaux 83: 249-264 (1962).

RUBIN, H.; LE COVER, M., and VENNARD, W.: Vocal intensity, subglottic pressure and air flow relationships in singers. Folia phoniat. 19: 393-413 (1967).

SCHILLING, R.: Untersuchungen uber die Atembewegungen beim Sprechen und Singen. Mschr. Ohrenheilk. 59: 51-56 (1925).

SCHOEN, M.: An experimental study of the pitch factor in artistic singing. Psychol. Monogr. 31: 230-259 (1922).

SEASHORE, C.: The vibrato. University of Iowa studies in the psychology of music. vol. 1, (University Press, Iowa City 1932).

SEASHORE, C.: Psychology of the vibrato in voice and instrument. University of Iowa studies in the psychology of music, vol. 3, (University Press, Iowa City 1932).

SJOSTROM, L.: Experimentellphonetische Untersuchungen des Vibratophanomens der Singstimme. Acta Oto-Laryng., Suppl. 67: 123-130 (1948).

SMITH, E.: An electromyographic investigation of the relationship between abdominal muscular effort and the rate of vocal vibrato. NATS Bull. 26: 2-17 (1970).

STANLEY, D.: The science of voice (Fischer, New York 1929).

STETSON, R.: The breathing movements in singing. Arch. Neerl. phon. Exp. 6: 115-164 (1931).

TIFFIN, J.: Some aspects of the psychophysics of the vibrato. Psychol. Monogr. Vol. 41. pp. 153-200 (1931).

VAN DEN BERG, J.: Direct and indirect determination of the mean subglottic pressure. Folia phoniat. 8: 1-24 (1956).

VENNARD, W.: Singing, the mechanism and the technic (Fischer, New York 1967).

WESTERMAN, K.: The vibrato: A specific integrational emergence upon fusure of somatic rhythms. J. Speech Dis. 6: 153-160 (1941).

WINCKEL, F.: Physikalische Kriterien fur objektive Stimmbeurteilung. Folia phoniat. 5: 232-252 (1953).

YANAGIHARA, N. and LEDEN, H., VON: The cricothyroid muscle during phonation — Electromyographic, aerodynamic and acoustic studies. Ann. Otol. Rhinol. Laryng. 75: 987-1006 (1966).

ZANTEMA, J. and VAN DEN BERG, J.: Zur Erzeugung des Vibratos der Singstimme. Z. Phonetik 9: 336-343 (1956).

ZEMLIN, W.: Speech and hearing sciences (Prentice-Hall, Englewood, Cliffs, N.J., 1968).

1. This research was supported by USPHS Research Grant NB 06670-05 from the National Institute of Neurological Diseases and Blindness.

2. Dr. John Large is an Associate Professor of Voice, School of Music, University of Southern California, Los Angeles, Calif.

3. Dr. SHIGENOBU IWATA is on leave of absence from the Department of Oto-Rhino-Laryngology, Nagoya City University, Japan.

4. Defined (USA Standard Acoustical Terminology, USA Standards Institute, 1960) as 'a family of tonal effects in music that depend upon periodic variations of one or more characteristics of the sound wave. Note: When the particular characteristics are known, the term "vibrato" should be modified accordingly; e.g., frequency vibrato, amplitude vibrato, phase vibrato, and so forth.'

5. Electronically, the intensity meter consists mainly of an input circuit, a linear range potentiometer, a direct-coupled AC-input amplifier and an unconventional DC-output amplifier. The signal is first fed to the continuously variable input potentiometer and then to the calibrated input attenuator. From the input attenuator the signal is fed to the range potentiometer. Different interchangeable range potentiometers are available, logarithmic (dB) as well as linear.

Singers' Formants

A Physical Definition
of "Good Voice-Quality"
in the Male Voice

Wilmer T. Bartholomew

Department of Research, Peabody Conservatory of Music, Baltimore, Maryland

INTRODUCTION

The need of bringing order out of chaos in the field of voice-teaching is nowhere felt more keenly than in conservatories of music, where the eternal conflict of traditional methods is often in evidence. Little of value can be learned from textbooks for there are very few if any points on which general agreement may be found. This widespread lack of agreement often extends even to the few select works which have been written by men who had some understanding of the acoustic principles involved, and is an emphatic warning of the danger of divorcing the physical aspect from either the physiological, the psychological, or even the aesthetic, in investigations of this sort. Musico-scientific studies of any sort must take account of more than just the aesthetic and more than just the physical. But this is doubly true of studies on the voice, because the voice mechanism is not only quite a complex structure muscularly, capable of tremendous and facile variation in the relations of its parts and the character of its surfaces but is in addition never entirely under conscious control.

The advantage of the objective approach is obvious. There is, fortunately, enough agreement among musicians as to what constitutes good vocal quality to enable us to speak of a typical good quality. Since every aspect of the sound we hear has its counterpart in the sound wave, careful registration of this sound wave by sufficiently sensitive apparatus should give us a record of the whole story. If we can find significant differences in such records between good voices and poor ones and can avoid the pitfalls of drawing wrong conclusions concerning something so transitory and subtle as is the voice, we can perhaps work backwards and deduce the physiological structure responsible for various qualities. With that basis, we would know how to proceed most intelligently in the psychological process of bringing the voice mechanism as much as possible under conscious control. That was our idea in commencing this investigation nearly four years ago.

APPARATUS

Our apparatus consisted of a highly damped studio with remote-control switches to an oscillograph room, a condenser microphone, resistance-coupled amplification, a specially-designed oscillograph vibrator and means for exposing long enough lengths of film to cover at least one complete cycle of the voice-vibrato,[1] a precaution which is absolutely necessary in analyses of voice-quality and which makes useless the short-film commercial apparatus, since the waves must also be sufficiently extended to make high frequencies readable. The most of the apparatus was designed by Mr. H. T. Rights of Westinghouse Company and was made possible through the financial assistance of the National Research Council. The apparatus and the film-speed are capable of separating frequencies in excess of 8000 cycles should they be present. To date nearly a thousand records have been taken, comprising various qualities from best to poorest, from over forty male and female voices, of all degrees of training and ability, at frequent points throughout the pitch series, on various vowels, at various intensities. The study of these records, and the harmonic analysis of a group of 46 wave forms of male voices, carried out on the Henrici analyzer in the Bureau of Standards at Washington, emphasizes four characteristic tendencies, which collectively give us a tangible, physical definition of "good quality," at least in the male voice. The first three of these have been reported at one time or another by other investigators, though perhaps not with the aid of such a large and controlled series of records, using singing voices and sufficiently sensitive apparatus.

VIBRATO

The first characteristic is the vibrato. Good voice-quality is inseparably connected with a smooth and fairly even variation occurring around a central mean about 6 or 7 times a second in usually all three of the variables: pitch, intensity and timbre. In a good voice, this variation is more marked the louder the tone. Fig. 1 shows the wave forms and spectra, plotting pressure-amplitudes, of four successive instants in one vibrato-cycle. The record is of a good-quality baritone voice singing "ah" loudly on Middle C. The variations in fundamental pitch and in total intensity are of course difficult to see from the wave form but the timbre change is very evident and is seen to consist of an interchange of energy between a relatively high region and a relatively low one. In the original film, the wave at a could be superposed on that at d, one vibrato-cycle later, with such considerable coincidence as to cause one to marvel at the precision of the vocal musculature as well as the fidelity of the recording apparatus.

Eleven male voices were ranked on the basis of their quality, by the judgment of teachers with experienced musical taste and extended acquaintance with the voices themselves. Records of single tones were taken under controlled conditions and classified visually on the rather indefinite basis of "amount and evenness of variation," by two persons who were unaware of whose records they were examining. The ranking secured even in this rough way approached very closely to a judgment of "quality" by ear. The importance of an even vibrato to the satisfying quality of a voice appears to be considerably greater than formerly realized. Tone-qualities which are quite disagreeable when sustained without a perceptible, even vibrato can be made passable if given artificially a proper amount of an even variation at proper vibrato speed. This does not mean that the vibrato is necessarily heard as a variation. Instead it imparts to the total complex tone a certain richness, to which we react unconsciously as part of the timbre, unless we learn to direct attention to it. The term "sonance," first used in this sense by Metfessel at the University of Iowa, has much to recommend it.

The vibrato appears to involve a large group of muscles and therefore is not to be explained as coming from this or that particular muscle. It is sometimes entirely unconscious in the singer, sometimes under partial conscious control, and in some individuals may be brought under definite voluntary control. The vocal "tremolo" is not entirely unrelated to the vibrato but is caused by incoordinated muscular tension, and expresses itself as an inartistic extreme of one or more of the three variables, or/and by a departure from the relatively "sinusoidal" variation of one or more of them. Also, it is often faster than 6 or 7 per second.

TOTAL INTENSITY

The second characteristic is found in the total intensity. The individual with good quality is usually able to produce a tone of considerably more intensity than an individual with a poor quality. The eleven men who sang the tones mentioned above were asked to sing them "as loudly as possible." The resulting records were harmonically analyzed and the amplitudes of the first 30 components added in each case, to secure a term representing loosely the total intensity of the tone. In the case of records showing an appreciable vibrato (such as Fig. 1), two or even three wave forms were selected from each record for analysis and their summations averaged to secure the "total intensity term." When the voices were ranked on the basis of these terms, they gave an order approximating the initial order-of-merit. The relatively large throat which is generally necessary to good tone makes possible this increase in intensity by permitting a more vigorous action of the cords, a free egress through the lower pharynx and over the tongue and a greater degree of resonating by tensing of the walls. Laryngoscopic photographs by Dr. G. Oscar Russell of Ohio State University, to whose pioneer work other investigators are indebted, show very clearly that in poor voice-production the opening that the sound has to go through to get to the mouth is sometimes nearly closed, either through a constricted pharynx or a partly closed epiglottis, or both, with consequent lessening of its strength.

LOW FORMANT

The third characteristic of good quality may be termed the low formant. Good male voices show a decided tendency toward strengthening a low partial somewhere in the general range of 500 cycles or lower. This in all probability takes place in the pharynx, which in the good tone is considerably enlarged and tensed through lowering of the larynx and stretchng of the epiglottis and sides of the throat. In the records so far analyzed, which were sung on Middle C, 262 cycles per second, the good voices had relatively strong 2nd partials (523 cycles), while the poorer ones shifted to 3rds, 4ths, or 5ths. Additional records should be analyzed on lower fundamental pitches, so a to produce more and closer partials in this critical range and permit more detailed study. Middle C was selected for harmonic analysis since many voices begin to show strain somewhere around this point.

This low formant may in some cases be the lower of the two vowel formants which contribute the particular vowel quality of the tone. However, there is usually a decided tendency in good voices to strengthen it relatively (sometimes at the expense of the upper vowel-determining formant) and sometimes to lower it still more. In such a vowel as "ah" in which the lower of the two vowel formants has been variously estimated around 800 cycles, our records show strong 2nds (523) in the better voices (though they do show strong 4ths as well, which correspond to one of the vowel formants). This is an explanation of the typical modification of vowel quality in singing, the vowel definition being weakened or even sacrificed so that the "tone" may be enlarged.

An illustration of the reality of the low formant in good tones is to be found in the fact that the voice teacher can secure a better quality "ah" by asking the student to add "oh." The vowel "oh" has a lower formant than "ah" and to change "ah" towards "oh" secures a larger resonator with tenser walls, which gives a somewhat lower pitch and larger amplitudes of vibration at this lower pitch. Even though the pharynx resonator should be greatly enlarged, it is very easy to keep its pitch from going down too low by slightly increasing the orifice. This, incidentally, will make it much easier for the sound to get out over the tongue.

Additional study is necessary to determine to what extent "chest resonance" may aid in the production of the low formant. The whole mechanism of the voice is so complicated and capable of so many different simultaneous adjustments that it is possible to get the same effect with various settings or quite different effects with what seem to be practically identical settings.

HIGH FORMANT

An overwhelming majority of the total number of records taken show the presence of a high formant, usually lying for male voices between approximately 2400 and 3200 cycles. This formant is present in varying amounts in all male voices tested, although in some poorer ones the range runs up higher, even occasionally as high as

5000 or 6000. Speaking generally, the better the voice, or the louder the tone, the more prominent this formant becomes, at least during some part of the vibrato cycle. Although its amount may vary with quality or with intensity, for the most part its pitch averages around 2800-2900 cycles, regardless of whether produced by a tenor or baritone, a good voice or a poor one, and regardless of the fundamental pitch, the vowel or the intensity. It has been found in pitches as low as A - 110 cycles, where it would correspond to about the 25th partial, and in pitches over two octaves higher such as tenor b'♭- 466 cycles, where it would correspond to the 6th partial. Table I shows how this occurs in a baritone subject, a concert artist with a recognized good voice-quality, for the vowel "ah." As the fundamentsl pitch is raised, successively lower-numbered partials are strengthened by resonance of some sort, in order that a large amount of the total energy of the tone may be kept in the formant region. Other vowels sung by this man show almost exactly the same high frequency.

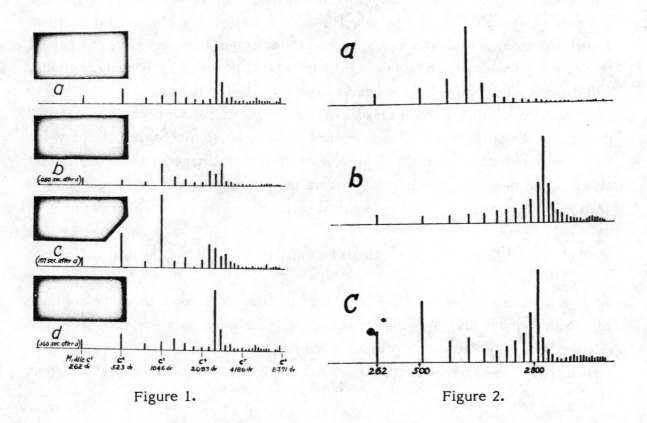

Figure 1.   Figure 2.

Table 1.

Subject	Vowel	Pitch		Partial	--High Formant-- Frequency	
FG(baritone)	(n)ah	A	110	25	2750	
	"	c	-131	23	3008	
	"	e♭	-156	20-21	3190	Aver-
	"	f♯	-185	16-17	3052	age
	"	a	-220	13	2860	fre-
	"	c'	-262	11	2878	quency-
	"	e'♭	-311	8-10	2800	2891
	"	f'♯	-370	7	2590	

Table II shows the same condition. It is of another vowel, "oh," from the records of a well-known Italian operatic tenor:

Table II.

Subject	Vowel	Pitch		Partial	--High Formant-- Frequency	
DB (tenor)	(n)oh	c	-131	21-22	2812	
	"	e♭	-156	18	2801	
	"	f♯	-185	16	2960	Aver-
	"	a	-220	13	2860	age
	"	c'	-262	11	2878	fre-
	"	e'♭	-311	10	3111	quency--
	"	f'♯	-370	8-9	3145	2921
	"	b'♭	-466	6	2797	

This same thing can be duplicated scores of times from our records.

Classical harmonic analysis, based as it is on arbitrary assumptions regarding the nature of the curve, does not tell the true story of the type of vibration present in a tone containing an inharmonic or even a damped harmonic component, as has been emphasized by Scripture and others, since it spreads the energy contained in such a component over several harmonic pitches. Fig. 2, a and b, shows the spectra of two synthetically drawn curves. a is from the analysis of a curve containing nothing but a damped 4th partial, b is from the analysis of a curve containing nothing but a logarithmically damped 12th partial. The spreading effect is very evident. In spite of this, however, it is equally evident that the harmonic technique can be used quite effectively in locating the midpoint or "center-of-gravity" of a formant region, particularly in statistical work averaging many records, and particulary in work on singing quality, where the relatively long sustained tone is much more the rule instead of the exception as in speech. Thus in Fig. 2 c, which is a composite spectrum secured by averaging the amplitudes of the harmonic components of wave forms from good male voices singing "oo" on Middle C, the presence of a low formant close to 500 cycles, and a high formant close to 2800, is clearly indicated. 11 wave forms were selected from the records of five good voices for these analyses in order to average out timbre-variations due to the vibrati.

But it must not be forgotten that a harmonic relation is not necessary between the formant frequency and the fundamental frequency of the cord tone. The high formant seems rather to be produced by a forced, shock-excitation of a resonant cavity, which is more or less damped during the period between two successive glottal puffs. Usually this high frequency is so prominent in the wave forms that it can be counted visually with ease. It has been found in records secured from two recording systems which were quite different in structure and characteristics from microphone to vibrator. And yet a search of the literature has failed to reveal any quantitative mention of it, with the exception of Helmholtz's observation (without apparatus) of "dissonant upper partials in the region for which our ear is so sensitive." However, Helmholtz considered this as "simply a characteristic of strained voices." An excellent acoustics text published within the last year reprints a spectrum of a bass voice completely lacking in this one characteristic which appears to be so typical of all good male voices, and even present in appreciable amounts in poor ones. The reason the dominance of this high formant and its relatively narrow limitation to a certain frequency region have apparently not been noted by other investigators is due either to frequency limitations in their recording apparatus, or perhaps to the fact that they have used "typical speakers." The typical speaking voice of the majority of individuals is produced with the throat in its normal position of relative constriction, which will lessen the amount of this high formant, whereas the singing voice is in this respect atypical, being generally produced by an enlarged and stretched throat.

The universal presence of this formant in at least moderate amounts, under all conditions of vocalization in the male voice (except the pure falsetto "oo"), points to a physiological structure of cartilaginous or even bony nature, incapable of the manifold and large changes of shape which most of the vocal organs can undergo. The only two such relatively constant structures which might be causing it are the nasal-head cavities, and the laryngeal chamber itself. The first of these has been ruled out by various considerations, the most conclusive of which is that with skill one may learn to lift the soft palate (velum) so as to close off completely the air-entrance to this nasal-head cavity, as may be demonstrated with a stethoscope applied to the nostril while singing, without appreciably changing the quality of the sung tone. This tone, when photographed, still shows the high formant, apparently as strong as ever. And besides, it is difficult to imagine how the narrow, irregular, and more or less soft-walled passages of the nasal-head system could be responsible for such strong resonance at such a high frequency.

This leaves only the larynx as the source of this ever-present frequency. Beyond doubt, the larynx itself is responsible for its generation, probably by acoustic reflections between the rima glottidis (the slit between the stretched cords at the bottom of the laryngeal chamber), and the top rim of the laryngo-epiglottal funnel (the rim formed by the top edges of the epiglottis and the aryteno-epiglottal fold). Euler, Willis, and others, in describing the act of phonation according to the glottal puff theory, which appears to be by far the most tenable theory of cord action, have explained how the vocal cords open explosively for a small fraction of the period of each fundamental vibration, emitting a sharp puff which travels with the velocity of sound to the mouth of the tube or funnel, where an echo of the pulsation will be formed which will run back again to the bottom (now closed by the touching cords, provided the cord-action has been explosive enough). Here it will "be reflected and again present itself at the mouth where a new echo will be produced, and so on in succession till the motion is destroyed by friction and imperfect reflection." This will result, says Willis, in the propagation of a succession of condensations and rarefactions, at intervals corresponding to the time required for the pulse to travel down the tube and back again. In other words, a short burst of the musical tone corresponding to a stopped pipe of the length in question, will be produced.

Willis was considering the whole pharynx, however, and apparently did not realize that the larynx itself could act as a pipe within a pipe, and (if its walls and rim were sufficiently stretched so as to minimize the damping, and perhaps with the resonating aid of the ventricles) even have a dominating effect on the wave form, since it is the first resonator to affect the cord-tone. When the throat is allowed to relax and become constricted, several things happen. The epiglottal tissues being no longer stretched, the aryteno-epiglottal rim becomes indistinct. The walls become softer. In addition, because of the disposition of the parts, the explosiveness of cord-opening lessens. In other words, the cords are open for a longer fraction of the fundamental period. If the cords do not close soon enough, the reflective power of the bottom of the larynx is greatly weakened, and the "2800" waves returning downward from the rim are met by an upward air-puff instead of a resisting surface. The ideal condition would perhaps be a near-instantaneous opening of the glottis to release a sharp and powerful compression wave, and an immediate closure of the cords to enable this compression wave to "echo" back and forth between the open rim-end and the closed bottom as a free, slowly-damping vibration of the air enclosed between the tensed walls. Actually, the glottis does not have to be perfectly closed each time after its opening in order to obtain the explosive action. It suffices that it oppose sufficient of an obstacle to the air to develop its elasticity, and a sufficiently closed bottom wall to make reflection of "2800" possible. When the throat is constricted, not even this condition holds. The sudden explosiveness of cord-action is lessened, the rim becomes indistinct, and the walls lose their tenseness. The result is that the effect of the short inside "pipe" lessens; i.e., there is a lessened production and a quicker damping of "2800." The outer pipe, from the cords to the curve of the tongue or even to the mouth, becomes the dominant factor. However, the pitch of this outer pipe - the low formant previously described - is then higher than in good tone-production, in which the larynx is pulled downwards. This lowering of the larynx increases the size of the lower throat, as is illustrated by the characteristic lowering of the low formant for good tones.

Convincing proof that the high formant is produced in the larynx itself is shown in Fig. 3. This is an oscillogram of the tone produced by blowing a completely excised larynx. For our purpose, the larynx of an animal, or even for that matter a mechanical larynx, serves almost as well as the human one, since we are here dealing merely with the phenomena of acoustic reflection, and whatever differences are present are more differences of degree than of kind. This record is from the larynx of a calf, and although the shape and dimensions of the calf-larynx are different from the human one, the differences are not so marked as to invalidate the testimony of this curve, in view of the striking parallelism in type between its damped high frequency and the simlar phenomenon at 2800-2900 in the human voice curves. The cord-tone (fundamental) is represented by the frequency of the cycle-groups, and the damped high frequency within each cycle-group corresponds to "2800." (The lower curve is a timing-wave.) It seems quite certain that a similar frequency would be secured by blowing an excised human larynx, although it has not been possible to verify this as yet. This photograph is interesting in its lack of any low frequencies, showing the absence of the effect of the pharynx and other higher-placed resonators, which in the good male voice bring ni 2ds, 3rds, 4ths, etc. It is difficult to avoid the conclusion that "2800" is produced immediately above the cords, probably in the manner outlined above, and before the low formant and the vowel characteristics are added to the tone, and certainly before any "head resonance" can have its effect.

The length of a stopped pipe which would give the tone of 2800 cycles would be approximately 3 cm. Although it is difficult to decide where the laryngeal pipe ends, with the epiglottis making one side longer than the other, with the prominence of the aryteno-epiglottal rim depending on the degree of stretching, and with the almost indeterminable effect of the ventricles, still it is within the range of possibility that its effective length is about 3 cm. In this connection, it is worthy of note that the length of the ear meatus is also about 3 cm, and that Helmholtz originally reported the ear as being unduly sensitive to the range (roughly) from 2640 to 3168 cycles, because of meatus resonance. Also, A. B. Wood has pointed out that the meatus, regarded as a closed pipe of effective length about 3 cm, has a resonant frequency about 2700 cycles. Although the results of audiograms secured by the Bell Laboratories do not appear to show a marked sensitivity at this point, the trough of their "threshold-of-audibility" curve, when the curve is considered as a whole, seems not far displaced from this region. For that matter, several threshold-of-audibility curves have been published, based on different sets of data, which do not entirely agree as to the position of the trough. Considering them all, the trough is evidently between 1000 and 4000 cycles, but it would seem difficult to say just where between these two points it should come, in view of the relatively low curvature, and in view of the fact that the curves have been smoothed.

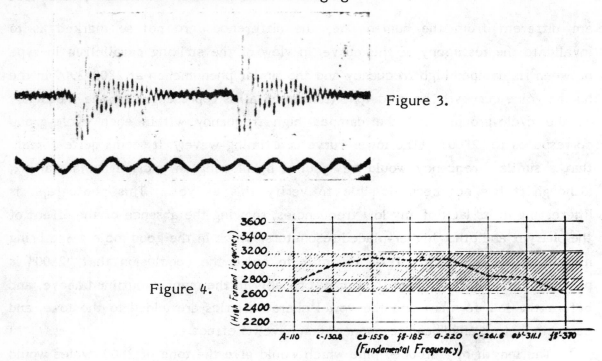

Figure 3.

Figure 4.

Figure 5.

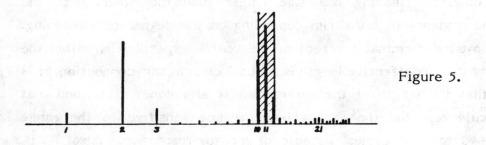

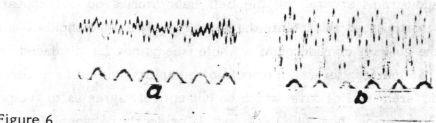

Figure 6

It is conceivable then that the better the voice, other things equal, the stronger does it make the high formant, and the more accurately and consistently does it center it around the center of the meatus resonance region. Fig. 4 shows how close this centering is for a good baritone, averaging the results of 41 records, using four vowels over the pitch range indicated. The shaded portion represents the area included between Helmholtz's roughly-deterined boundaries of meatus resonance (2640-3168).

In the case of a promising student with an "excellent natural voice," the high frequency was markedly prominent throughout a series of 24 records (4 vowels on 6 pitches), and was contained within the boundaries of 2640 and 3145 cycles, with an average at 2839. These figures, which seem too good to be true, were determined from a rough visual analysis, and tabulated, before the striking coincidence was noticed between them and Helmholtz's figures for the ear.

However, since the high formant is determined by the dimensions of the larynx itself, it is not surprising to find its <u>pitch</u> at least fairly constant in all voices, good and bad, although its <u>prominence</u> usually varies with the excellence of the voice. It would seem to be more than just coincidence, that the condition of the throat that makes possible a loud, full, "round" tone-production with minimum strain to the singer, should produce precisely that tone which, at least during a part of the vibrato-cycle, contains such a large amount of energy (sometimes well over 50 percent) in the relatively narrow frequency region for which his, and the listener's, ear is most sensitive. One is tempted to draw some interesting evolutionary conclusions.[2]

It must be borne in mind, however, that "2800" is not the <u>sole</u>, nor even the most important, determinant of good quality. Voices which possess it at the proper point and even which possess it in large degree, may still be of poor quality due to the lack of a suitable vibrato, of a low enough low formant, or of sufficient power. If these latter are present, the addition of a strong high frequency at the point for which the hearer's ear is most susceptible will have the effect of adding a very desirable "ring" or brilliance.

Additional corroboration of the reality of this high frequency is to be found in the fact that in good voices, which have considerable energy at this point, a slight peaking is sometimes found around 5700 cycles, showing that when the larynx pipe is energized strongly enough, its natural octave begins to appear. Fig. 5 has been selected to illustrate this. It shows the spectrum of a wave selected from that phase of the vibrato-cycle when the high formant was most prominent, and is from a baritone with a very good tone-quality, singing "(n)oo" on Middle C. The shaded portion represents Helmholtz's roughly-determined region of meatus resonance. The 10th and 11th partials appear to carry the bulk of the high frequency energy here. Remembering that the harmonic analysis has spread a single damped component over several harmonics, we would estimate its frequency to lie between the 10th and 11th partials, probably near the 10-1/2 point. The octave of 10-1/2 would be 21, and at the 21st partial we see a slight peaking. The effect is never marked, but appears in a sufficient number of spectra to warrant mentioning. If the above explanation is correct, however, it is evident that the larynx is not following the laws of simple stopped pipes whose length is large in comparison with their width, because the first natural overtone of such a pipe is the 3rd partial, giving the musical interval of a perfect twelfth. Perhaps the irregular shape of the larynx or its branching ventricles are in some way responsible for the introduction of the octave.

Fig. 6 illustrates the four characteristic attributes of good quality. A good tone and a poor one were produced by a baritone voice. a and b are from the good tone, and c and d from the poor one. a and b, and also c and d, have been selected approximately 1/13 second apart in order to indicate the timbre change between extremes of the vibrato cycle. A 500 cycle timing wave is visible also. Notice in this figure: first, the lack of the timbre-vibrato in the poor tone (the wave forms c and d being quite similar, and a and b quite different); second, the greater intensity of the good tone, indicated by the greater amplitude; third, the fact that the low characteristic, which is a third partial in the poor tone, has lowered to a second in the good one; and lastly, that the high frequency, which is quite marked in the good tone, is almost completely absent from the poor one.

These tones were sung on e'♭ - 311 cycles, so that the third partial in the poor tone falls at 933. There is some evidence to indicate that the presence of any considerable energy in the region around say 900 1500 cycles, when supported by a strong lower resonance, gives a tenorish quality to the voice, but when not so supported gives it a distinct ugly quality.

Investigations on the female voice have indicated the same four tendencies that have been noted in the male voice, with the exceptions that: (1)the high formant centers still higher, perhaps around 3200 cycles, corresponding to a somewhat smaller larynx; and (2) some types of tone with much smaller percentage of high formant are accepted as good. The coloratura type will sometimes have practically no high formant at all, but is also called good precisely because of its purity, and also because of its agility. As a matter of fact, in women there is a marked tendency for the high formant to drop out at some point as the pitch rises. It would seem that in women a much larger part is played by the light "head-voice" register which corresponds to the "falsetto" in men, and in which the cords are more bowed than used explosively as reeds. Stork's experiment (reported by Scripture), shows that if the larynx be illuminated below the cords by a light through the neck and be observed with a laryngoscope, the light is seen in increasing brightness through the cords as the pitch rises until in the head register there seems to be only a thin membrane in front of it. This shows that in high tones the time of closure diminishes in comparison with the time of opening, or in other words the explosiveness is lost. As this occurs, the high formant drops out, the vibration tending toward a sinusoidal form. If this tone lacks a satisfactory vibrato, it can become very objectionable indeed, especially if sustained at a high or loud pitch.

This paper has necessarily been lmited to the physical and physiological aspects of the problem. A fuller presentation of the physiological implications, and a discussion of the pedagogical principles involved in such matters as the so-called "placement," nasality, registers, etc., will be published elsewhere.

REFERENCES

1.   W. T. Bartholomew, A Technique for the Taking of Long Oscillograph Records, J. Exper. Psychol. 16, No. 2, Apr. (1933).

2.   It has also been reported that dogs are peculiarly sensitive to e'''', which is close to 2800. Perhaps this is why they frequently howl when hearing singing.

Quantitative Studies
on the
Singing Voice

S. K. Wolf, D. Stanley and W. J. Sette

Electrical Research Products, Inc., New York

INTRODUCTION

Heretofore exact consideration of the art of singing has been handicapped by the lack of suitable quantitative means for simply evaluating voice characteristics. Recently developed acoustical devices have made possible the inauguration of a series of physical tests on the singing voice resulting in a large amount of objective data of considerable potential significance. The factors studied include intensity as a function of time and pitch, vibrato, vibrato-tremolo and tremolo and quality. The fundamental aim of our work is to evaluate the caliber of a voice as completely as possible insofar as its external physical manifestations are concerned. Ultimately, we hope that it will be possible to establish a definite correspondence between these external manifestations and a singer's vocal equipment, thus obtaining an objective method for rating the latter. On the basis of present information it is possible to evaluate the performance of a singer in regard to some characteristics of his voice, and to demonstrate improvement or deterioration. It has also been found possible to evaluate certain phases of artistry depending on physical factors and mechanical control. We are, at this time, presenting a preliminary report of our findings.

DESCRIPTION OF INSTRUMENTS

The instruments used included an automatic level recorded,[1] a crystal analyzer[2] and an acoustic spectrometer,[3] all developed at the Bell Telephone Laboratories. As its name suggests, the automatic level recorder is a device for automatically securing a record of fluctuating sound pressure levels in decibels as a function of time. The frequency range extends from 30 to 10,000 cycles. The sensitivity of the stylus may be adjusted to follow intensity level changes up to 360 db per second. By driving the recorder paper and crystal analyzer tuning control synchronously, the horizontal axis may be made frequency instead of time, and a quick harmonic analysis obtained. The crystal harmonic analyzer has two separate filters incorporated, one giving a band width of 20 cycles, and the other of 200 cycles. The frequency range extends from 40 to 10,900 cycles. The acoustic spectrometer employs 144 reeds, each responding to a different frequency. The lowest reed frequency is 50 cycles, the other reeds being tuned at progressively increasing frequencies with a 2.93 percent interval; i.e., there are 24 reeds per octave. The maximum frequency is 3109 cycles. The reeds are adjusted to give equal response for equal input voltages, the deflections being proportional to the voltages and therefore to sound pressures at the pick-up microphone. A photographic attachment permits records to be obtained.

For all of our measurements the singers were located in an acoustically dead room with the instruments in an associated laboratory. A loud-speaking communication system between the two rooms permitted the transmission of instructions and the singing pitch. Normally, one experimenter remained with the singer for aural check and coaching, while another operated the electrical equipment. The use of a dead room with close microphone pick-up minimized the possibility of errors due to reflection interference. A Western Electric moving coil microphone was always employed as the sound pick-up.

PITCH INTENSITY MEASUREMENTS

If we consider ordinary physical experience, one type of measurement we would make on a singing voice is an examination of the acoustic output as a function of the singing pitch. In rating mechanical or electrical equipment, one criterion is the efficiency of the equipment over a given range of working conditions. In our case we have plotted the power as a function of the pitch range. While the ability to make a loud sound on a few tones does not indicate a good or well-used voice, the ability to sustain a high level of intensity over a wide range does indicate that the voice is being produced at high efficiency. In any case, one criterion for evaluating a voice is the power output available.

With this in mind, pitch-intensity measurements were made for more than fifty voices of various calibers, ranging from untrained singers and beginners to successful professional artists. The voices tested included various types of baritones, tenors, contraltos and sopranos. Unfortunately, no true, fully developed bass voice was available.

For such measurements, we used our automatic level recorder. The singer was placed in the acoustically dead room at a distance of fifteen inches from the pick-up microphone. He was told to sing the vowel "ah" at full intensity and as freely as possible. He was asked to start with the lowest tone which he could produce and to hold each tone for about five seconds. Readings were taken at whole tone intervals until the highest tone which he could produce was reached. The microphone was orientated on a level with the mouth and in such a direction as to secure sound incidence at an angle of thirty degrees from the normal. The microphone and level recorder were calibrated daily by means of a standard sound source.

In reading intensity values, the highest sustained part of the tracing was considered and where vibrato appeared, the repeated maxima were read. In most cases two sets of readings were made and the higher value for each tone plotted.

In the cases of women whose registers were isolated, but not coordinated, separate readings of the falsetto and the lower registers were taken so that, over a certain area of the range, two points were obtained. Where the registers were not isolated, only one curve could be obtained. A few readings were made of men's falsettos, but this test was not taken in most cases, since men should not use the falsetto in performance.

Figures given in this paper are all total sound output levels relative to one microwatt. They were computed from the measured intensity levels assuming hemispheric radiation from a singer's mouth. The assumption of hemispheric radiation seems the most likely one to make. However, a few tests we made indicated that the level existing fifteen inches from the side of the head were in the order of 4 db lower than those existing fifteen inches in front of the mouth.

This difference varied with the singing pitch. With the singer facing away from the microphone and his lips fifteen inches from it, the intensity was down an additional 2 db.   For vowel sounds other than "ah," the differences were of varying magnitudes. In general, the darker vowels showed smaller differences.

"Ah" was selected as the standard vowel to be sung, primarily because it is an open vowel and widely used in exercising. In order to investigate the relative intensities of the different vowels with regard to pitch, we took measurements over the ranges of five good baritones singing on the vowels "ah," "ay," "oo" and "ee." We then plotted the mean of these readings, as shown in Fig. 1. It will be noted that "ah" and "ay" are at a somewhat higher level than "oo" and "ee." This is not surprising in view of the fact that the mouth is generally in a somewhat closed position for the latter and relatively open for the former. The relatively smooth rise in intensity with pitch of three of these curves is an outstanding character-istic. For the vowel "ee" there is a sudden drop centering at the pitch of A below middle C (C = 261.6 cycles). This effect was extremely pronounced for some of the singers, but repeated measurements of the same voices did not show it to be consistently present. It is accompanied by a noticeable change in the quality of the vowel and the original quality being sung determines whether or not the drop occurs.   The effect was also noticed for a good contralto and apparently is connected in some way with the vowel determinants.

Our subsequent measurements are all concerned with the vowel "ah."

In order to obtain a basis of comparison, it was decided to draw two reference curves, one for male and one for female voices. For these curves the points used corresponded to the highest levels obtained by any singer on the various tones. In drawing the curve for men's voices, allowance was made at the extreme low end for the fact that no real bass voice was available. The curves, as well as the determining points, are shown in Fig. 2.

The ranges considered were from A_3 to G' (55 to 784 cycles) for men's voices and from A_2 to C''' sharp (110 to 2216 cycles) for women's voices.

It will be seen that there is a uniform rise in intensity in both curves as the pitch rises, except at the extreme upper end. The extreme high points are not well determined since, in the women's curve, only one girl tested was able to sing above G'' and, in the men's curve, only one man was able to sing above D' sharp. This may account for the droop at the top of both curves, For the balance of the curves, various singers were able to contribute.

It is possible that, if enough readings were taken from the voices of really great singers, the men's and women's curves would be exactly similar but an octave apart.

Various hypotheses are possible in order to explain the increase of intensity with pitch. As the pitch rises the tension on the vocal cords and on the muscles of the thorax increases. The resultant increase in breath pressure should partly account for the rise in intensity. Another possible explanation of increased intensity lies in the fact that, as the pitch rises, the lower harmonics generated by the larynx more nearly coincide with the resonance frequencies of the vowel sounds. If the assumption made by various people[4] that the distribution of energy among the partials generated by the vocal cords varies inversely as the cube of the harmonic number, then, when the lower partials of a high tone are accentuated through resonance, a higher level of energy should result. Still another consideration is that, if the amplitude of vibration remains constant with frequency, the energy should increase according to the square of the frequency. It is possible that all three factors enter into the phenomenon in some proportion. In any case, it is well known that a great deal more exertion is involved in singing a high tone than in producing a lower one. The phenomenonn is in accordance with the common observation that, when one speaks loudly, he raises the pitch.

The maximum values measured for both men and women were of the same order of magnitude, i.e., one watt. This compares with the value of forty-one microwatts given by Fletcher[5] for the average phonetic power of the vowel in the word "talk." For extremely loud speech, Fletcher gives one thousand microwatts. The values we found do not appear excessive when the fact that a soloist can be heard over a large orchestra and a chorus is remembered.

As already stated, the reference curves are a composite of all types of voices. We find that good voices of lower tessitura (contralto and baritone) meet or cross the reference curves for the lower and middle tones while those of higher tessitura (soprano and tenor) meet or cross them for the upper tones and tend to fall below at the middle and, more especially, at the low ends. Of course, this is only true where the voice is properly developed.

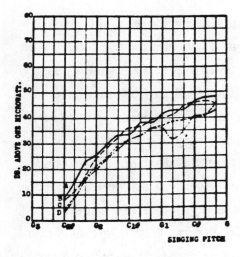

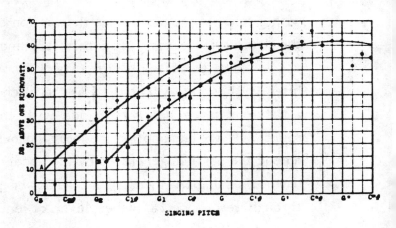

Figure 1.
Full voice power level vs. singing pitch.
Average levels produced by five
baritones.
A. AH——————. B. AY——————.
C. OO——————. D. EE——————.

Figure 2.
Full voice power level vs. singing pitch.
Reference curves. A. Men. B. Women.

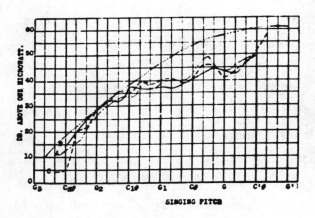

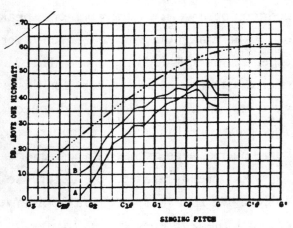

Figure 3.
Full voice power level vs. singing pitch.
Stabilized baritone.
A. 6/13/34 ——————.
B. 7/25/34 ——————.
C. 9/5/34 ——————.
Reference——————.

Figure 4.
Full voice power level vs. singing pitch.
Beginner baritone.
A. 6/7/34.
B. 10/17/34.
Reference——————.

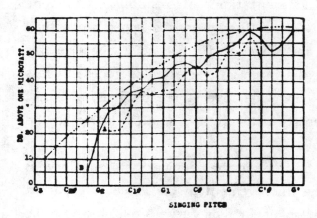

Figure 5.
Full voice power level vs. singing pitch.
Advanced student tenor.
A. 5/23/34 ------
B. 9/26/34 ————
Reference ——·——

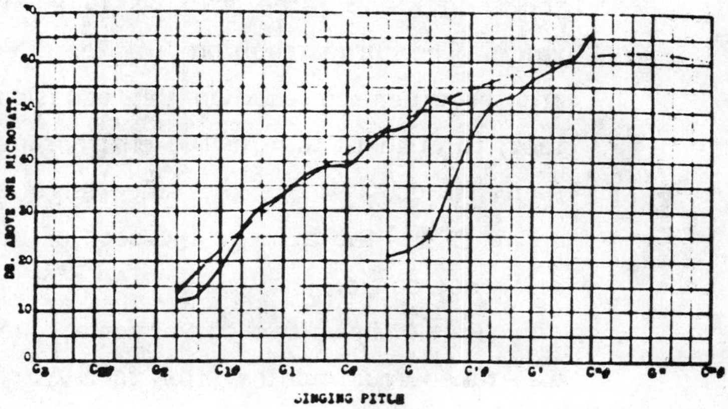

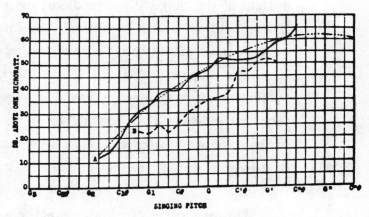

Figure 6.
Full voice power level vs. singing pitch.
Advanced student contralto.
Reference ——·——.

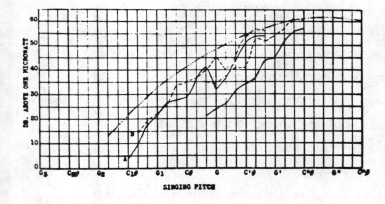

Figure 7.
Full voice power level vs. singing pitch.
Soprano (See Text).
A. 6/13/34 ———— .
B. 9/12/34 ------ .
Reference ——·—— .

Figure 8.
Full voice power level vs. singing pitch.
Two contraltos.
A. Student ————
B. Opera performer ------
Reference ——·——

EXAMPLES OF PITCH-INTENSITY READINGS

We will now consider some "pitch-intensity" curves take on the voices of individual singers. In order to demonstrate the relative consistency of our results, there are shown in Fig. 3 three tracings taken at different times of a stabilized baritone voice. The curve taken on July 25, 1934 is lower throughout the upper range than are the other curves. On this occasion, the singer had a bad cold. Despite this fact, throughout almost the entire range the intensity variation is generally less than five db. Notice that the range is very wide, over three octaves, and that above $D_1\sharp$ the average increase of intensity with pitch is small relative to the reference curve.

Fig. 4 shows two curves for a young baritone in the beginner's stage. Curve B was taken four months later than A. The improvement in his voice is apparent since curve B is situated from five to eight db higher than curve A over most of the range. Note in curve A the sudden drop which starts at D sharp. In curve B this effect does not take place until the tone F is reached. Notice also that the range has been extended by one whole tone. The voice is of limited range and the power level is rather low. Curve A is over 20 db below the reference curve at the top and bottom of the range. The middle of the range is somewhat better, but even here it is about 13 db down. In curve B the intensity has risen, and in the middle of the range, comes within about 8 db of the reference curve.

The drops starting at $D\sharp$ and F, i.e., at the uppermost tones, are paralleled by similar drops at diverse pitches for other voices. Pronounced drops of this sort seem to indicate that the higher tones are poorly produced. One physiological explanation we may offer is that a constriction of the throat occurs at such points. Whatever it is due to, the condition apparently is ameliorated in the course of training.

The two curves in Fig. 5 are for a fine tenor voice under training. Curve B was taken four months later than A and shows not only a striking increase in power but also a wide increase in range at both ends.

Curve A is somewhat irregular, and through the middle of the range is often ten or more db below the reference curve. Curve B is more regular and comes up throughout the range to within 5 db of the reference curve except for the lowest tones. The slight drop of 2 db between B and C' sharp in curve B may indicate a somewhat faulty adjustment for the C'$\sharp$ but the marked drop at D'$\sharp$, which does not occur for the contralto of Fig. 6, may be taken to indicate some physiological effect; i.e., improper resonation, reduced laryngeal efficiency, or both. Except for this drop and the minor one at C♯ , curve B has a relatively smooth rise, which we might assume to be a desirable attribute.

That the young man has exceptional talent may be assumed because of his high power level over a wide range, uniform rise of intensity with pitch, and from his susceptibility to training, judging by the progress shown by curve B.

Fig. 6 shows the curves for a fine contralto voice. In this case the lower register and the falsetto are plotted separately. Since equal intensities are shown on two consecutive tones; i.e., C'♯ and D'♯ , the former tone being produced with lower register adjustment and the latter with falsetto, she is able to sing up the scale without any sharp transition in intensity. The point at which she should change from lower register to falsetto at full intensity is, therefore, D'♯ . The curve crosses the reference curve at several points throughout the range with no material drop at any point and with the highest tone in the voice considerably above the reference curve. An unusually good voice of great power which should be effective throughout its extremely wide range is indicated. We have found with women's voices, that, where the range is wide and the intensity high over the range, the lower register is well developed.

Fig. 7 shows the "pitch-intensity" curves of a young soprano. These tracings are of particular interest because this girl, whose voice had been injured, had developed nodules on her vocal cords. At the inception of study, she was unable to sustain any tone and even her speaking voice broke. Before this time only the falsetto register had been employed for both the singing and the speaking voice and it had apparently been strained. The first curve was made some time after corrective treatment had been started. At this stage the lower register was well developed but the falsetto was still weak and the nodules on the vocal cords had not entirely disappeared. The second reading was made three months later when the nodules had disappeared and the strain on the falsetto mechanism was considerably alleviated. The interest in these curves lies principally in the wide change in the intensity of the falsetto throughout the range. The two registers were plotted separately for each occasion. The A curves are so far apart that there is obviously no point at which she could change register without an abrupt drop in intensity. The B curves show a smoothed out lower register of somewhat higher intensity, especially at G; while the falsetto shows an increase in intensity of up to 16 db. In this latter reading it may be seen that, if she changes register at B, there is no drop in intensity. The curves show a high intensity in the lower register at about C' sharp and in the upper part of the falsetto which touches the reference curve at B'. The range covered is three octaves, although as yet the intensity does not rise uniformly.

Fig. 8 shows the "pitch-intensity" curves of two contraltos. Curve A is that of the student shown in Fig. 6 and curve B is for the voice of an opera singer of some standing.

Considering curve B we find an intensity about 15 db below the reference curve throughout the middle of the range, and about 10 db below for the low tones. For the medium high tones (F' and G') the intensity is down less than 10 db. At A', the highest tone which this singer can reach, the intensity is down 10 db. The upper tones are lacking. Notice that the range covered by the opera singer is six whole tones less than that covered by the amateur. It was also observed that the former lacked lower register development.

It may be concluded from this and other similar cases we have tested that some singers are successful in spite of poor vocal equipment by reason of exceptional musical, dramatic or artistic attainments. It seems reasonable to assume, however, that such singers would have attained greater success with better vocal equipment.

CONSIDERATION OF VIBRATO CURVES

Another factor of great importance in singing is the movement of the voice, which imparts a live, pulsating character to sung tones. Some sort of movement is essential not only from a listener's viewpoint, but when correctly effected, is considered to be technically advantageous.

A consideration of the physiological mechanism involved leads to the conclusion that voice movements of quite different characteristics may occur. We are arbitrarily classifying them as vibrato, tremolo-vibrato, and tremolo. We have reason to believe that, for what we define as vibrato, there occurs a movement of the thorax as well as of the laryngeal and pharyngeal muscles, whereas in the other cases there is no such thorax action. The vibrato is of lower frequency, ranging from about 4.5 to 6.4 per second, whereas the tremolo and tremolo-vibrato range from about 6.5 to above 8 per second. The distinction between the latter is one of degree. When there is considerable variation in pitch and intensity at the higher range of speeds we term the movement tremolo-vibrato; otherwise we term it tremolo.

The intensity variation accompanying movement of the voice we measure with the automatic level recorder. As was to be expected, the variations differ between individuals and between separate readings for the same individual. Fig. 9 gives some examples. Specimens a and b show medium and wide vibratos, having a relatively even form. Specimens c and d have a sort of square characteristic. Specimens e and f are quite irregular, f suggesting the presence of either two unphased movements or harmonics of one fundamental movement.

Specimen g shows a tremolo, there being no intensity variation (within the one decibel minimum indication of the recorder) until the last second or so of the tone. Specimen i was taken from the same voice and on this tone an almost true vibrato is found. Specimens h and j are tracings of the tremolo-vibrato, the speeds being respectively 7.0 and 7.6 per second. It appears impossible for what we term the true vibrato to occur at this frequency. Specimen m shows a tracing from a recording of the voice of a baritone who at one time was one of the world's greatest singers. This tracing was made with the aid of the crystal analyzer in order to permit more definite measurement of the frequency of fluctuation, which turned out to be 7.5 per second. Other measurements of the movement of this singer's voice showed that he had a true vibrato for many of his tones. It is interesting to note that a little while after this recording was made, this singer practically lost his voice.

Specimen k shows a tracing of a tone started softly and swelled to fortissimo on the vibrato. It will be noted that at pianissimo there is no vibrato and that, as the intensity increases, the swinging of the vibrato increases until an intensity fluctuation of about 15 db is reached. Specimen e shows the intensity and frequency of fluctuation of a trill. The intensity change is of the order of 10 db and the frequency about 6.7 per second.

We have made measurements of the frequency of voice movements of some of the world's greatest artists, using phonograph records as our source of material. Out of 115 measurements the frequencies in the vicinity of 6.0 per second occurred thirty-one times and predominated over all other frequencies. We take this to mean that 6.0 per second is in the nature of an optimum frequency of variation, at

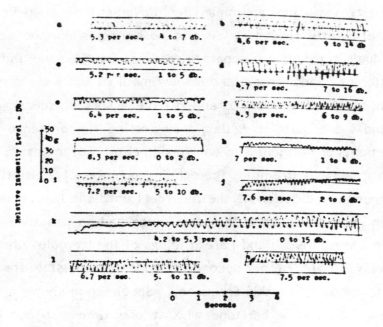

Figure 9.

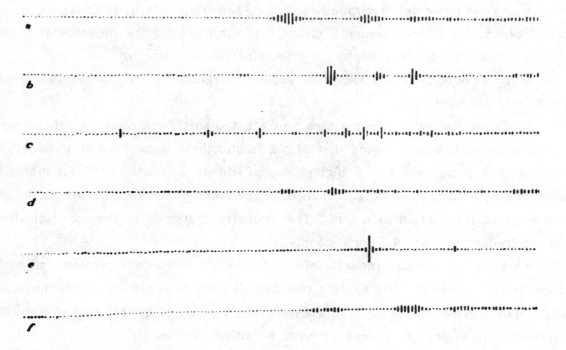

Figure 10.

least from the point of view of the person producing a tone. A frequency of less than about 4.5 per second does not appear as pleasing as do higher ones.

In our work we have studied the development of the vibrato in students undergoing training, and find that, as this development progresses, vibrato is introduced to a greater extent, the movement is intensified, and the frequency raised. The majority of students' readings fell between 5 and 6 per second.

The pitch variation occurring in the voice movements is also of considerable interest. In order to study this phenomenon our acoustic spectrometer was employed. The singers were requested to hold the tone and the acoustic spectrograms, shown in Fig. 10, were taken, using a three-second exposure. The deflections along the vertical axis are proportional to the sound pressure and the reed number is proportional to the pitch, along the horizontal axis.

In Fig. 10 are given specimens showing the various types of pitch fluctuations which may occur. The pitch variation which accompanies the vibrato may be very wide or relatively narrow. The graduation from wide to narrow is illustrated by specimens a, b and c. Specimen d shows the pitch variation occurring in a tremolo-vibrato. It will be observed that the pitch change is a relatively wide one. Specimen e shows the true tremolo frequency variation of a successful radio "crooner" of the better type of music; the frequency variation is so small as to be negligible. The pitch change occurring in the trill is a very wide one, as will be seen from specimen f. The trill is usually characterized by an intensity peak in the neighborhood of both high and low intensity points.

The results obtained with the spectrometer serve to indicate the relative amount of pitch variation occurring, but the absolute amount is not determined. This follows from a consideration of the physical and mathematical nature of the vibrato. In some respects, a vibrato tone is similar to what the engineer calls a frequency modulated signal, that is, it involves a tone whose frequency is varying periodically. In addition, the true vibrato also involves a periodic intensity variation. If only that part of it in the nature of a warble tone is considered, it will be recalled that it could be represented mathematically by the sum of an infinite number of components for each partial tone, these components being separated from each other by the frequency of the vibrato, i.e., by approximately six cycles per second. The amplitude of these components, or "side-bands" is determined by Bessel's functions, involving the vibrato rate and the percentage pitch variation occurring.

QUALITY

With regard to singing, the term "quality" takes on several aspects. In its strict scientific sense the term is used relative to the harmonic composition of a complex tone. However, with respect to the singing voice, it has assumed more general significance and is used with reference to the total impression created by sung tones. It includes not only harmonic distribution, but also the ability to vary it, maintenance of proper pitch and intensity, and the vibrato or tremolo movement of the tone. For the present we shall be concerned with the strict physical interpretation and discuss it as a factor in singing.

The quality of a phonated tone is then determined by the number, frequency and relative intensity of its components. That a singer has some control over this is evident since he can vary the "color" and change the vowel quality. Furthermore, it may be observed that quality and vowel quality both depend on the harmonic distribution. Only a few frequencies are necessary to determine a vowel although the other partials which are present must modify the impression created, i.e., impart such characteristics as "brilliance," "shrillness," etc. It may be possible to consider that frequencies outside the vowel bands determine vowel "timbre," whereas variations in relative levels of the partials within the bands determine merely the vowel. However, this can be true only within unknown limits, and we are not at this time prepared to make such a division. Accordingly the term "vowel quality" will be employed for that general factor in singing dependent on the harmonic configuration and corresponding to the physical conception of quality. With this in mind we may proceed to a discussion of experimental results.

Harmonic analyses were made with both the crystal analyzer-level recorder combination and the acoustic spectrometer. With the former the 200 cycle band was used giving adequate separation for pitches above and including middle C (261.6 cycles per sec.). The use of the 20-cycle band is impractical because of the wide frequency spread introduced by vibrato, especially for the higher partials. A motor was used to drive the analyzer tuning control from 100 to 4600 cycles per second in ten seconds. A few readings have also been made from 4600 to 10,900 cycles, but the amount of power contained within this range is usually very small. The acoustic spectrometer observations extended from 50 to 3100 cycles per second. Photographs were taken using a three-second exposure. Because of the influence of vibrato, and the contraction of the frequency range at the upper end (the instrument has a uniform pitch scale) which causes a crowding together of the partials, the spectrometer results serve mainly as qualitative indications.

To lay the foundations for a thorough investigation of vowel quality observations were made on the vowel "ah" intoned in different manners. Fig. 11 is a plot of readings taken with the crystal analyzer for a baritone voice singing middle C. The partial number is plotted along the horizontal axis, and the relative intensity level in decibels along the vertical axis. In the figure continuous curves are drawn through the intensity levels of the various partials. The upper set shows the spectra for "dark," "normal" and "white" intonations. When listened to, these are heard as "aw," "ah" and "ah" with a suggestion of a, respectively. It will be noticed that the dark quality is differentiated from the normal by a shift of energy to the lower partials in the region of the vowel determinants, whereas the reverse takes place with the white timbre. These shifts are a general occurrence and are, of course, directly traceable to the vowel characteristics. Variations in the relative intensity of the partials above the sixth (1570 cycles per second) are also apparent, but we are not yet ready to discuss their significance beyond stating that the brilliance of the tone must be affected. The lower set of curves are for dark nasal, normal and white nasal "ahs" on middle C, produced by the same singer using a purposely "shut off" technique. The so-called normal one differs from the normal one produced with an "open" technique, and a difference is audible. For the nasal tones there is present a relatively sharp peak in the determinant region. The appearance of such a peak, which does not always occur, seems to depend on the degree of nasality and the singing pitch.

When different singers are asked to sing the same vowel, marked differences in vowel quality are frequently noticeable. The question arises: Are there any general trends in the harmonic distributions of phonated tones which would indicate whether or not the vowel quality would be considered pleasing, and whether or not a singer is using his voice properly? For the former there is some affirmative evidence; for the latter our data have so far led to mainly negative conclusions. We present some typical data relative to these points.

The acoustic spectrometer was at first used to perform harmonic analyses. The types of results obtained are shown in Fig. 12. The vowel sung in all cases is "ah" on middle C. The first three, a_1, a_2 and a_3 are for a good baritone singing with dark, normal and white colors, respectively. It will be noticed that, as the vowel is brightened, there is a shift of energy upward along the pitch scale.

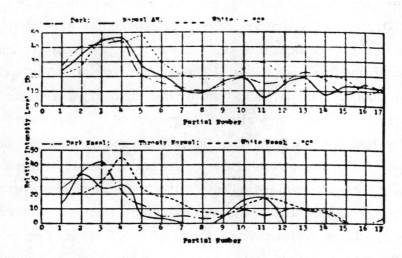

Figure 11.
Vowel "AH," "middle C," six qualities,
baritone.

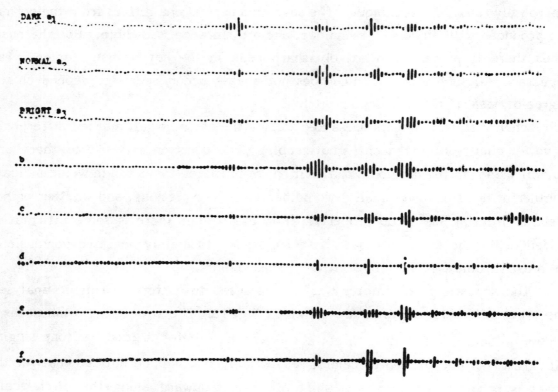

Figure 12.
Vowel "AH" — "C" — Different singers.

Specimens b, c and d are for three baritones who sang well, fairly well, and poorly, respectively; and e and f are two sopranos who sang well and poorly. The outstanding difference between the better and the bad singers is the lack of vibrato frequency spread which characterizes the poor voices. In regard to harmonic distribution, there is no pattern which may be selected as indicative of a good singer. For example, the good singer, b, has a prominent partial in the vicinity of 2500 cycles per second which is not present in a_1, a_2 and e. The fair singer c has an area of strong intensity in the vicinity of 2700 cycles, which is missing in the other voices. The poor singers, d and f, have prominent third and fourth partials, indicating a whitish quality, but the good singer, e, with a predominant fourth partial is whiter than either of these, and the fairly good singer, c, is the whitest of all the specimens.

A more limited amount of data taken with the crystal analyzer is similar in import. Fig. 13 shows the analyses for normal and white "ahs" as produced by three baritones. Two of these used their voices well. Their curves are shown in dotted form. Except for the fact that the singer who produced his voice badly (solid line) gives a lower intensity than the others, there is no consistently outstanding characteristic.

In Fig. 14 are shown analyses of the voices of three women. The upper curve corresponds to the pitch G above middle C and the lower curve to the pitch G below high C. The former was produced in the lower register and the latter in the falsetto. Here again the two good singers are shown by dotted lines and the poorly-produced voice by the solid line. It will be noticed that for G there is a very pronounced area of high intensity in the vicinity of the ninth partial (3528 cycles per second) for the poor singer. This voice, in the lower register is of shrill, disagreeable character. The curves of the lower set are rather similar in contour, despite the fact that the solid curve is of a throaty poorly-produced voice, while the other two curves are of well-produced voices. At this higher pitch, G', the vowel quality is relatively pleasing.

Our harmonic analyses represent averages over a period of time, and, as portrayed here, do not indicate the timbre variations occurring during the vibrato cycle. With the crystal analyzer the amount of time allowed for any one partial is of the order of one-half second, i.e., long enough to include about three vibrato cycles. Curves obtained using the level recorder and the crystal analyzer to

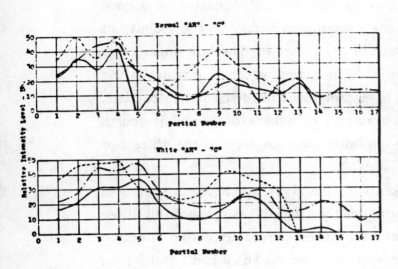

Figure 13.
Analyses of tones produced by three baritones.

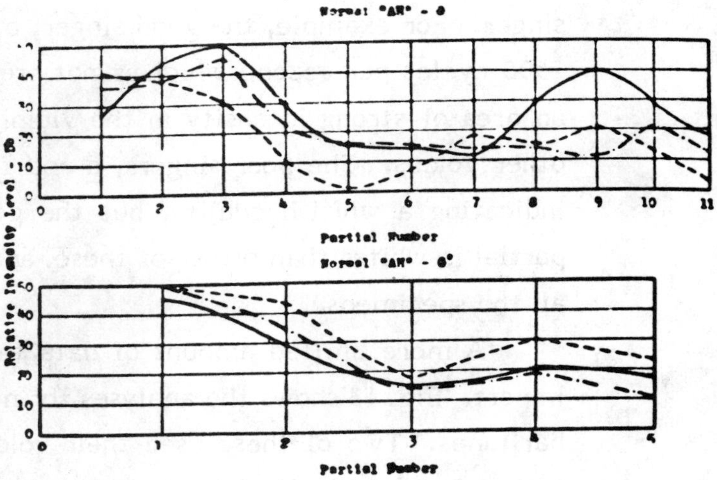

Figure 14.
Analyses of tones produced by three sopranos.

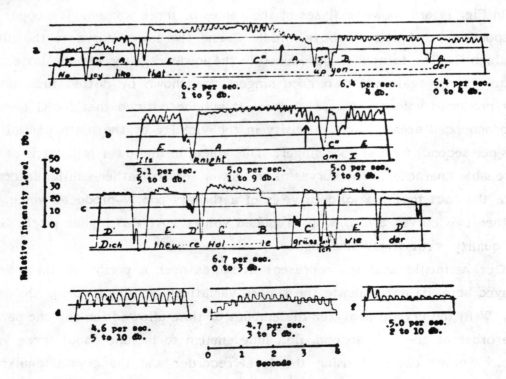

Figure 15.

indicate a few db change in level for any one partial in a vibrato cycle, but as yet we have made no attempt to determine the phase relations of these variations.

Another requirement for good singing concerns the ability of the singer to hold a constant mean pitch as long as the tone is sustained. If the pitch varies, apart from the vibrato fluctuation, the quality is not pleasant. It is not improbable that good musical quality, from the acoustical standpoint, lies primarily in accuracy of intonation and in proper vibrato variation, provided that the harmonic distribution is not abnormal.

In discussing Fig. 8 we showed how an artist could have a certain measure of success with limited vocal equipment. While this statement was not intended to depreciate the vital importance of voice, it did indicate the equally great importance of artistry. While many phases of artistry are a matter of temperament and can, therefore, hardly be measured in scientific terms, certain other phases involve mechanical skill.

Fig. 15 gives some illustrations of the use of the level recorder as an aid in studying a singer's performance.

One important factor in the interpretation of music lies in the singer's ability to start, or attack, a tone in the center of the pitch and to hold the tone constant at the desired intensity. When the tone is badly attacked, the singer starts under the pitch softly and slurs up, increasing the intensity as he raises pitch.

Specimen _e_ shows a level recorder tracing of a hesitant attack. Note that the intensity starts low and rises about ten db. It then almost immediately starts to drop and, just before the end, the intensity is down again about 7 db. This inability to attack and hold intensity suggests a singer of inferior artistic rating and also gives the impression of a weak voice, since the full intensity is not sustained. This singer could not interpret a song with a smooth legato.

Specimen _f_ shows an extremely vigorous, somewhat explosive attack. In this case the intensity of the tone, at the moment of attack, is about eight db higher than the intensity at which it is sustained. Constant use of an ultravigorous attack is inartistic, but for certain dramatic effects this device may be employed artistically. Notice that this singer is able to maintain a constant intensity. Specimen _d_ shows a well attacked and well sustained tone.

Specimen _a_ shows a musical phrase sung by a young man who is a good musician and who also uses his voice quite well. Notice that, except for the second tone $G_1\sharp$, and the E, which is intentionally swelled, each tone is struck at the desired intensity (or with a slightly too vigorous attack — as on the E) and maintained at a constant intensity. Notice the increase in the amplitude of the vibrato as he swells the E, and the relative smoothness and almost ideal frequency of the vibrato throughout. Notice also the vibrato run-down (see arrow) from C♯ to A_1. An inartistic or bad singer slurs from tone to tone and the vibrato disappears.

Specimen b shows a well-sung phrase from Wagner's Lohengrin. Each tone is struck squarely in the center. The high A is swelled and run down on the vibrato (see arrow). Notice that each tone rises to its proper intensity level, i.e., the A is at higher intensity than are the E's and both E's are at about the same intensity level. In specimen a, this relative intensity level is not always correct, since the E is no louder than the C♯ . A criticism of singer b lies in his vibrato which is somewhat too slow.

Specimen c shows an inartistically sung phrase from Wagner's Tannhauser. The voice is soprano. Notice the lack of proper vibrato throughout and the presence of a fluctuation at tremolo frequency. Notice that the D' at the end is about eight db below the C' which is nearly as loud as the E's. These deviations are not accountable for by vowel differences. There is a sag in intensity for each tone sung except the first. This indicates rendition which is poorly-balanced and lacks proper legato. Notice the absolute cessation of all movement of the voice as she slurs from G' to B on the word "Halle," and the failure to establish the tone D' on the syllable "re" of the word "theure." Notice the three rolled "r's."

CONCLUSION

The studies reported here represent a preliminary attempt to evaluate the mechanics of the singing voice. The continuation of such investigations we hope will lead eventually to norms of considerable practical value and shed new light on the voice mechanism and the manner in which it functions.

We are now undertaking a series of measurements, similar to those outlined here, on some of the world's great artists. Such tests were recently made on Giovanni Martinelli. His pitch-intensity curve showed a generally uniform increase of intensity with pitch, with the levels approximating those of the reference curve. The vibrato frequency was about 5.7 per second, the shape of the intensity variation being of a smooth rounded form, amplitude of 1 to 4 db. Harmonic analysis of several tones showed the presence of strong components between 2000-3300 cycles per second, partially explaining the well-known carrying power of the voice. Individual tones were well attacked and well sustained.

REFERENCES

1.   E. C. Wente, E. H. Bedell and K. D. Swartzel, J. Acous. Soc. Am. 6, 3 (1935).

2.   W. P. Mason, Bell Sys. Tech. J. July, 1934.

3.   C. N. Hickman, J. Acous. Soc. Am. 6, 2 (1934).

4.   J. C. Steinberg, J. Acous. Soc. Am. 6, 1 (1934).

5.   H. Fletcher, Speech and Hearing, pp. 67, 68.

Certain Results
of the
Analysis of
a Singer's Voice

S. N. Rzhevkin

In the voice of a highly qualified singer it is possible to detect the presence of sharply expressed "singer's formants" in the regions near 500 and 2500 cps; these "singer's formants" are identical for all vowels over the entire range from low notes to high notes. A comparison with the voice of an inexperienced singer shows that in the case of the latter the "singer's formants" are not sharply defined and are not stable; the upper formant, which controls the degree to which the voice sounds metallic, is absent. A hypothesis is offered concerning the rapid readjustment of the voice of an experienced singer from the speech position at the beginning of a vowel sound to the singing position which is characteristic of the steady-state extended portion of the sound.

Up to this time, a singer's voice as an acoustic phenomenon has seldom been examined, and then only superficially. The first important investigations in this field were made by V. D. Zernov (1), who determined the strength of the sound produced by a voice and the law according to which it varied with the height of the tone in singers with different kinds of voice training (F. Shaliapin, G. Pirogov, et al).

In 1927 V. S. Kazanskii and the author (2) recorded the voices of a number of singers by means of a mechanical oscillograph; we discovered that for well-trained singers' voices there is a characteristic region of amplified overtones (a singer's formant) which lies in the vicinity of 500 cps. Our data were then verified in papers by Bartholomew (3), as well as Wolf, Stanley and Sette (4). Bartholomew discovered a second singer's formant in the region 2800-3200 cps, in addition to the singer's formant in the region of 500 cps.

The cause of the insufficient study of a singer's voice by the field of acoustics results from the fact that only random individual work is being done in this field, i.e., no systematic investigations are being conducted. The utilization of the methods of modern acoustics is completely inadequate in vocal pedagogy as well as in the study of the physiological and psychological aspects of the singing voice. A survey of papers on the study of the singing voice is given by Hutton and Bell (5). Up to this time there is actually no theory of the singing voice. In order to create a voice theory, it is necessary to correlate the anatomic physiological characteristics of the vocal apparatus with the resulting acoustic effect. A deep acoustic-physiological investigation of the singing voice is a problem of great complexity and scope. In this paper we have only attempted to illuminate a small group of problems related to the analysis of the sound of a singing voice.

The material which is subjected to analysis in this paper was obtained as a result of recording a number of singers in one of the studios of the Moscow Radio Center. The recording of the curves which are characteristic of the acoustic pressure was accomplished by means of a loop oscillograph. We utilized a high-quality condenser microphone which permitted us to record sounds of frequencies from 50 to 6000 cps without distortion. The microphone was located approximately 2 m from the singer. The recordings were made during a brief time interval of approximately 0.2 sec; this interval was selected to coincide with the instant when the sound of the voice was completely steady. The curves for the majority of the sounds go through a certain variation with the passage of time; their amplitudes alternately increase and decrease, and this phenomenon is the result of "vibrato".

Basically, this paper provides detailed data resulting from the analysis of recordings which were made of just one singing voice -- that of the bass, D., a gifted singer with a very beautiful voice timbre; the range of his voice extended from sol-94 cps to sol-386 cps (47 recordings were made). For the purposes of comparison certain data for an inexperienced singer, R., are given (6 recordings); the voice of singer R. was quite powerful, but it dropped in richness on high notes (above re-288 cps).

The analysis of the recordings was accomplished by means of magnifying one cycle of the curve by means of magnifying one cycle of the curve by means of an epidiascope to an amplitude of 8-15 cm and then decomposing it into its harmonics by means of a mechanical analyzer using the Madier system; this device permits analysis to be made up to the 25-th harmonic. Not nearly all of the recordings were analyzed in view of the difficulty in this work. The most interesting recordings were investigated in several places, since the character of the curve often varied radically and it was thus essential to investigate the spectrum at various instants of sonority. Such repeated analyses, notwithstanding the difference in the shape of the curve, as a rule yielded similar results. The maximum number of the analyzed curves (49) was made for the voice of the bass D; 7 analyses were carried out for the baritone R.

Figures 1 and 2 show two spectra for the sounds of different singing voices for the vowel $\underline{a}$* at a frequency of 217 cps ($1a_1$). The scales of the graphs are plotted on a relative scale along the ordinates; one unit was everywhere considered to be the amplitude of the greatest harmonic. The envelopes of the curves were drawn through the tops of the ordinates of the spectra. The maximums of the envelopes determine the position of the formant regions which characterize the resonant frequency of the coupled system consisting of the throat and mouth cavities. In the voice of bass D. (Fig. 1), an amplification of harmonics is observed in the region near 500 cps and near 2800 cps; in the spectrum of the voice of Baritone R., there is a maximum amplification in the region of 1100 cps and a number of secondary maxima in the regions of 500, 1600, 3400 and 3700 cps. The difference in nature of these spectra is very substantial.

The resultant data given below in the graphs represents only a portion of the material that we have obtained; from among all of the spectra obtained we selected the typical and most characteristic ones. However, the general conclusions which are given below are based upon the entire experimental material. We did not observe any substantial deviations from the data provided.

The results of the analysis of a male singer are illustrated by means of graphs (Fig. 3-8) upon which several spectra are depicted at once; these results can be briefly formulated in the following manner:

1. In the sound of a high-quality singing voice (male) a sharp amplification of the overtones is observed in a narrow band of the high frequencies; the width of this band is approximately 1 tone (Fig. 3 for the vowel $\underline{a}$, Figs. 4-7 for various

---

* (Translator's Note: The most probable phonetic values for the Russian vowels mentioned in this article are, according to Webster's New Int. Dict., 2nd Ed., Unabridged, (1949) p. 75; a = ä, e = ā, i = ē, o = ō, u = o͞o).

vowels).   The center of this band lies in the interval 2500-3000 cps (re ♮ $_4$ - sol$_4$). It is convenient to call this characteristic region of amplified overtones the "upper singing formant".

2. In addition to the upper formant region a lower formant region is observed in the majority of sounds made by a good singing voice (Fig. 3 for the vowel a, Figs. 4-7 for various vowels); the center for this region lies between 400 and 600 cps (sol$_1$ - re$_2$). This region has a somewhat greater width than the upper region (2-3 tones). In the sounds of the vowels u and i which have a low speech formant, the lower singing formant sometimes is lowered to 250-400 cps. At the limiting upper note (fa ♮ -345 cps, Fig. 7) the position of the lower formant region is unstable.

3. The positions of the singing formant regions are identical for tones of all frequencies used and for all vowels (Figs. 4-7) and do not correspond to the formant regions of vowels in speech pronunciation. Speech formant regions are substantially wider than singing formant regions, and they are disposed differently.

4. The amplitude of the sound-pressure harmonics in the upper singing formant region for the vowel i is always greater than it is in the lower region (2-10 times greater). Conversely, for the vowel u the harmonics in the region of the lower formant are often stronger, although sometimes the reverse is observed. For the vowels o and e the amplitudes of the harmonics in both regions are approximately the same.

5. The fundamental tone in a forte singing sound is always weaker than the higher harmonics. The vowel u presents an exception in rare cases.

6. The investigation of sounds which are sung piano did not show a substantial difference in terms of their spectrum in comparison to sounds which were sung forte.

7. The investigation of the voice of an untrained singer (Baritone R.) with a sharp timbre showed that the lower formant in the sound produced by various vowels changes from 600 to 900 cps (Fig. 8). No sharply defined upper formant region is observed; only a certain general amplification of the harmonics is noted in the region of from 2500 to 3500 cps.

From the results which we obtained it is evident that the width of the formant regions of the singing voice is small in comparison to the speaking voice. This can be explained by the greater rigidity of the walls in all of the cavities of the voice apparatus in singing phonetics, in comparison to the situation for speech phonetics. This rigidity is evidently caused by the tension of the musculature of the larynx, throat and mouth cavity and produces a sharper tuning of the resonant cavities.

The other essential feature of the singing voice in comparison with the speaking voice is the fact that the singing formant regions are practically identical for all vowels and do not correspond to the formant regions which occur in speech pronunciation. In this connection the following question arises: in what manner is it possible to guarantee the articulation of vowels in singing phonetics, and how can sufficiently clear diction be achieved? This paradox can be explained if it is assumed that the introductory portion of the sound of the vowels (the period of "sound attack") is reproduced by the singer in a manner corresponding to the speech position of the resonant cavities, and thus the "impression" of the true articulation of this or that vowel is produced (i.e., the sound of the overtones in the corresponding frequency regions is guaranteed). After this introductory period the singer must readjust his entire voice apparatus as quickly as possible into the singing position in order to guarantee the necessary sonority and power in his voice.

It is only possible to attain sufficient speed in making such a readjustment by means of intensive training, and therefore only qualified singers can simultaneously guarantee both a clear diction and the mastery of singing tone. Beginning singers who can produce a good sound in their exercises can easily lose their singing tonal quality when rendering arias or romances, especially when they are rendered at a rapid tempo.

The conclusion which is thus underlined, that singing tone (vocale) is identical in its physical structure for all vowels, is of great importance. This fact indicates that the physiological-anatomic mechanism of a singer's voice is the same for all vowel sounds. This concept is without question essential for vocal pedagogy. In our work we did not investigate the initial portion of the vowel sounds; the proof of the postulates which we have stated concerning the rapid readjustment of the voice apparatus of singers requires additional investigation.

The presence of strong overtones in the region of the upper singing formant (corresponding to the region of maximum sensitivity of the ear) undoubtedly is the cause of that particular brightness of timbre in good singing voices which is often characterized by the word "metallic". Therefore a sharply defined upper singing formant should be considered fundamental and most important as a sign of a correctly trained singing voice.

The lower singing formant (which lies in the vicinity of 500 cps) evidently plays a less important role than the upper one. It corresponds to an amplification of the first harmonics of a male singing voice and most probably causes the impression of "power" or "bigness" in a voice.

The results we obtained here are based, for the time being, upon extremely tentative material. However, our results permitted us to note certain working hypotheses and paths for further investigations which must, in our opinion, be carried out in the future. The results of such investigations, undoubtedly, would have great scientific and practical significance.

LITERATURE CITED

1.   V. D. Zernov, Absolute Measurement of Sound Intensity (Moscow, 1909).

2.   V. S. Kazanskii and S. N. Rzhevkin, "Investigation of the sound timbre of the voice and of bow instruments," J. Appl. Phys. 1928, No. 5, 87-103.

3.   W. Bartholomew, "A physical definition of good voice quality in the male voice," J. Acoust. Soc. Am. 1934, 6, 25-33.

4.   S. Wolf, D. Stanley and W. Sette, "Quantitative studies on the singing voice," J. Acoust. Soc. Am. 1935, 6, 255, 266.

5.   Hutton and Bell, Central States Speech Journ. 1954.

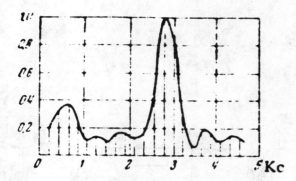

Figure 1.
Bass D., 1a-217 cps, the vowel a, forte.

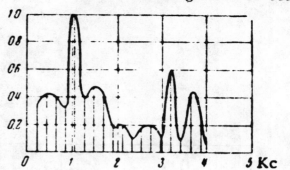

Figure 2.
Baritone R., 1a-217 cps, the vowel a, forte.

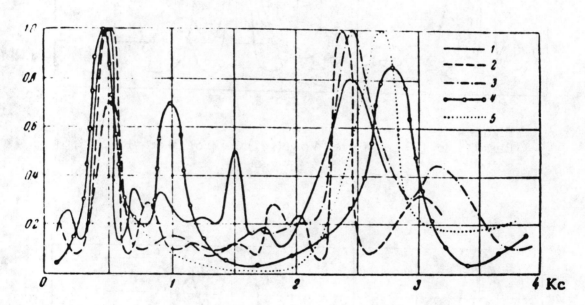

Figure 3.
Bass D., the vowel a, forte. 1) sol-94 cps; 2) do-129 cps; 3) 1a-169 cps; 4) do-259 cps; 5) re-288 cps.

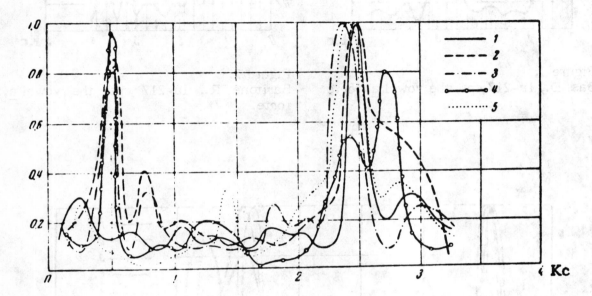

Figure 4.
Bass D., do-129 cps, forte. Vowels: 1) u; 2) o; 3) a; 4) e; 5) i.

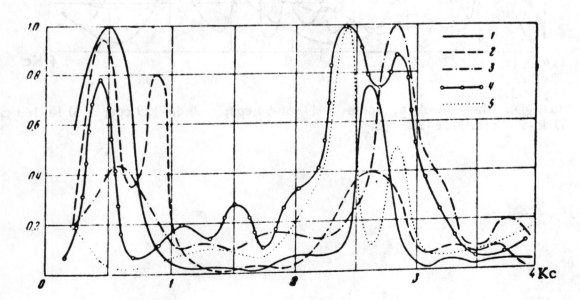

Figure 5.
Bass D., 1a-217 cps, forte. Vowels: 1) u; 2) o; 3) a; 4) e; 5) i.

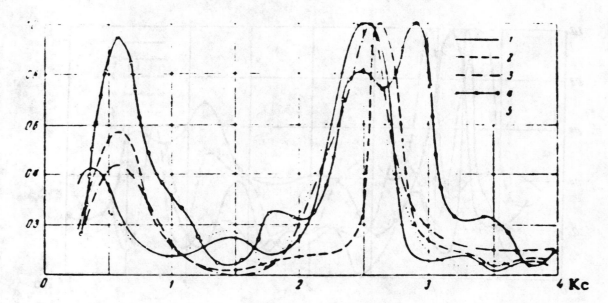

Figure 6.
Bass D., re-288 cps, forte, closed sound. 1) u; 2) o; 3) a; 4) e; 5) i.

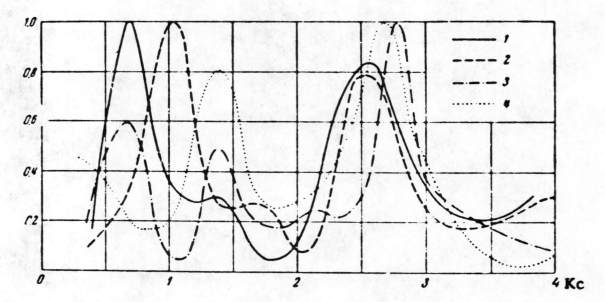

Figure 7.
Bass D., fa-345 cps, forte; closed found. 1) o; 2) a; 3) e; 4) i.

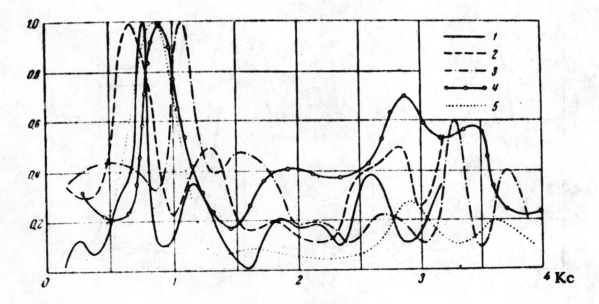

Figure 8.
Baritone R., vowel a, forte.   1) do-129 cps;   2) mi-167 cps;   3) la-217 cps;
4) re-288 cps; 5) mi-3$\overline{2}$5 cps.

Formant Structure
and Articulation of
Spoken and Sung Vowels

J. Sundberg

Department of Speech Communication

Royal Institute of Technology (KTH),

Stockholm (Head: Prof. G. Fant)

Acknowledgements. This work was supported by the Tri-Centennial Fund of the Bank of Sweden. The author wishes to thank Prof. Fant and his staff at the Department of Speech Communication, Royal Institute of Technology (KTH), Stockholm for valuable discussions and the singers for their kind co-operation.

I. FORMANT STRUCTURE

It is a common observation, that the vowel quality differs between speech and professional singing (1). This quality difference may be an effect of articulatory differences or by differences in the glottal wave form. The formant frequencies of a vowel is exclusively determined by the articulation (2). Thus, a difference in the formant frequencies between two items of a vowel articulated by one and the same subject justifies the conclusion, that the articulation was changed. An analysis of the formant frequencies of spoken and sung vowels thus enables us to tell, whether the difference in vowel quality is an effect of differences in the articulation. By means of synthesis experiments we also attain certain possibilities to determine to what extent differences in the glottal wave form may contribute to the quality differences.   The purpose of the present investigation is to study 1. those differences in the formant frequencies that seem characteristic between spoken and sung vowels and 2. those articulatory differences that correspond to these characteristic differences in the formant frequencies.

SUBJECTS

Four trained bass singers were engaged as subjects: B1, B2, B3, and B4. B1 and B4 are frequently engaged as soloists in church music performances and sometimes also at the Royal Opera in Stockholm. B2 is an experienced soloist of this Opera. B3 is to be considered as an amateur, but has twelve years of vocal training.

The singers represent different types of voices: B1 has an extremely dark voice quality and a range from C_2 to F_4, B2 a rather dark voice ranging from F_2 to G_4, B3 a rather light voice ranging from D_2 to F_4, and B4 a light voice ranging from F_2 to G_4.

THE ACOUSTIC MATERIAL

The formant frequencies of nine long Swedish vowels, (u), (o), (a), (æ), (e), (i), (y), (ʉ), (ø), were studied. Each of these were repeated three times preceded by an English r-sound in a carrier phrase: (De va̱ rV rV rV ja sa̱; It was rV rV rV I said). In a first series the spoken vowels were recorded, and in a second series the same phrases, sung on a constant fundamental frequency, F0, or on a simple melody, were recorded (F0 $\approx$ 110 Hz).   The tape recordings were made in a non-reverberant room with the microphone placed at a distance of about 17 cm in front of the mouth.

MEASUREMENTS

The formant frequencies were measured on sonagrams. As each vowel was repeated three times in each carrier phrase, three values of each formant frequency were obtained. No trend could be observed in these three values, and the mean values were calculated. These mean values are shown in figure 1. The fifth formant frequency is plotted only in those cases, where it appeared in all vowels.

The lighter voices tend to show more formants on the sonagrams than the darker, i.e. to have higher levels on the higher formants: The darkest voice B1 produced only four visible formants on the sonagrams, the rather dark voice B2 produced four in speech and five in singing.

Among the subjects some differences were found also in the formant frequencies. The darkest voice generally shows the lowest and the lightest voice the highest formant frequencies. In most cases, thus, the voices can be ordered B1, B2, B3, B4 using the formant frequency values as a ranking principle. Probably these differences in the formant frequencies of the individual singers are mainly due to different lengths of the vocal tracts.

The four diagrams in figure 1 all show grossly the same differences between the spoken and the sung vowels. Therefore, the mean value was calculated for the formant frequencies of each vowel in speech and in singing for all four subjects. These mean values are shown in figure 2. Fant has given mean values of the formant frequencies of the same vowels for seven male Swedish speakers (3). These values are also plotted in figure 2 for comparison.

Figure 2 shows that there are only small differences in the values of the first formant frequency, F1, between speech, singing, and Fant's data. For the second formant frequency, F2, only small differences appear between Fant's data and the singers' spoken vowels except for (ʉ) and (ø), whereas F2 is much lower in the sung vowels, the back vowels excluded. The third formant frequency, F3, also shows clear differences: Fant's data are higher than in the singers' speech, and considerably higher than in the sung vowels. This is not true for the back vowels, where the relations are approximately inversed. The values of the fourth and fifth formant frequencies, F4 and F5, show the most evident differences: Fant's data are highest, and the values of the sung vowels are lowest, and this statement applies to all vowels.

In table I are shown the relations between the third and fourth formant frequencies in spoken and sung vowels. The mean value of F4-F3 is for the spoken vowels 0.63 kHz and for the sung 0.50 kHz. The corresponding mean value for Fant's data is 0.90 kHz. Thus, F3 and F4 are closer in singing than in speaking and appear to be closer in trained voices than in untrained speaking voices.

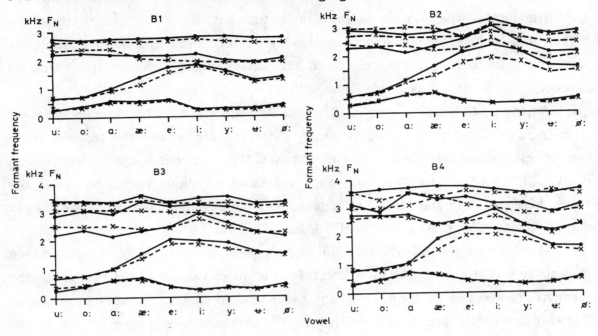

Figure 1.
Formant frequencies of four singers' long Swedish vowels. Solid lines: spoken vowels; dashed lines: sung vowels.

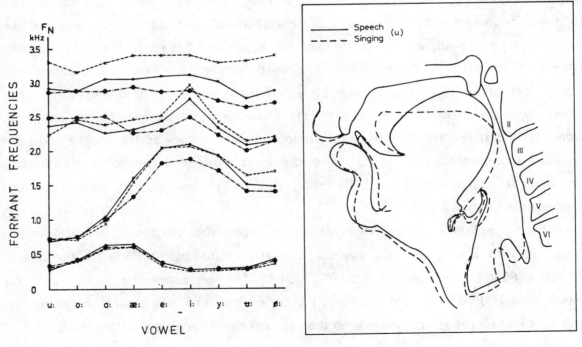

Figure 2.
Mean values of formant frequencies of long Swedish vowels. Dashed lines: Fant's data; solid lines: singers' spoken vowels; chain-dashed lines: singers' sung vowels.

Figure 3.
Tracings of lateral X-ray pictures for the vowel (u). Solid contour: spoken vowel. Dashed contour: sung vowel.

Table I. Frequency distance in kHz between F4 and F3

Vowel	Fant's mean values	Singers' spoken vowels	Singers' sung vowels
(u:)	1.07	0.55	0.38
(o:)	0.69	0.46	0.39
(a:)	0.81	0.79	0.38
(ae:)	0.95	0.74	0.67
(e:)	0.89	0.66	0.57
(i:)	0.44	0.35	0.39
(y:)	0.88	0.68	0.51
(ʉ:)	1.17	0.69	0.64
(ø:)	1.19	0.74	0.56
Mean value	0.90	0.63	0.50

To conclude, sung vowels as compared with the spoken vowels displayed the following four characteristics as regards the formant frequencies:

1. F2 is lowered in the non-back vowels; 2. F3 is raised in the back vowels and lowered in the other vowels; 3. F4 and F5 are lowered in all vowels; 4. the frequency distance between F3 and F4 is reduced in all vowels.

II. ARTICULATION

The mentioned differences in the formant frequencies between spoken and sung vowels obviously have some articulatory background, i.e. the singers introduce modifications in their ordinary vowel articulation when they sing. The nature of these presumed articulatory differences between spoken and sung vowels was analyzed by means of X-ray pictures and, as regards the lips, photographs[1]. The acoustical implications of the articulatory differences or perturbations were determined by means of an electrical line analogue (LEA) simulation technique (4).

X-RAY PICTURES

Three of the subjects presented above served as subjects. One of them, B2, had no possibility to submit himself to the radiological investigations. This, however, was of minor importance, since his formant frequency changes above was shown to be of the same nature as those of the other subjects.

The vowels were spoken in the context (en dV :t), and lateral X-ray pictures were taken during the articulation of the sustained vowel. The sound produced was simultaneously registered on a tape recorder. The same procedure was repeated for the sung vowels produced on a constant note (F0 $\approx$ 110 Hz).

The X-ray pictures included the entire vocal tract with lips, glottis and the frontal part of the cervical vertebrae (fig. 3). Neither filter nor contrast were used.

Frontal X-ray pictures of the larynx were also taken when the subjects spoke and sung an (a).

FORMANT FREQUENCY CHANGES

The formant frequencies of the vowels, spoken and sung during the X-ray photographing, were determined from sonagrams. The differences in the formant frequencies between the spoken and sung vowels were found to be of the same type as the above-mentioned.

However, one of the subjects, B4, did not produce these differences as clearly as in the preceding experiment. Also his articulation differences between the spoken and sung vowels were much smaller than for the other subjects. A formant frequency analysis was therefore made of vowels produced by this subject in some Swedish songs with piano accompaniment. Here, the formant frequencies differed clearly from those of the spoken vowels and in the same manner as for the other subjects. Therefore, the articulation of the sung vowels that this subject produced when the X-ray pictures were taken was not fully representative of his articulation in actual singing. It was concluded, that the mentioned differences in the formant frequencies between spoken and sung vowels seem to be typical and not very dependent on the articulatory context.

AREA FUNCTIONS

A meaningful study of the acoustical implications of articulatory differences requires knowledge of how the cross-sectional area varies as a function of the length of the vocal tract, i.e. of the area function. The exact procedure used for deriving area functions from the measures available on lateral X-ray pictures of the vocal tract, the frontal lip photos, and X-ray pictures of the larynx, is described elsewhere (5).

The accuracy of the computed area functions were tested on an electric line analogue, LEA, consisting of a series of electrical circuits, each corresponding to a length section of 0.5 cm of the vocal tract. Each section is adjustable to simulate a given cross-sectional area. In this way, the area values at every half centimeter of the vocal tract may be simulated on the analogue, and the formant frequencies of the complete area function may be measured. The agreement between the formant frequencies of the subject and those measured on the analogue thus informs us about the accuracy of the estimated area function.

Area functions were worked out for the spoken and sung vowels of one of the subjects (B1). The agreement between the formant frequencies of the subject and those measured on the analogue was acceptably good. The mean values of the differences between the formant frequencies of the subject and those measured on the analogue amounted to 5.7% for F1, 3.1% for F2, and 3.0% for F3. This provides an indication that the procedure for deriving area functions and computing formant frequencies is reasonably accurate and essentially correct. Moreover, the results support the assumption that the vowels were articulated without nasality also in singing (6).

The effects of articulatory differences were analyzed in the following way. On the area functions, simulated on the analogue, the area was reduced by 26% over a length of 1.5 cm. The effect of this modification was systematically evaluated at eleven different places along the vocal tract. Thus, the first four formant frequencies were measured after each perturbation. The percentual changes in formant frequency plotted as a function of the length of the vocal tract inform us about the acoustical sensitivity to small articulatory perturbations at different places in the vocal tract. Experiments with area functions obtained from other subjects than B1 showed that, between subjects, the perturbation sensitivity curves differ only slightly, provided that the place of maximum constriction is located at the same place in the vocal tract.

Perturbation sensitivity curves were worked out for the area functions pertaining to the spoken vowels of subject B1. In order to obtain a general view of the effects of perturbing the vocal tract at different places, the perturbation sensitivity curves for each formant of all nine vowels were plotted on the same graph. To make such plots feasible the length was normalized from $\underline{l} = 0$ at the lips and $\underline{l} = 1$ at the glottis. These plots, figure 4a-d, yield the information needed for a study of the acoustical implications of differences in the articulation of a given vowel.

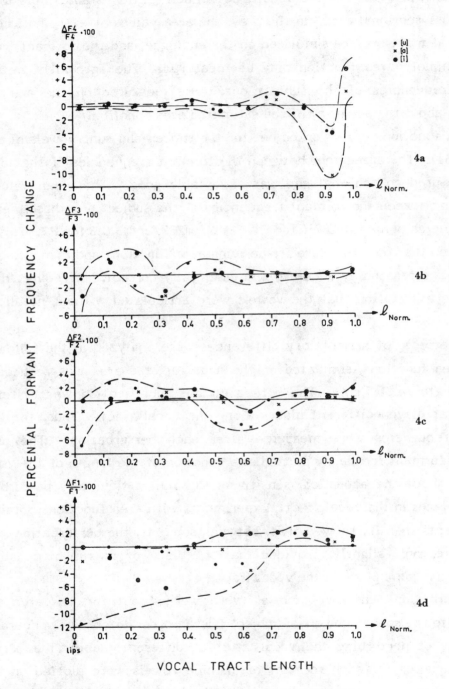

Figures 4a-d.
Percentual changes in the first four formant frequencies due to a perturbation inserted at eleven different places along the vocal tract simulated on the electrical line analogue LEA. The perturbation involved a narrowing of the area by 26% over a length of 1.5 cm. The area functions of the Swedish vowels (u), (o), (a̱), (æ), (e), (i), (y), (ʉ), and (ϕ) give values within the dashed lines.

Figure 4d shows, that the subject has to increase his mouth cavity or decrease the volume in the lower pharynx region, if he wants to rise his first formant frequency. According to figure 4c a narrowing in the middle of the pharynx will make F2 sink substantially in all vowels, but a narrowing of the cross-sectional area in the mouth will give a rise to F2 only if the area is not constricted before as is the case in (i). Figure 4b shows, that F3 can easily be altered by articulation differences in the mouth: a reduced volume immediately behind the incisors and an expanded volume in the soft palate region will rise F3. Finally, figure 4a illustrates, that F4 is practically insensitive to articulation differences outside the larynx tube. An expansion of the sinus morgagni and a narrowing of the entrance to the larynx tube lowers F4 essentially. This confirms the assumption made by Bartholomew, that the 'singing formant', located in the frequency region 2.5-3.0 kHz, is strongly dependent on the larynx tube (8). Actually, the larynx tube appears to behave as a Helmholtz resonator for the fourth formant, the volume element of which is constituted by the laryngeal ventricle. We will next proceed to study how the subject uses these possibilities to alter his formant frequencies in singing.

ARTICULATORY DIFFERENCES

From a physiological point of view there are several elements in the articulatory organs that are independently variable. In some of these dimensions, notably 1. larynx position, 2. the jaw and the lip openings, 3. the cross-sectional area of the vocal tract in the velum region, and 4. the tongue shape in the back vowels, typical differences were found between spoken and sung vowels. We will now describe these articulatory differences and discuss their consequences as regards the formant frequencies.

1. The position of the sagittal mid point of the rima glottis related to the lower frontal corner of the second cervical vertebra is shown in figure 5a. In speech the larynx assumes a high position in (e) and (i), whereas the rounded front vowels (y), (ʉ), and (ø) are articulated with a lower larynx. A high larynx position in vowels where the tongue is pulled upwards seems natural, since the tongue root and the larynx are attached to each other via the hyoid bone and the epiglottis.

Our acoustic analysis indicates that the larynx depression would be especially effective in (y). In singing, however, the big differences in larynx positions are smoothed out and the average position is lower (fig. 5b). This is in accordance with the findings of Faaborg-Andersen and Vennard, that muscles lowering the larynx are active in singing (7).

Singing teachers often recommend their pupils to sing (i) as (y). This might be a simple way to make the pupil lower his larynx, since the normal speech position of the larynx in (y) is much lower than in (i).

A lowering of the larynx implies a lengthening of the pharynx part of the vocal tract. The X-ray pictures showed that this length expansion takes place immediately above the epiglottis. A lowering of the larynx by 1 cm could therefore be simulated by simply inserting two extra length sections at the corresponding place on the analogue. The obtained lowering of the formant frequencies are shown on figure 5c. F3 is the least sensitive measured formant irrespective of vowels. F1 is the most sensitive formant in the back vowels, and F2 is the most sensitive in the front vowels. F4 is rather sensitive for all vowels.

Thus, the lowered F2 in the sung vowels may be an effect of the lowered larynx, since the degree of larynx lowering as well as the sensitivity of this formant to a lowered larynx both culminate in the front vowel series. Also the reduced frequency distance in the sung vowels between F3 and F4 may be partly explained with reference to the larynx lowering, since F4 is much more sensitive than F3 in all vowels.

2. The lip and the jaw openings were examined not only on the X-ray pictures, but also in a series of frontal and lateral photos, at least two for every spoken and sung vowel. From these photos it is possible to estimate the relations between the width of the mouth opening and its height and the position of the mouth corners (9). These relations are required for the estimation of the lip opening area.

The lip opening seems to be strongly dependent on the vocal effort. This circumstance appears likely when we examine figure 6 which shows a comparison of the degree of jaw opening with various efforts (10). As the effort increases, jaw opening - and thus, by implication, lip opening - also tends to increase. The depression of the mandible was observed to be larger in the sung vowels. The sound levels of the spoken vowels were lower than those of the sung vowels. The vocal effort was therefore presumably bigger when the subjects sang than when they spoke the vowels. Thus, the larger lip opening in the sung vowels, evident on figure 7a, and the lowered jaw could be effects of a difference in the vocal effort rather than characteristics of the sung vowels.

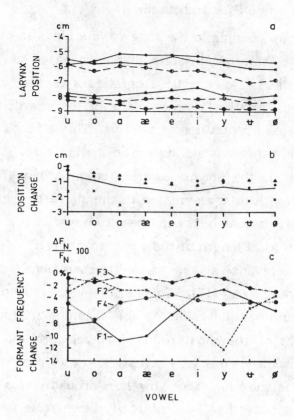

Figure 5.
(a) Larynx position in different Swedish vowels. Solid lines: spoken vowels; dashed lines: sung vowels. Subjects: ●, ⊙B1; x, ⊗B3; ▲, ⊕B4. (b) Difference in larynx position between spoken and sung Swedish vowels. Subjects: ● B1, x B3, ▲ B4. The solid line shows the mean values. (c) Changes in the formant frequencies due to a 1 cm lowering of the larynx as measured on the electrical line analogue LEA.

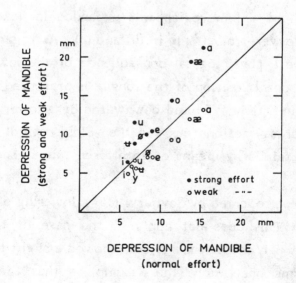

Figure 6.
The effect of the vocal effort on the depression of mandible. Measurements made by B. Lindblom, who also offered figure 6.

If, however, the lip opening in the sung vowels tends to be of the same size as in the spoken vowels or smaller, in spite of an increased jaw openings, as is the case with (e) and (i), this is likely to be a significant feature of the articulation of these vowels in singing. Another characteristic of the vowels (e) and (i) in singing is a considerably increased protrusion of the lips. This effect is also observed in (y) but is negligible in the other vowels, as shown in figure 7b. It is interesting that the protrusion as well as the larynx lowering culminate on the two spread front vowels. This observation is in agreement with the suggestion of Perkell, that there seem to be some interrelations between the larynx position and the lip protrusion, together governing the total length of the vocal tract (11).

An acoustically relevant variable of the lip conditions is the ratio between its effective length and rea, l_o/A_o (12). This ratio was increased by 50% in the area functions, and the obtained lowering of the formant frequencies are shown in figure 7c. F1 and F2 of the most rounded vowels are most sensitive. F3 is insensitive in the back vowels but very sensitive in the front vowels (e), (i), and (y). Thus, the lowered F3 in the sung front vowels is probably an effect of the changed lip articulation. F4 appeared to be practically insensitive to the lip perturbation introduced on the area functions: the maximum change amounted to $5^o/_{oo}$.

The main effect of a lowered jaw is a rise in F1, provided that the tongue shape is preserved (13). If the lowered jaw really is a characteristic of the sung vowels, it can be interpreted as a compensation of the effect on F1 of the lowered larynx.

3. The area in the velum region was expanded in nearly all sung vowels. Exceptions to this rule were found only in (ʉ) and (ø). As regards the front vowels this expansion may be a physiological consequence of the lowering of the larynx and the jaw. If the frontal position of the tongue is preserved and the tongue root and the jaw at the same time is pulled downwards by a lowered larynx, the result will be an expanded cross-sectional area in the velum region. In the back vowels the same effect is obtained by means of an altered tongue shape, as we shall see below.

In an investigation reported by Sovijarvi (14) a lowering of the soft palate was observed in singing. This does not apply in the case of the subjects of this investigation, even though one of the subjects showed a slight tendency on the back vowels. This confirms once more the assumption that the sung vowels were articulated without nasalization. The disagreement may be due to different singing methods or to the difference in F0 between this investigation and that of Sovijarvi.

Singing teachers frequently speak of the necessity of 'widening the throat' in singing. Probably, it is the mentioned expansion of the area in the velum region that gives this sensation. If so, this sensation would mainly be a sign of a lowered larynx in the front vowels.

The velum is situated at about 0.35 l-0.45 l in the normalized vocal tract. The acoustic consequences of an area expansion in this region are illustrated in figure 4a-d. F1 will rise in the front vowels and be rather unaffected in the back vowels. F2 will drop a little in all vowels. F3 will tend to rise, especially in the back vowels. Thus, the lowering of the larynx and the area expansion in the velum region both contribute to the lowering of F2 in the sung vowels. The rise in F3 of the back vowels may to a certain extent be an effect of the same articulatory difference.

4. The tongue shape is changed considerably only in the back vowels. In (u) and (o) the tongue tip is given a more frontal position in singing than in speech. At the same time the tongue root is pulled downwards by the slightly lowered larynx. The velar tongue shape in (u) and (o) is thus replaced by a pharyngeal shape, more resembling the tongue shape of an (a). Similar observations were made by Sovijarvi (14). This means, that the entire form of the frontal cavity is altered in the way demonstrated in figure 3. For the spoken back vowels the largest area is found immediately behind the incisors, and for the sung vowels the maximal values are situated in the velar region of the mouth, since the tongue tip fills out a good deal of the frontal part of it. These changes mainly affect F3, as is seen on figure 4a-d. The filled out frontal part of the mouth cavity and the expanded posterior part of it both tend to rise F3. The effect on other formant frequencies is small. Here we have a probable explanation of the raised F3 of the sung back vowels. The frontal X-ray pictures of the larynx, taken when the subjects spoke viz. sung an (a), displayed a pronounced expansion of the laryngeal ventrical and of the sinus piriformis in singing (fig. 8). In view of other investigations it seems probable, that this expansion belongs to the characteristics of the articulation of sung vowels (15). Such an expansion would lower all formant frequencies but substantially only F4. However, van den Berg has observed differences in the shape of the larynx tube between vowels, and it did not seem advisable to check this by means of a complete series of 18 frontal X-ray pictures because of the risk of

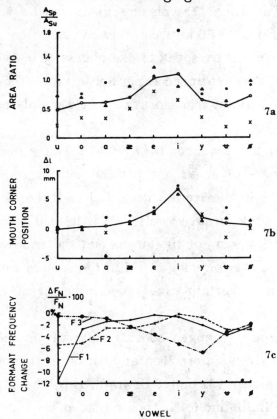

Figure 7.

(a) Ratio between the lip opening area of spoken (A_{sp}) and sung (A_{su}) vowels. Subjects: ●B1, x B3, ▲B4.   The solid line shows the mean values.   (b) The difference in mouth corner position relative to the insicors between spoken and sung vowels. Subjects: ●B1, x B3, ▲B4. The solid line shows the mean values. (c) Changes in the formant frequencies due to an increase in $\underline{l}_o/A_o$ by 50% as measured on the electric line analogue LEA.

damaging the larynx (16). This question is therefore left open. The same is true with the eventual difference in the sinus piriformis, even though experiments showed that an expansion there tends to lower F5 substantially.

DISCUSSION

Above we have found support for ascribing certain formant frequency differences between spoken and sung vowels to certain articulatory differences: 1. The lower F2 in the front vowels is an effect of the lowered larynx and its physiological consequence in the velum region; 2. the rise in F3 in the back vowels is an effect of an altered tongue shape involving a decrease of the cavity immediately behind the incisors and an increase of the posterior part of the mouth cavity. In the front vowels the lowered F3 is an effect of the lowered larynx and, as regards the spread front vowels, also of an increased lip protrusion; 3. the lowered F4 is an effect of the lowered larynx; 4. the reduced frequency distance between F3 and F4 is a consequence of articulatory differences mentioned under 2. and 3.

Let us now discuss why the spoken and sung vowels are articulated differently. Is it in order to achieve certain aesthetical, or better, acoustical characteristics of the sung note, or is it for physiological reasons?

It is a common observation that the sound level in the frequency range 2.5–3 kHz is abnormally high in sung vowels (8, 17, 18, 19, 20). This increase is often referred to as the 'singing formant'. When F2 is low in frequency, as in the back vowels, the spectral level in this frequency range is low (21). However, it can be raised if the higher formants are brought closer in frequency. This is illustrated in figure 9a, showing the spectral envelope of an (u) with the formant values normal for this vowel according to Fant, and with the source characteristic – 10 dB/oct (3). The graph also shows what happens to the spectral level if F3, F4, and F5 are brought closer in frequency.

It is seen on figure 9b that this spectral envelope matches an actually sung vowel spectrum envelope of an (u). Experiments indicated that the 'singing formant' can be explained in the same manner in other vowels.

The source characteristic, –10 dB/oct, is not typical of untrained voices according to Martony (22). The source spectrum of untrained speakers falls between 12 and 18 dB/oct. This indicates that the vocal training changes the source characteristics substantially (23). Another fact, supporting the same

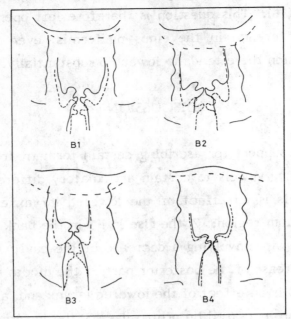

Figure 8.
Tracings of frontal X-ray pictures of four singers' neck and chin when articulating an (a)-sound.

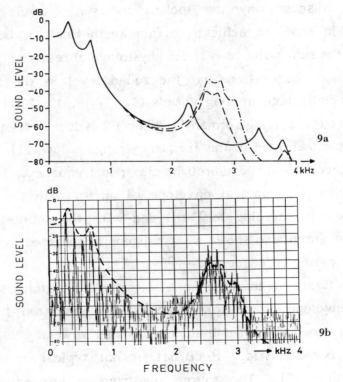

Figure 9.
(a) Spectral envelopes of the vowel (u) simulated on a terminal analogue and demonstrating the effects of a reduced frequency distance between the third, fourth, and fifth formants. Source characteristic: -10 dB/oct. (b) Spectrum of a sung (u). The dashed curve is the same as the chain dashed curve on the upper figure.

conclusion is the 8 dB discrepancy in the level of the fundamental between the sung and synthesized note. The differences in the source spectrum between spoken and sung vowels remain to be investigated in greater detail.

The 'singing formant' mentioned by several authors, thus seems to consist of a group of two or three formants. When these formants come very close in frequency, as in the sung (u), (a), and (i) (tab. I), they will appear as one single peak in a broad band spectral analysis. Several investigations of the acoustical characteristics of sung vowels have been restricted to these three vowels, giving the corners in an F1-F2 formant diagram. This might be an explanation to why the formant group has been interpreted as one single 'singing formant'.

The 'singing formant' appears especially in the back vowels to give the timbre 'brilliance'. The singer seems to bring about this spectrum characteristic by a skilled control of the higher formant complex apparently obtainable without nasalization. However, needless to say, other singers may employ different methods.

So far, we have found a plausible reason for the articulatory modifications of the back vowels. In the front vowels, the big difference appears in the larynx position and in the lip opening. Probably, the larynx lowering is made for physiological reasons. It is well known that singing with a high larynx position may damage the vocal cords (24). A reason for this might be that a low larynx position makes the tissues between the thyroid and cricoid cartilages more lax. The shifts in the relative position of these two cartilages, required for the big pitch variations in singing, could be made with less muscular activity, if the tissues joining them are lax (25). However, this is a question for future research. The differences in the lip opening might be due to habits associated with the adjustment of the larynx position.

Finally, it should be emphasized, that this investigation is based on observations from a restricted number of bass singers singing a rather low note. It is of course possible that the observed articulation in singing is dependent on the type of voice, the pitch, and the shape of the vocal tract.

SUMMARY

The formant frequencies of nine Swedish vowels spoken and sung on a low pitch by four trained bass singers are analyzed. Certain typical differences are hereby observed between the spoken and sung versions of the same vowel. The articulation in speech and singing of these vowels is studied by means of lateral X-ray pictures of the entire vocal tract and photographs of the lip opening. Certain typical differences in the position of the various articulatory organs are hereby observed. The sensitivity to perturbations in different parts of the vocal tract of the area functions pertaining to the vowels is investigated by means of experiments with an electrical line analogue. Using this information, the differences in the formant frequencies between the spoken and sung version of the same vowels could be correlated with the observed modifications of the articulation of the vowels in speech and singing. An acoustical explanation to the generation of the 'singing formant' is suggested, and the reason for the articulatory differences is discussed.

REFERENCES

1. Cornut, G. et Lafon, J.-C.: Etude acoustique comparative des phonemes vocaliques de la voix parlee et chantee. Folia phoniat. 12: 188-196 (1960).

2. Fant, G.: Acoustic theory of speech production (Mouton & Co., 's-Gravenhage 1960).

3. Fant, G.: Acoustic analysis and synthesis of speech with applications to Swedish. Ericsson techn. 15: 64 (1959).

4. Fant, G.: Acoustic theory of speech production, p. 99 (Mouton & Co., 's-Gravenhage 1960).

5. Sundberg, J.: On the problem of obtaining area functions from lateral X-ray pictures of the vocal tract. STL-QPSR 1/1969: 43 (KTH, Stockholm).

6. Vennard, W.: An experiment to evaluate the importance of nasal resonance in singing. Folia phoniat. 16: 146 (1964).

7. Faaborg-Andersen, K. and Vennard, W.: Electromyography of extrinsic laryngeal muscles during phonation of different vowels. Ann. Otol. Rhinol. Laryng. 73: 248 (1964).

8. Bartholomew, W. T.: A physical definition of 'good voice quality' in the male voice. J. Acoust. Soc. Amer. 6: 27 (1934).

9. Fromkin, V.: Lip position in American English vowels. Language and Speech 7: 215-225 (1964).

10. Lindblom, B.: Personal communication.

11. Perkell, J. S.: Physiology of speech production: Results and implications of a quantitative cineradiographic study (M.I.T.-Press, Cambridge, Mass. 1968).

12. See ref. (2).

13. Lindblom, B. and Sundberg, J.: A quantitative model of vowel production and the distinctive features of Swedish vowels. STL-QPSR 1/1969: 14-32 (KTH, Stockholm).

14. Sovijarvi, A.: Die gehaltenen, geflusterten und gesungenen Vokale and Nasale der finnischen Sprache (Annales Academiae Scientiarum Fennicae B XLIV, 2, Helsinki 1938).

15. Flach, M.: Uber die unterschiedliche Grosse der Morgagnischen Ventrikel bei Sangern. Folia phoniat. 16: 67-74 (1964).

16. van den Berg, Jw.: On the role of the laryngeal ventricle in voice production. Folia phoniat. 7: 57-69 (1955).

17. Fry, D. B. and Manen, L.: Basis for the acoustical study of singing. J. Acoust. Soc. Amer. 29: 690-692 (1957).

18.   McGinnis, C. S.; Elnick, M. and Kraichman, M.: Study of the vowel formants of well-known male operatic singers. J. Acoust. Soc. Amer. 23: 440-446 (1951).

19.   Rzhevkin, S. N.: Certain results of the analysis of a singer's voice. Sov. phys. acoust. 2: 215-220 (1956).

20.   Vennard, W.: Singing, the mechanism and the technique (Fischer, Inc., New York 1967).

21.   See ref. (2).

22.   Martony, J.: Studies of the voice source. STL-QPSR, 1/1965: 4-9 (KTH, Stockholm).

23.   Donovan, R.: Variables of laryngeal tone. Folia phoniat. 19: 281-296 (1967).

24.   Luchsinger, R., and Arnold, G. E.: Lehrbuch der Stimm- und Sprachheilkunde (Springer, Wien 1959).

25.   Fant, G.: Personal communication (1969).

The X-ray pictures were obtained by kind co-operation with Dr. Lagergren, Karolinska Sjukhuset, 104 01 Stockholm 60, Sweden.

Studies of
the Soprano Voice

Johan Sundberg

Acknowledgement. This research was supported by the Bank of Sweden Tercentenary Foundation.

Acoustic investigations of female singing are rather rare. The reason for this certainly is the difficulty of explaining the acoustic data. In vowels with fundamental frequencies in the range of 250 to 1000 Hz or even higher, it is hardly possible to identify the effects of the two major acoustic spectrum determinants, i.e., the glottal sound source and the vocal-tract sound transfer characteristics, normally described in terms of the formant frequencies. In other words one can seldom be sure if a difference between two vowel spectra is due to a difference in the phonation or in the articulation or both.

However, an attempt was recently made to estimate the formant frequencies in a professional soprano singing various vowels on different pitches. The present paper is centered around the results of that study. The purpose is to point out a couple of questions raised by the results and to suggest answers to some of them. The questions deal with audibility, vowel identification, vibrato, the glottal sound source, and registers.

Our starting point will be a study of the formant frequencies in a soprano subject, and that study will first be recapitulated (Sundberg, 1975a). It is a common observation that female singers have extremely wide jaw openings when they sing high pitches. This is illustrated in figure 1.

Figure 1 shows photos of the lip opening for the vowels (u) (upper series) and (i) (lower series). The fundamental frequency, f_o, i.e., the pitch, increases from left to right in the picture. We see that the normally small lip opening for these vowels is considerably increased as the fundamental frequency rises. Empirical knowledge along with a systematic study of other sopranos tells us that this is typical for sopranos.

What is the reason for this pitch-dependent articulation? It is well known that articulatory changes affect the formant frequencies, and that the jaw opening is particularly influential on the first formant frequency. Thus, we have reason to suspect that at least the first formant frequency is changed in a pitch-dependent manner. Using different and independent methods an attempt was made to estimate the formant frequencies in a soprano subject. The resulting values are shown in figure 2.

Figure 2 shows the frequencies of the two lowest formants in six vowels sung at different pitches. The dotted lines refer to the first formant and the dashed lines to the second formant. Evidently, the formant frequencies change with the fundamental frequency. As regards the first formant, the principle seems to be that it retains a speech-like value as long as this value is higher than the fundamental frequency. Above that fundamental frequency the first formant joins the fundamental. This can be observed in the picture, as the thin solid lines coursing diagonally indicate the frequencies of the eight lowest spectrum partials: the first formant frequency is never considerably lower than the frequency of the first partial. Recalling that an increase of the jaw opening tends to raise the first formant frequency, we realize that the results shown in the figure seem to explain why the jaw opening is increased with the pitch. The pitch-dependent jaw opening in female singing seems to reflect a tuning of the first formant to a frequency close to the fundamental in high-pitched vowels.

Facing these results we may ask why the first formant matches the fundamental at high pitches. A spectrum partial is more emphasized, the closer it is to a formant frequency. If the fundamental almost coincides with the first formant, it will gain considerably in amplitude and dominate the spectrum. The fundamental is normally the strongest of the source spectrum partials. Therefore the soprano produces vowels with maximum amplitude when she tunes the first formant to the fundamental, other things being equal. Moreover, if she kept the formants constant, the overall spectrum amplitude would vary considerably with the pitch, depending on the frequency distance between the formants and the partials.

The obvious benefit of tuning the first formant to the fundamental in high-pitched vowels is that the loudness - and thus the audibility - of the voice is raised to a maximum without extra costs in terms of vocal effort. Additionally, dramatic amplitude variations with pitch are avoided. We may conclude that the soprano saves her voice by varying her jaw opening with the pitch.

We have seen that the soprano deviates considerably from the formant-frequency values that are normal when she speaks. Also, we know that the vowel quality is largely determined by the formant frequencies. This raises the next question: How much of vowel intelligibility does the soprano lose when she sings with these abnormal formant frequencies? There is no exhaustive answer to that question as yet, but we may anticipate it by comparing results from two analogous experiments that have been made, one using a living soprano as stimulus generator, the other working with synthetic sounds. The first-mentioned experiment was published by Stumpf in 1926. He asked subjects to identify vowels sung by three sopranos at various pitches. One soprano was a professional singer, and according to the just recapitulated findings there are good reasons to presume that this soprano used a pitch-dependent articulation so that the frequency of the fundamental was made to match the frequency of the first formant at high pitches. Stumpf's two other subjects were "naive" singers lacking formal voice education. The other investigation (Sundberg, 1975b) was essentially the same, even though the stimuli were synthesized and the same formant frequencies were used regardless of the pitch. The formant frequencies were those observed in our soprano study when she sang the six above mentioned vowels at a 263 Hz fundamental. These stimuli represent a case where the soprano would retain the same articulation and formant frequencies even in her high pitches. The stimuli were all presented at the same overall SPL. The subjects were ten phoneticians, and they gave their interpretations of the stimulus sounds in terms of any of 12 given Swedish long vowels.

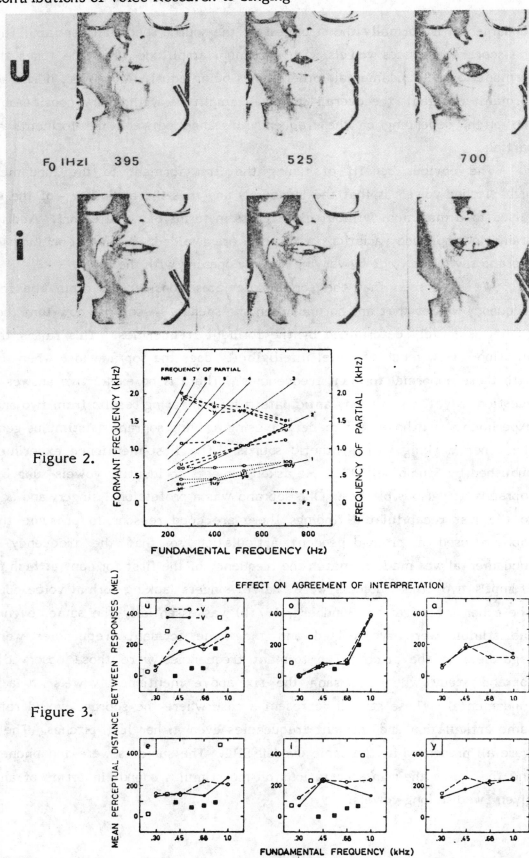

Figure 1.

Figure 2.

Figure 3.

It is reasonable to assume that the scatter between the response vowels obtained for a specific stimulus reflects the difficulty with which this stimulus was identified as a specific vowel. A measure of the scatter was derived in the following way. Each of the 12 response vowels was ascribed a set of formant frequencies, expressed in mels, in accordance with Fant's (1959) data for Swedish female speakers. Then, each of these three formant frequencies was averaged over all responses pertaining to the same stimulus. The resulting <u>average</u> <u>response</u> was then represented by a set of three mel values. Then, the perceptual distances between this average response and each of the individual response vowels were computed using the equation which was recently proposed by Plomp (1970) and by Lindblom (1975) for such purposes. Finally the average perceptual distance from the average response to each individual response was determined. This value can be assumed to reflect the degree of difficulty that the subjects had in interpreting a stimulus as a specific vowel. The resulting mean perceptual distances between the responses are shown on the ordinates in the graphs in figure 3. The values are arranged according to the formant-frequency combination used in synthesizing the stimuli. For instance, the top left graph shows the values pertaining to the stimuli synthesized with formant frequencies as in a low-pitched sung (u). The abscissa is the fundamental frequency of the stimulus. Stumpf's results are represented by the squares and our data by the open circles. For the moment we disregard the filled circles. As can be seen, Stumpf's test did not include the vowels (a) and (y). The question is now how much vowel intelligibility the soprano loses by using pitch-dependent formant frequencies. As mentioned, this case can be assumed to be represented by Stumpf's professional soprano, i.e., the filled squares in the figure. The other case is that the soprano would use the same formant frequencies in all pitches, and this case is represented by the open circles. We can see that, mostly, the professional soprano wins the game with wide margins. The trend is that constant formant frequencies cause a degree of identification difficulties which is in between the cases of the professional soprano and the two untrained singers which are represented by the open squares in the graphs. Evidently Stumpf's experiment should be repeated using fully controlled synthetic stimuli, before any definite conclusions can be drawn. However, the results shown here seem to support the hypothesis that in the pitch range considered the soprano does not lose very much at all, and that indeed she would lose more of intelligibility if she retained her normal speech formants. Part of this effect certainly is a consequence of the fact that a rise in pitch requires a slight rise in the formant frequencies if the vowel shall keep its quality (Slawson, 1968).

Vowel identification is often assumed to be facilitated by the vibrato. The background of this is illustrated in figure 4. Basically, it is assumed that vowel identification is easy to perform as soon as the spectrum envelope clearly depicts the frequencies of the formants. The vibrato corresponds to a frequency modulation of around six undulations per second. The result is that all partials move up and down in frequency. The relative amplitude of a partial depends on its frequency distance to its closest formant. If a partial is somewhat lower in frequency than a formant, a rise of the frequency of that partial will increase its amplitude, other things being equal, and if the partial lies slightly higher than the formant, the reverse will occur. Incidentally, this interrelationship between frequency and amplitude modulation in vibrato tones does not seem to be observed in many studies of the vibrato. Anyway, a vibrato will theoretically add to the information on the formant frequencies, as each partial scans a portion of the idealized spectrum envelope, and consequently vowel identification may be facilitated by a vibrato.

This hypothesis was tested in the experiment just mentioned, since all of the synthetic vowel stimuli were presented both with and without vibrato. The results pertaining to the non-vibrato case are represented by the filled circles in figure 3. We can see that the differences between the vibrato and the non-vibrato cases are small as a rule, and of various signs. Thus, in some instances the vibrato facilitates, in some cases it complicates, and in some cases it has a negligible effect on vowel intelligibility. It can be concluded that the effect of a vibrato on vowel intelligibility is not at all universal. If an effect exists at all, this is only under certain conditions, but a trained singer would know these conditions quite well from experience. It should be mentioned that in the majority of those cases, where the vibrato changed the average response significantly, the scatter between the responses increased. This may lead us to speculate that the vibrato is systematically used by skilled sopranos in order to conceal the substantial deviations from her normal formant frequencies.

Let us now turn to another question caused by the pitch-dependent choice of formant frequencies in our soprano. As mentioned, the fundamental becomes dominating in the spectrum as soon as it is close to the frequency of the first formant. A dominating fundamental may remind us of the acoustic characteristics of mid-register tones as opposed to the chest-register tones in female singers, as shown by Large (1968) in his acoustic study of an (a) vowel sung by seven subjects at a fundamental of 330 Hz. There is no reason to doubt that the glottal sound source is involved in registers. This is evident from the differences in air flow between the registers as revealed by Large et al. (1970), just to mention one example. Rather, the question is the following: Are the formant frequencies another factor involved in the perceptual discrimination between chest-and mid-registers?

This problem was investigated by means of another experiment. A singer, experienced in demonstrating register differences, sang a series of vowel pairs in chest- and mid-register at different pitches. In the case of two pairs of (æ) vowels sung at different pitches, the spectrum of the glottal source could be determined with a fair degree of certainty, because here the first formant was considerably higher than the lowest spectrum partials. Interestingly, the formant frequencies were observed to differ slightly between the chest- and mid-register tones. The source spectra are shown in figure 5. It shows the source spectrum deviations from a standard slope of -12dB/ octave and the abscissa is not the frequency but the number of the partials on a log scale. First, we observe that the two spectra sung in the same register resemble each other rather closely even though they differ with respect to the fundamental frequency. Second, we observe that the lowest partials are stronger in the mid-register samples than in the chest-register samples. Evidently, this will contribute to the dominance of the fundamental in the mid register.

The dashed lines show straight line approximations of the two source spectrum types. The conclusion that these straight line approximations are typical of the source spectra in the two registers would indeed be rather ridiculous in view of the body of underlying experimental material. But it can be used as the basis for a tentative hypothesis, and this hypothesis can be tested. For instance, the differences in the partial amplitudes between our idealized source spectra could be compared with the differences that Large found in his study of the (a)-spectra. This comparison can be made in figure 6. The points represent averages of Large's data, and the line shows the differences between our hypothetical mid and chest register source spectra. There is a considerable disagreement in the third and fourth partials, which can be explained if we assume that the second formant frequency was lower in the mid register than in the chest register in Large's material.

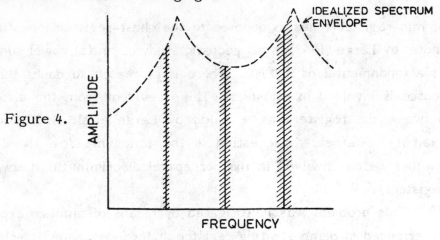

Figure 4.

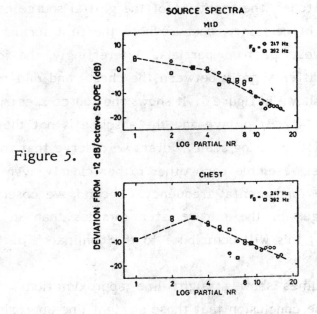

Figure 5.

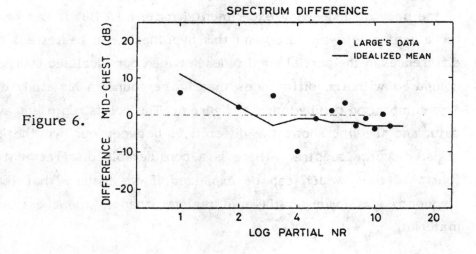

Figure 6.

Apart from this difference, the points and the line show a fair degree of agreement, and consequently Large's data seem to support our hypothesis that the differences between our idealized source spectra are representative of the glottal source spectrum differences between chest and mid register.

Our hypothesis can also be tested in an independent way. We can synthesize vowels with these two source spectra and ask experienced listeners if the stimulus sound like chest- or mid-register tones. Also, we can combine different sets of formant frequencies with these two source spectra and find out the effect which a shift in that parameter may have in terms of registers.

The stimulus material comprised one (i) and one (u) and two (æ) vowels with different pitches. In the (æ) synthesis the formant frequencies observed in the subject's mid- and chest-register versions were used. The (i) and the (u) had one formant-frequency combination where the first formant matched the fundamental frequency, and another combination was observed in sung vowels in which they were further apart. The stimuli were arranged in pairs in which either the source spectrum or the formant frequencies differed. Each pair was presented four times in random order to seven singing teachers. Their task was to decide which one of the two stimuli in the pair sounded most like a vowel sound sung in the mid register. The results can be seen in the table which follows.

Number of "Correct" Votes
(N = 28)

Source	Stimulus Formants	Vowel Quality			
		i $f_o = 263\,Hz$	ae $f_o = 263\,Hz$	ae $f_o = 394\,Hz$	u $f_o = 394\,Hz$
Chest	Varied	23	12	19	14
Mid	Varied	20	21	22	16
Varied	"Chest"	22	22	20	15
Varied	"Mid"	21	22	22	17

The table shows the number of "correct" responses, or, more accurately, the number of mid-register votes which according to our hypothesis should be expected to sound more like mid register because of the formants or because of the source. The underlined numbers deviate from guessing beyond a 95% level of significance.

The (u) stimuli gave no responses that surpassed mere guessing. This result is probably a consequence of the fact that the fundamental was very dominating in all these stimuli regardless of source and formants. In the case of the (æ) stimuli the first formant never did match the fundamental, for obvious reasons. It can be seen in the table that the subject's formant-frequency differences between chest and mid registers are not as influential on register quality as the source-spectrum difference between the registers. In the case of the (i) stimuli all cases surpass the 95% level of significance. Placing the first formant on the frequency of the fundamental had the same effect on perceived register as shifting the source.

The results of this study support two conclusions. First, our hypothetical source spectra seem to differ from each other in a way which is representative of the source spectra in chest and mid registers. Second, it is evident from the results obtained for the (i) stimulus that the timbre qualities characteristic of the two registers can be affected not only by the source spectrum, but also by the formant frequencies. The effect is probably not very great in most vowels, because the formant frequency variability within a specific vowel with a given pitch is certainly rather restricted. Still, our results show that a dominating fundamental contributes to the impression of mid register regardless of whether its dominance is a consequence of the source spectrum or of the formant frequencies. This finding is not very surprising, because it would be difficult for a listener to separate source and formants in an isolated vowel. For instance, a change of the source spectrum may easily change the perceived vowel from a clear (u) to a clear (o), even though the formant frequencies are identical. Still our finding is not uninteresting. It shows that the formant frequencies, i.e., the articulation, can be used by a singer in order to reduce the timbre differences which result from a shift between registers. In other words, it may be used in order to make register transitions gradual and harder to observe. This is not to say that the soprano cannot reach the same or at least a similar goal by a skilled handling of the glottal sound source. But the articulation seems to offer another means to the smoothing of register transitions.

It seems also that the results relate to what has been called isoparametric tones, i.e., tones which differ in register but are similar with respect to vowel, pitch, and SPL. Vowels that meet these demands are probably produced with compensatory changes as regards formant frequencies and vocal effort.

It may also seem legitimate to conclude from our results that the idealized source spectra used in the test are typical of the chest and mid registers. This is not so, though. The source spectra seem to correspond to those which are typical of our singer subject, but other subjects can be assumed to use different source spectra. For instance, it can be assumed that the slope of the source-spectrum envelope in our subject is steeper than in professional opera singers. Rather, it is the <u>differences</u> between our idealized source spectra which seem to comprise features that typically distinguish chest and mid registers.

The main question considered in the present paper is why sopranos match the fundamental frequency with the first formant frequency at high pitches. Several reasons have been found. First, she produces strong sounds at the lowest possible price as regards vocal effort: her voice can be heard more easily when accompanied by an orchestra, and this appears to be a rather sensible criterion of a successful solo singer. Second, she avoids substantial, pitch-dependent loudness variations, which otherwise would have to be compensated for by means of vocal effort. Thirdly, she does not seem to lose very much as regards vowel intelligibility as compared with a case where she uses the same formant frequencies for a given vowel regardless of pitch. Rather, the opposite appears to apply. It is possible but not yet shown that the vibrato plays a role in this connection. Fourth, she may probably use the formant frequencies to reduce the timbre difference between vowels sung in chest and mid registers. We may then conclude that the soprano has very good reasons indeed for articulating a vowel differently at various pitches.

It appears that the experimental evidence supporting these conclusions is rather limited at certain points. This fact will serve as a good stimulus in this first international conference on research in singing: it points to the need for much future research.

REFERENCES

Fant, G. (1959). "Acoustic Analysis and Synthesis of Speech with Applications to Swedish," Ericsson Technics, pp. 3-108.

Large, J. (1968). "An Acoustical Study of Isoparametric Tones in Female Chest and Middle Registers in Singing," The NATS Bulletin, Dec., pp. 12-15.

Large, J., Iwata, S., and Von Leden, H. (1970. "The Primary Female Register Transition in Singing," Folia Phoniat. 22, pp. 385-396.

Lindblom, B. (1975). "Experiments in Sound Structures," paper presented at the 8th International Congress of Phonetic Sciences, Leeds, G. B., August.

Plomp, R. (1970). "Timbre as a Multidimensional Attribute of Complex Tones," in Frequency Analysis and Periodicity Detection in Hearing (ed. by R. Plomp and G. F. Smoorenburg), Leiden.

Slawson, W. (1968). "Vowel Quality and Musical Timbre as Functions of Spectrum Envelope and Fundamental Frequency," J. Acoust. Soc. Am. 43, 1, p. 87.

Stumpf, C. (1926). Die Sprachlaute, Berlin, pp. 77-85.

Sundberg, J. (1975a). "Formant Technique in a Professional Female Singer," Acustica 32, 2, pp. 89-96.

Sundberg, J. (1975b). "Vibrato and Vowel Identification," STL-QPSR No. 2-3/1975, pp. 49-60.

Intelligibility

Vowel Color
and
Voice Quality

Pierre Delattre

ABOUT THE AUTHOR. He is not a specialist of singing. However, as a linguist and experimental phonetician, he has had opportunities to deal with the problems of pronunciation in singing and has lectured several times before the members of NATS during the Colorado Workshops. He is especially known for his successful study of the acoustic cues that cause the perception of speech sounds -- consonants as well as vowels. He has used a research technique that combines spectrographic analysis and synthesis. The latest results of his research by this technique have appeared in the "Journal of the Acoustical Society of America," "Journal of Experimental Psychology," "American Journal of Psychology," "Psychological Monographs," "Word," "Publication of the Modern Language Association of America," "French Review," "Studia Linguistica," and a summary of the last ten years of research will be in the next issue of Phonetica (S. Karger, Basel). For most of his work, he has used the facilities of the Haskins Laboratories, New York.

Singing-voice quality and vowel color are in articulatory conflict. The good production of one tends to impair the good production of the other. The X-rays presented by Professor Raoul Husson in the October 1975 Bulletin in "Special Physiology in Singing with Power," pp. 12-15, demonstrate what the vocal tract cavities can do to preserve good voice quality without loosing too much of the vowel color. As they present side by side the same vowels spoken and sung, they emphasize the differences and make them easy to observe because the latter are sung with great acoustic intensity. We asked Professor Husson to let us use his X-rays for a discussion of this important subject and he was kind enough to grant us immediate permission. (It is only to avoid confusion that we use "color" for vowels and "quality" for voice, for the two terms are synonymous.)

Our examination of the X-rays will be based on two hypothetical "conditions" for singing-voice quality. Before attempting to state those conditions perhaps we should recall together the latest facts on vowel theory.

As you know, the production of any speech sound, whether spoken or sung, involves a source of sound and a resonance of the sound issued by the source, the result being radiated to the external air. For instance, the source of an "s" is at the linguo-dental slit and its resonance takes place mainly in the cavity limited by the slit and the lips; the frequency of the turbulent friction noise of "s" is very high because that frontal cavity is small and open — 3500 cps to 7000 cps. The source of an "a" is at the glottis and resonance operates in the whole vocal tract, from glottis to lips, involving all the cavities that might form therein and interact among themselves and with the source.

The wave issued at the source is called a "carrier wave" because without it the distinctive qualities that are implicitly present in a given shape of the vocal tract would not be carried to the ear of a listener.

For a spoken vowel, the vocal cords (the source) produce a generous series of harmonics (harmonically related overtones) whose intensity decreases from low to high by at least 6 decibels per octave above 1000 cps, and whose frequency does not have to reach any higher than 2500 cps (3000 cps for i) because the distinctive (differentiating, significant) formants of vowels are all under these frequencies. For instance, when a man speaks at a fundamental frequency of 100 cps, the larynx emits a series of at least 25 to 30 harmonics at the frequencies of 100, 200, 300 . . . . 2500 cps, etc. Then resonance takes over: In going through the vocal tract, from glottis to lips, the series of harmonics is "filtered" and only some of the harmonics are "passed." In principle, the "passed" harmonics are those whose frequency merely coincides with that of the various modes of natural resonance of the whole tract and of the various cavities of the tract; the others are "absorbed." The "passed" harmonics bunch into formants, or frequency regions of greater energy on the spectrum. For a male voice speaking at a fundamental frequency of

100 cps, formants average a frequency width of some 200 cps and include from 2 to 3 harmonics -- typically one strong harmonic between two weaker ones. The three first (lowest) formants are mainly the first, second, and third mode of resonance of the whole cavity, but they can be influenced by the first, second, etc. modes of resonance of each of the composing cavities.

Obviously, formant frequency is independent from the fundamental frequency, subjectively called voice pitch and whose variations make "intonation" in speaking and "melody" in singing. For example, if the utterance of an "a" vowel is sustained while the pitch is made to fall, the spectrum will show that all the formants of the "a" keep a constant frequency while the individual harmonics have falling frequencies (Fig. 1); conversely, if the pitch is sustained while vowel color is changed — let us say, from a to ε — the first formant falls by some 200 cps and the second rises by some 600 cps while all the harmonics keep a constant frequency (Fig. 2). Changes in formant frequency are due only to changes in the shape of the vocal tract cavity or cavities; changes in pitch frequency to stretching of the vocal cords. If the two physiological events are independent, so are the acoustic results of each event — formant frequency changes and overtone frequency changes.

The color of vowels — what causes one vowel to be perceived as linguistically the same or different from another -- is mainly characterized by formant frequency. In artificial speech (for example, speech produced by cords of pure tones imitating the overtones of a spectrum), all vowels can be synthesized with as few as two formants. In natural speech, however, the three first formants play a part in the linguistic identification of front-unrounded vowels, that is to say, in vowels whose third formant is close to the second; and the two first formants only in the identification of the back-rounded vowels. (For details, see "An experimental study of the acoustic determinants of vowel color . . ." Word, 8, 3 1952, pp. 195-210.) In the latter, for instance, in "o," "u," the intensity of the third formant is very low (about 40 db down) and serves only to such factors as naturalness, personal voice quality, etc. — not to linguistic differentiation.

Beside formant frequency, an acoustic factor that occasionally plays a part in linguistic distinction is formant intensity. In the present state of research, there are only two known cases in which relative intensities of the first and second formants play a distinctive role. (1) The perception of vowel nasality results mainly from the low intensity of the first formant relative to the second. For instance, when the first-formant intensity of "a" in back is lowered by 12 db, the

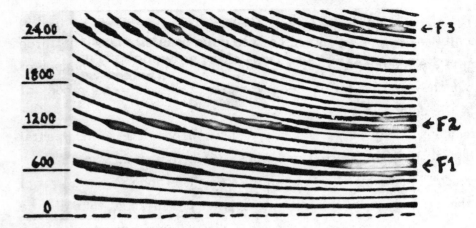

Figure 1.
A spectogram of a showing that voice pitch can be independent of vowel color: The voice melody frequency falls by about one octave (about 240 cps to 120 cps), but the formant frequencies of a (about 700, 1200 and 2400 cps) remain unchanged throughout.

Figure 2.
A spectogram of a-eh showing that vowel color can be independent of voice pitch: The frequencies of formants one and two change from about 700 cps and 1200 cps for a to 500 cps and 1800 cps for eh but the voice melody frequency remains unchanged at about 110 cps throughout.

word is understood as bank, the absence of a velar nasal consonant before the "k" being hardly noticeable.   (2) Conversely, the perception of syllabic consonants results mainly from the low intensity of the second formant relative to the first. For instance, when the second-formant intensity of "o" in meadow is lowered by some 12 db, the word changes to medal. Duration also plays a role in the linguistic identification of American vowels, but here the formants behave alike -- not differently from another.

Now, the acoustic features that characterize vowel color linguistically are very clear. Unfortunately, the acoustic features that characterize voice quality, either in speaking or in singing, are not so clear, the objective research being more difficult and less advanced. Only two years ago, the opinion of Paul B. Oncley, one of the researchers in the field of the singing voice, was that ". . . we still have only a superficial knowledge of the factors which contribute to the proper production of the singing voice . . ." (J. A. S., 28, 4, 1956, p. 780). The work of correlating voice formants with types and classes of voices has not yet been done successfully. It is generally agreed, however, that voice quality in singing is mainly characterized by the two or three formants whose frequencies are just above the vowel formants. (In the American terminology the word "formant" applies to any concentration of energy on the spectrum, whether or not it characterizes vowel color.) This agrees with spectrograms we have made and with the 28 pages of spectograms found in Visible Speech (New York, Van Nostrand, 1947, pp. 376-404), sampling the voices of known singers from Caruso to Bing Crosby. These voice quality formants vary from person to person, but mainly lie, for a man, between the frequencies of 2400 cps to 4000 cps. With the back-rounded vowels, voice quality uses formants as low as the third (2400 cps). Evidence of this is in the commonly known fact that spoken "u," "o," have practically no third formant (40 db down), whereas when sung they always have an intense one (the intensity is comparable to that of third formants in front vowels, about 20 db down). With the front-unrounded vowels, the formants of voice quality begin above the third since this formant is used in the perception of vowel color.

With the preceding paragraphs as an accepted basis, we can now attempt to formulate the two conditions of singing voice quality, the second of which will be explained by the Husson X-rays, and the first making the second possible.

Condition A: The source

For singing voice quality, the vocal cords must produce a much richer series of overtones (harmonically related) than for spoken vowels. Otherwise the cavities will have nothing to "resonate" in the high frequencies since the cavities can only operate resonance on what comes to them from the source. "Richer" means a more numerous series of overtones, a wider range reaching up to higher frequencies with sufficient intensity. The oscilloscope image of this richer tone is a narrower spike wave; the spectographic image, a higher pile of harmonics decreasing more slowly in intensity from low to high. Physiologically, this richer tone is produced by a longer closure and shorter opening of the glottis in each cycle, thanks to stronger musculation and a wider contact of the vocal cords resisting to stronger breath pressure (cf. the Husson article from which our X-rays are borrowed, p. 13, under "Attainment of the Intensity Requirement").

Condition B: The resonance

For singing voice quality, the vowel strictures at the tongue and lips must be wider than for spoken vowels. Otherwise, the high overtones that characterize singing voice quality cannot be "passed" by the vocal tract. This applies more as a stricture is nearer the front of the vocal tract.

The fact that the higher overtones are "passed" more as the strictures are wider was already noted by Sir Richard Paget, who, in experiments with plasticine analogs of the mouth, could detect a third formant and above when the shape of the tract approached that of a uniform pipe (Human Speech, New York, Harcourt, Brace, 1930). It is also noted in an all-important work by two Japanese physicists, Tsutomu Chiba and Matasa Kajiyama, who say, for instance: "The high resonance of 'o' is usually weak, but when the mouth is comparatively wide open, a fairly strong high resonance will be produced even in the case of 'o'." (The Vowel, its Nature and Structure, Tokyo, Kaiseikan, 1941, p. 145). Finally, it finds support in a recent study by the Swedish physicist C. Gunnar Fant: "On the predictability of formant levels and spectrum envelopes from formant frequencies: (For Roman Jakobson, The Hague, Mouton, 1956, pp. 109-120). Actual spectograms showing the intensity decrease of formant three from a to "u" (maximal strictures, both at the lips and at mid-tongue) and strong intensity of formant three in a vowel like ə (minimal strictures throughout the tract and closest approximation to uniform pipe) can be found in "Un triangle acoustique des voyelles orales du francais," (The French Review, 21, 6, 1948, pp. 477-485), or "The physiological interpretation of sound spectograms," (PMLA, 66, 5, 1951, pp. 864-876), and in "Control methods in a study of the vowels," by Gordon E. Peterson and Harold L. Barney (J. A. S., 24, 2, 1952, pp. 175-185). In the latter work, the intensity of third formants are given as: 43db down for a back vowel like "u," but only 24 and 22 db down for front vowels like ɛ and æ, the closest approximation to ə that can be found in that article.

Let us survey the main vowels from the viewpoint of the difficulty encountered in singing them. The vocal tract varies in shape from that of a uniform pipe (same section area throughout), closed at one end (the glottis) and open at the other (the lips) to that of a double resonator (narrow strictures at mid-tongue and lips). The more the vocal tract approximates the shape of a uniform pipe, the more the high formants are favored by resonance, and inversely. When the vocal tract is nearly equally open from larynx to lips, it produces a vowel in the vicinity of ə (schwa vowel or neutral vowel) with color variations depending on the subject's tract length (average: 17.5 centimetres but quite variable). This ə should be the easiest vowel to sing with good voice quality. Departing from its position by tongue fronting and raising, from ɛ to "i," singing quality should become increasingly difficult to obtain without opening the lips and tongue stricture wider than in speaking. Toward the back, backing and raising the tongue from ɔ to "u,", the difficulty increases even more rapidly because there are two major strictures forming in this series, one at the lips and the other at mid-tongue. As to the "a" family, although they are more "open" than ə they should be more difficult to sing because of their pharyngeal stricture which increases from æ to a. Among French vowels, "y" should offer more difficulty than "i" but less than "u"; ø more than "e" but less than "o"; œ should be very easy, yet not so much as the American schwa since it is not quite so open.

The X-rays borrowed from Professor Husson's October 1957 article in The Bulletin show (a) that the tract strictures, especially the front ones, at the lips or front of the tongue, are wider in singing than in speaking; (b) that considerable articulatory compensations are made in an effort to regain the vowel quality that was lost through too much stricture widening.

To study these articulatory compensations, we must recall the most elementary acoustic laws of cavities: The larger its volume and the smaller and longer its opening, the lower the natural note of resonance of a cavity. For

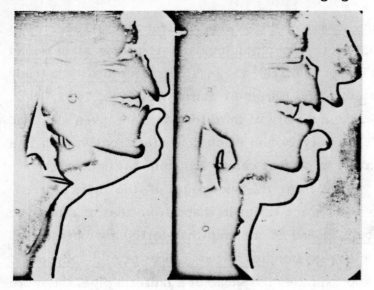

Figure 3.
The ee vowel sound, emitted on 290 cycles by the same singer and under the same conditions as described under Figure 5. To the left: position of the speaking voice. To the right: position of the singing voice.

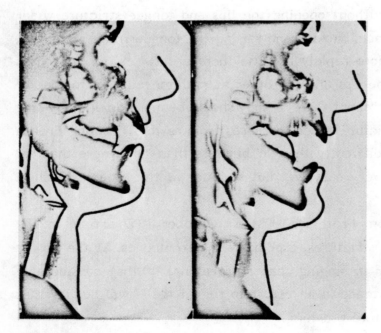

Figure 4.
The open eh vowel sound, emitted on 580 cycles by Mlle. Genevieve Settes, strong mezzo-soprano of the Paris Opera. Radiographic plates taken, February 20, 1957. Recurrent chronaxy: .098 of a second; 115 phonemes at one meter from the mouth. To the left: position of the speaking voice. To the right: position of the singing voice.

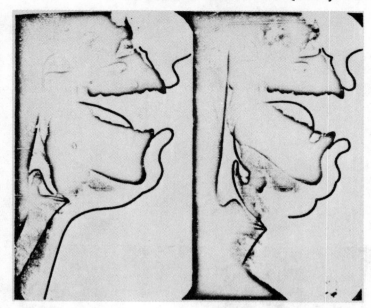

Figure 5.
The a vowel sound, emitted on 290 cycles by M. Ernest Blanc, the most powerful baritone of the Paris Opera.   Radiographic plates taken, February 20, 1957. Recurrent chronaxy: .095 of a second; 130 phonemes or decibels at one meter (3 ft. 3-3/8 in.) from the mouth. To the left: position of the speaking voice. To the right: position of the singing voice.

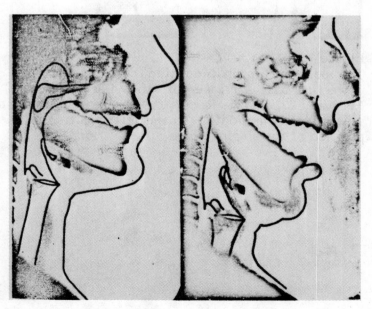

Figure 6.
The French close o vowel emitted on 580 cycles by the same singer and under the same conditions as described under Figure 4. To the left: position of the speaking voice. To the right: position of the singing voice.

Figure 7.
The oo vowel sound, emitted on 290 cycles by M. Georges Vaillant, the most powerful bass-baritone of the Paris Opera.   Radiographic plates taken, February 20, 1957. Recurrent chronaxy: .110 of a second; 130 phonemes at one meter from the mouth. To the left: position of the speaking voice. To the right: position of the singing voice.

instance, a large cavity with a small and long opening has a low note (that is the case for both cavities of "u"); a small cavity with a wide and short opening has a high note (that is the case for the front cavity of "i"); a very large cavity with a very large and short opening can have a medium note (that is the case for the front cavity of "a"). Let us examine the differences between the spoken X-ray and the sung X-ray, and apply the law of cavities from lips to larynx. We shall multiply all measurements by three in order to approximate natural size.

Front cavity for sung "i" (ee). A wider lip opening (frequency raising effect on front cavity) is offset by enlarging the front cavity volume (lowering effect) through lip protruding, jaw opening and backing of tongue stricture by some 10 millimeters.

Back cavity for sung "i" (ee). Opening the tongue stricture by 3 mm (raising effect) and backing it by 10 mm thereby reducing the volume (raising effect) are offset by lowering the larynx by some 30 mm, thereby enlarging the back cavity (lowering effect).

Front cavity for sung "e" (eh). A wider lip opening is offset by enlarging the cavity through jaw opening and backing the stricture by some 6 mm.

Back cavity for sung "e" (eh). Widening the tongue stricture by 6 mm (raising effect) and backing it by 6 mm, thereby decreasing the volume (raising effect) are offset by lowering the larynx by 18 mm, thereby enlarging the back cavity (lowering effect).

Front cavity for sung "a." A wider lip opening (raising effect) is offset by enlarging the front cavity (lowering effect) through jaw opening and lowering the stricture by 24 mm.

Back cavity for sung "a." Lowering the tongue stricture by 24 mm is offset by lowering the larynx by 27 mm, so that the volume and opening of the back cavity for sung "a" are about equal to those of spoken "a."

Front and back cavities for sung "o." The reasoning is the same as for "a." The tongue stricture is lowered by 24 mm and the larynx by 27 mm.

Front and back cavities for sung "u." The reasoning is the same as for "a." The tongue stricture and the larynx are both lowered by 24 mm.

To summarize the compensations we can say that widening the opening at the lips is offset by enlarging the front cavity, which forces the front tongue strictures to widen and all tongue strictures to back and/or lower. In turn, the latter effects on the back cavity are offset by lowering the larynx.

Summary. The best conditions for speaking vowels require the presence of constrictions along the vocal tract; the best conditions for singing require the absence of such constrictions in order to allow the high frequency overtones that characterize voice quality to be passed by the resonating cavities. A comparison between X-rays of spoken vowels and those of sung vowels indicates what compensations the shape of the vocal tract can make in order to preserve vowel color while producing voice quality.

An Experimental Study of the Effect of Pitch on the Intelligibility of Vowels

John Howie and Pierre Delattre

Once more we present contributions from scholars whose field is not primarily music. Both authors are teachers of French language and linguistics who have specialized in experimental phonetics, that is, in the acoustic and articulatory study of the nature of speech by instrumental means. It is adequate equipment that makes this sort of research possible. In a way, therefore, the real author of this study is the Linguistic Research Laboratory of the University of Colorado, where speech can be analyzed, synthesized, taken apart, put together again, manipulated nearly at will, thanks to combined electronic and radiographic equipment. Pierre Delattre directs its research activities, and John Howie worked there when this investigation took place. If purely musical competence was needed, Berton Coffin provided it very generously.

INTRODUCTION

Everyone agrees that the intelligibility of vowels in singing becomes worse as the musical pitch rises. The purpose of this study has been to investigate this subjective observation by means of objective experiments, in order to learn, first, how listeners identify a variety of vowels in isolation over a wide range of pitches, and, most important, why the intelligibility varies in certain ways with changes in pitch.

The interpretation of the results of these experiments is based on formant analysis. The notion of analyzing the voice in terms of formants has been discussed previously in this review.[1]   Briefly, the theory of formants is as follows: The cavities of the vocal tract possess natural notes of resonance which "pass" or reinforce certain harmonics of the vocal cord tone. These emphasized harmonics from concentrations of acoustic energy at frequency regions on the spectrum corresponding to the natural notes of resonance of the cavities. The term formant refers to the selective resonance in a particular frequency region which contributes to the timbre of a complex tone. It is mainly the two lowest formants of a spoken or sung sample which characterize the timbre, or color, of vowels, while the higher formants contribute mostly to the timbre, or quality, of the individual voice.

Two acoustic concepts are essential to the present discussion. The first one relates to the lowest possible frequency of formants: since all formants, in singing, are composed of harmonic components of the fundamental (also called first harmonic), no formant can have a lower frequency than that of the fundamental. The second concept concerns the relation between changes in fundamental frequency and changes in formant frequency:

> "Obviously, formant frequency is independent from the fundamental frequency, subjectively called voice pitch and whose variations make "intonation" in speaking and "melody" in singing. For example, if the utterance of an "a" vowel is sustained while the pitch is made to fall, the spectrum will show that all the formants of the "a" keep a constant frequency while the individual harmonics have falling frequencies; conversely, if the pitch is sustained while vowel color is changed — let us say, from a to ε — the first formant falls by some 200 cps and the second rises by some 600 cps while all the harmonics keep a constant frequency. Changes in formant frequency are due only to changes in the shape of the vocal tract cavity or cavities; changes in pitch frequency to stretching of the vocal cords. If the two physiological events are independent, so are the acoustic results of each event — formant frequency changes and overtone frequency changes."[2]

Thus, formant frequencies can vary while the fundamental frequency is fixed, and conversely, the fundamental can vary while the formants remain fixed on a determined vowel. This does not mean, however, that vowel color is necessarily independent of fundamental pitch variation. In one case at least it should be very much dependent on it. This case occurs when one attempts to sing a vowel at a fundamental frequency higher than the normal frequency of the lowest formant of that vowel. Then the lowest formant is absent. That is, it is absent at the frequency it should have for that given vowel. Theoretically, a substitution takes place: the fundamental itself serves as lowest formant, and the frequency of the fundamental being too high the color of the perceived vowel is altered, is different from that of the intended vowel.

The importance of the lowest formant in characterizing vowel color is well established. Recent experiments with synthetic vowels at the Haskins Laboratories have, in fact, determined that the first formant is generally as important as the second in the recognition of vowels.[3] It has been shown that removing the first formant either destroys vowel color altogether or else alters the color appreciably.

It is reasonable to assume, then, that it is impossible to produce recognizable vowels at musical pitches very much higher than their first formants. And, on the basis of this assumption, the number of unintelligible vowels in singing must be considerable, since the first formants of all vowels lie within the normal pitch range of the soprano voice: i.e., from about 250 cps (roughly middle C) for (i) and (u) to about 750 cps (roughly high G) for (a) as in father.

Fig. 1 gives the formant frequencies of American vowels as averaged by Peterson and Barney.[4] Fig. 2 gives the formant frequencies of French vowels as established by P. Delattre.[5] Nasal vowels differ from oral vowels by the low intensity of the first formant and by the addition of a weak formant at about 250 cps. German, Italian, and Spanish vowels can also be taken from this table.

EXPERIMENTAL PROCEDURE

Intelligibility tests were constructed, in which nine vowels (a i e o u y ɸ ɔ ɛ) as in English father, beet, bait, boat, boot and French bu, boeufs, bon, bain, were presented to a group of fifteen listeners for identification. The vowels were first recorded on magnetic tape, as sung by a baritone and a soprano, both native-American speakers with trained singing voices. The two singers uttered each of the nine vowels on the pitches listed in the following table (with the frequencies shown in cycles per second).

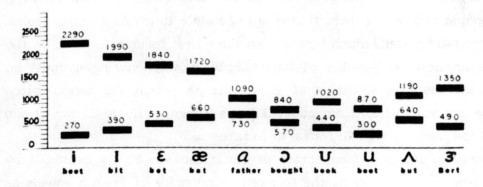

Figure 1.
Schematized spectra showing first and second formant frequencies of American vowels, as averaged by Peterson and Barney. These measurements are for men's voices; the formant values for women's and children's voices will all be some 10 to 15 pc higher.

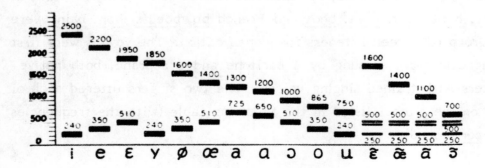

Figure 2.
Schematized spectra showing first and second formant frequencies of French male vowels, as established by P. Delattre. The nasal vowels differ from the oral vowels by the low intensity of the first formant and by the addition of a formant at about 250 cps.

	BARITONE		SOPRANO
		C	1056
		G	792
		E	660
		C	528
G	396	G	396
E	330	E	330
C	264	C	264
G	198		
E	165		
C	132		

The tape recordings were then cut and spliced together again in random order to form four listening tests, each one containing one utterance of each vowel at each pitch. Of the two tests from the baritone, and of the two tests from the soprano, one consisted of the initial half-seconds of utterance and the other consisted of the middle half-seconds of utterance. It was thus possible to test separately the initial and middle segments of each vowel to determine what effect the singer's vocal attack might have on vowel intelligibility. The stimuli tones were connected with five seconds of blank tape, providing a uniform silent interval between the vowels heard by the listeners.

The listeners, graduate students in French, were given test blanks with nine key words for each stimulus, and were asked to draw a line through the one word which illustrated the vowel they heard in each tone. The stimulus vowels were represented by both English and French words: father (faΘər), beet (bit), bait (bet), boat (bot), boot (but), bu (by), boeufs (bø), bon (bɔ̃), bain (bɛ̃). The fifteen subjects were familiar with these vowels and their key words, but they were not instructed in the problems of vowel production in singing. The subjects were required to identify every vowel they heard, no matter how hard the choice. No provision was made for an impossible choice since it was desired to have complete data on the subjects' interpretation of the least intelligible utterances. This data furnished clues to what happened acoustically in the singers' efforts to produce vowels at the higher pitches.

RESULTS

According to the responses from the listening tests, it is possible to conclude that vowels do indeed have poor intelligibility at high pitches, and that, in general, the

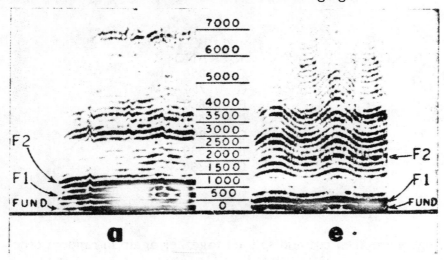

Figure 3.
Spectograms of samples sung by a soprano (taken from our listening test stimuli); initial segments, with vocal attack, of (a) as in <u>father</u> and (e) as in <u>bait</u>, sung on middle C (264 cps).   The differences between the formant structures of these vowels are made perfectly clear when the fundamental is low enough to provide at least one harmonic to represent each formant.

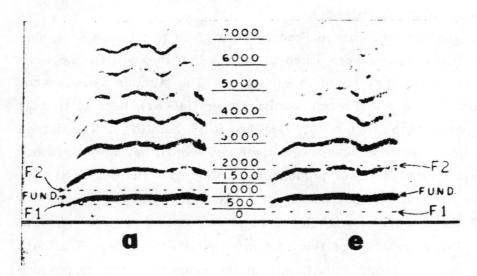

Figure 4.
Spectograms of samples sung by a soprano (taken from our listening test stimuli); initial segments, with vocal attack, of (a) as in <u>father</u> and (e) as in <u>bait</u>, sung on high C (1056 cps). Dotted lines indicate the formant frequencies of the intended vowels. For good intelligibility of a vowel the harmonics (horizontal bands) would have to coincide with both dotted lines. Normal differences between the formant structures of these vowels are no longer evident when the fundamental is sufficiently higher than the normal first formants. Since all vowels sung at this high pitch have harmonic structures that look almost alike, it is not surprising that they sound almost alike.

higher the pitch, the poorer the intelligibility. Furthermore, it is apparently the relationship between the fundamental frequency of the voice and the two principal formant frequencies characterizing the vowel — especially the lower formant — which determines the degree of intelligibility of vowels at different pitches. This relationship between fundamental frequency and formant frequency may be expressed in terms of four generalizations:

1. The best intelligibility occurs when the fundamental frequency is well below the frequency of a vowel's first formant, allowing each formant to be strongly represented by one or more harmonics of the vocal cord tone. Fig. 3 shows the harmonic and formant structures of the vowels (a) and (e) sung by a soprano on C 264. These spectrograms were made from the _initial_ half-seconds of utterance and show the vocal attack as well as the singer's vibrato.

2. When the fundamental has a frequency coinciding, or nearly coinciding, with the first formant frequency of a given vowel, it seems, as had been assumed, to play the role of a strong first formant of that vowel — resulting in good intelligibility. For example, a fundamental of 264 cps may play the role of a normal 250 cps first formant of (i), contributing to nearly perfect intelligibility for (i) sung on middle C; and a fundamental of 792 cps may play the role of a normal 750 cps first formant of (a) sung on high G. (The intelligibility of such an (a) at 792 cps is interior to that of (i) at 264 cps because the _second_ formant of (a) (ca 1200 cps) will not come as close to coinciding with a harmonic — the second harmonic of this (a) is at 792 x 2 = 1584 cps. -- as the second formant of the (i) (ca 2400 cps) -- the ninth harmonic of (i) sung at 264 is at 264 x 9 = 2376 cps).

3. When the fundamental has a frequency appreciably higher than the first formant frequency of a given vowel, this fundamental tends to impose the perception of one of the vowels that would have a first formant at that frequency. An extreme example is singing vowels on G 792 -- a fundamental frequency nearly equivalent to the normal first formant frequency of (a). The result, here, is very poor intelligibility for all vowels except (a), with the other vowels being largely interpreted as (a) under the conditions of our listening tests.

4. And when the fundamental is well above the first formant of (a) -- which has one of the highest first formants -- intelligibility of the intended vowel is still worse, except for (a). Now, the most interesting result of our tests is that all

vowels sung at C 1056 were quite consistently identified as (a), whose normal first formant frequency is only about 750 cps for a soprano. This phenomenon should be difficult to explain since the harmonics of "high C" (1056, 2112 ... cps) do not coincide in any way with either the normal first formant (ca 750 cps) or the normal second formant (ca 1200 cps) of the vowel (a). Fig. 4 shows the harmonic structures of the vowels (a) and (e) sung by a soprano on C 1056. This pitch is obviously higher than the first formants should be for either of these vowels, and the great intervals separating the successive harmonics allow all normal formant structure of vowels to disappear.

A likely explanation for such consistent perception of (a) at C 1056 is to be found in the assumption "that the ear effectively averages two vowel formants which are close together, receiving from these two formants an impression which is highly similar to that which would be heard from one formant placed at a position somewhere intermediate between them."[6] In a study designed to verify this assumption, the investigators at the Haskins Laboratories were able to conclude that "the back vowels (whose formants are close together) can be rather closely approximated by a single formant, whereas the front vowels, with the possible exception of (i), cannot."[7]

The fundamental tone C 1056 is thus considered to play the role of a single "average" formant for the vowel (a), since its frequency is nearly midway between the frequencies of (a)'s normal first formant (ca 700 cps) and normal second formant (ca 1200 cps). The result is that all utterances on "high C" are interpreted by listeners as (a), no matter what vowel the singer may attempt to produce.

For singers who have been discouraged by vain efforts to sing certain vowels at high pitches, it may be a comfort to learn that it is theoretically impossible. This should also be a warning to the music teacher who literally expects "the impossible" from a student! Of course, this problem affects male voices much less than female voices since the first formants of only the close vowels (i u y e o ø) lie within the normal range of the tenor voice, i.e., about 250 cps (roughly middle C) for (i u y) and about 360 cps (roughly middle F) for (e o ø); and even these first formants lie sufficiently above the normal range of the bass voice to escape any serious loss of intelligibility.

The vocal attack, heard in the initial half-seconds of utterance, seems to have contributed something to the intelligibility of most of the vowels. The attack made its greatest contribution to the intelligibility of the close, rounded vowels (u y o ø), where the singers evidently tended to round the lips more in the initial segment than in the middle segment — resulting in less intelligible middle segments of these vowels. This observation is consistent with the notion that an open vocal tract is essential for good singing voice production, and that the degree of closure — both by the tongue and by the lips — necessary for the articulation of close, rounded vowels is incompatible with singing voice quality.

An acoustic explanation for this situation is given in the article, "Vowel Color and Voice Quality," mentioned above. "For singing voice quality, the vowel strictures at the tongue and lips must be wider than for spoken vowels. Otherwise, the high overtones that characterize singing voice quality cannot be "passed" by the vocal tract. This applies more as a stricture is nearer the front of the vocal tract." Since the lip-stricture of the rounded vowels is nearest the front, it results in the greatest conflict between vowel color and singing voice quality. In singing, then, the vowel color of (u y o ø) appears to be conveyed to some degree by an effort to round the lips at the instant of attack — only to be lost as the singer strives for good voice quality in the succeeding half-second of utterance.

On the other hand, the vocal attack had the opposite effect on the intelligibility of the two nasal vowels studied. Both [ɛ̃] and [ɔ̃] were generally less intelligible in the initial segment than in the middle segment -- which suggests that English-speaking singers do not completely lower the velum for nasal vowels during the initial half-second of utterance.

CONCLUSION

To summarize the results of these experiments, it may be stated (1) that vowels generally lose intelligibility as the pitch rises, and (2) that the theoretical assumption is generally correct that recognizable vowels cannot be produced with a fundamental frequency appreciably higher than the frequency of the first formant. The following table is offered as a practical guide:

VOWELS START SERIOUSLY LOSING INTELLIGIBILITY
WHEN THE FUNDAMENTAL REACHES THESE FREQUENCIES:

(i u y)	350 cps	(roughly middle F)
(e o ø)	450 cps	(roughly middle A)
(ɛ ɔ œ)	600 cps	(roughly high D)
(æ a a̲)	750 cps	(roughly high G)

It should be noted, however, that the vowels (æ a a̲) will tend to retain their intelligibility when sung at high pitches. It has been found that listeners rather consistently hear the vowel (a̲) for all utterances on the higher tones of the soprano's range, regardless of the vowel intended by the singer. This effect is explained by assuming either that the fundamental tone coincides closely enough with the first formant frequency of (a̲) to be identified as that formant, or else that the fundamental approximates a single "average" formant whose frequency is midway between the frequencies of the two lowest formants of an (a̲).

REFERENCES

1.   "Vowel Color and Voice Quality," The Bulletin, XV, 1, 1958, pp. 4-7.

2.   Ibid., pp. 4, 5.

3.   For details, see "An experimental study of the acoustic determinants of vowel color." Word, 8, 3, 1952, pp. 203, 204.

4.   "Control methods in a study of the vowels," Journal of the Acoustical Society of America, 24, 2, 1952, pp. 175-185.

5.   "The Physiological Interpretation of Sound Spectrograms," Publication of the Modern Language Association of America, 66, 5, 1951, pp. 864-876.

6.   Word, 8, 3, 1952, p. 203.

7.   Ibid., p. 208.
     The Bulletin, XV, 1, 1958, p. 5.

Intelligibility in Singing
as a Function of
Fundamental Voice Pitch

V. P. Morozov

Institute of Evolutionary Physiology, Academy of Sciences, USSR, Leningrad

Translated from Akusticheskii Zhurnal, Vol. 10, No. 3, pp. 330-334,
July-September, 1964
Original article submitted June 25, 1963

The syllable articulation method was used to measure the intelligibility of the singing voice. The existing method was modified to the extent that the singers vocalized rather than spoke from the syllable articulation tables a different predetermined fundamental voice pitches.
It was established that singing intelligibility is a maximum at pitches in the medium voice range, falls off somewhat in the low notes, and declines very abruptly at the high notes.

It is a well-known fact that the vocal speech pattern of singers is marked by low intelligibility. This is why the opera-goer finds it necessary to glance over the program notes prior to the performance. It seems to us that an important part of any inquiry into the causes behind insufficient intelligibility of singing should be the explanation of how the intelligibility depends on the fundamental pitch of the singer's voice over its two-octave range.

Inasmuch as there does not exist any quantitative method for measuring the intelligibility of singing, we decided to use our basic tool the method of syllable articulation normally applied to the investigation of speech over radiotelephone communication lines (1). This method was modified in our own experiments so that the subject was instructed to sing rather than speak the syllables in his normal singing voice at certain rigidly prescribed notes played for him on the piano. Each syllable in the sequence was sung at a pitch differing by a whole or half tone from the one just preceding it. This sequence of tones ran the entire range alternately down the scale then up the scale. A test run disclosed that this tired the subject less than singing many syllables in a row at the same pitch. As a result of this test, it was also known to the experimenter at what pitch each of the 50 syllables from the articulation table were sung. The sequence of tones specified to the subject were ordered such that in singing three tables an equal number of syllables were produced at each of the selected tones. Consequently, knowing the total number of syllables sung by the subject at a given pitch and the total number of these correctly interpreted by auditors, the percentage articulation (A %) could then be calculated for each note of the subject's voice range.

The articulation team (auditors) in our experiments consisted of six or seven persons with normal hearing. The distance from the singer to the auditors was a constant 12 m throughout all of the tests. The tests were performed in a room of the Leningrad State Conservatory.

The singers used for subjects were divided into three groups: men, women, and children. The men and women were students and graduates of the conservatory: two bases, one baritone, three tenors, two mezzo-sopranos, two sopranos. The children's group was made up of seven high sopranos from the children's choir of the M. I. Glinka Leningrad Academic Chorale, their ages ranging from 10 to 14 years. The investigated adult range was about two octaves, the children's range about an octave and a half.

The total percentage articulation was derived for each group of subjects -- men, women and children -- and for each note of the tested voice range according to the data of all members of the articulation team.

The total number of estimates (n_Σ) obtained in this way for each note of the investigated voice range are shown in Table 1 with the number of correct estimates (n_x); these figures were used to derive the percentage articulation.

As is apparent from the table, the total number of estimates at each pitch level (n_Σ) fluctuated approximately between the limits from 150 to 400. This is a sufficient number of estimates to level out the factor of chance in deriving the

Fundamental voice pitch	G	A	H	c	d	e	f	g	a	h	c'	d'
Vocal chord vibration frequency, cps	98	110	123	131	147	165	175	196	220	247	262	294
Men n_Σ	150	150	320	320	320	320	320	315	270	305	300	295
Men n_x	122	132	282	284	294	277	272	273	224	258	241	235
Women n_Σ	–	–	–	–	–	–	–	–	–	–	140	140
Women n_x	–	–	–	–	–	–	–	–	–	–	115	123
Children n_Σ	–	–	–	–	–	–	–	–	–	–	420	420
Children n_x	–	–	–	–	–	–	–	–	–	–	307	317

Fundamental voice pitch	e'	f'	g'	a'	b'	h'	c''	d''	e''	f''	g''	a''	h''
Vocal chord vibration frequency, cps	330	349	392	440	446	494	524	587	659	698	784	880	988
Men n_Σ	295	245	220	170	150	80	–	–	–	–	–	–	–
Men n_x	238	181	167	109	100	35	–	–	–	–	–	–	–
Women n_Σ	149	140	140	140	–	140	140	140	140	140	140	140	60
Women n_x	122	121	119	119	–	115	103	88	71	53	35	25	5
Children n_Σ	420	420	420	420	–	420	420	245	245	–	–	–	–
Children n_x	337	343	310	295	–	294	271	150	119	–	–	–	–

Table 1.

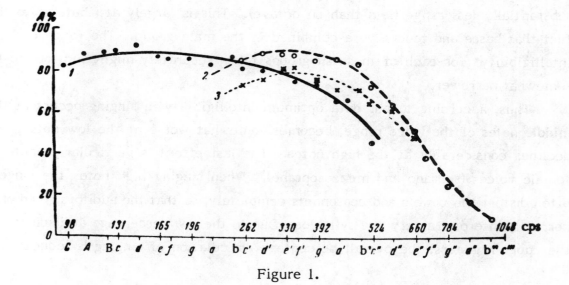

Figure 1.

percentage articulation for each graduation of pitch. It is clear that a certain element of chance may be introduced by the fact that the number $n\Sigma$ included syllables that are not entirely distinct in their phonemic content, since at each note the entire table was not sung but only a specific portion of it appointed to that note. The latter also appears to explain the conspicuous, albeit very slight, scatter of points about the curves representing the pitch dependence of the articulation (see the figure) for men (1), women (2), and children (3). In these graphs the syllable articulation of "vocalized speech" (A %) is plotted on the vertical axis. The upper scale of the horizontal axis represents the frequency of the fundamental voice tone in cycles per second, the lower scale gives the corresponding note designation of the pitches.

As shown by the behavior of the curves, for each group of test subjects there are intervals of best and worst intelligibility. The interval of maximum articulation (about 90%) for men lies roughly between the notes A and c', corresponding to fundamental frequencies from 110 to 262 cps. The syllables sung at higher pitches give a lower percentage articulation, but still better than 50%.

The articulation of the female voice is a maximum ($\sim$90%) at the low and medium pitches, approximately from 330 to 524 cps (e' to c") and suffers a severe drop at the high notes. On approaching the upper limit of c''' (1048 cps) the syllable intelligibility of women tends to zero.

The syllable articulation curve for children lies about 10% lower than the curve for women and has a maximum within approximately the same pitches. Hence the male group has the broadest range — about an octave and a half — of high intelligibility (above 80%), while the female and children's groups have substantially less range (less than an octave). This is largely attributable to the fact that bases and tenors were combined in the male group. The range of high intelligibility* for each of these subgroups taken separately might turn out to be somewhat narrower.

Thus, according to our data optimum intelligibility in singing occurs at the middle notes of the voice range, becomes somewhat worse at the low notes, and declines considerably at the high notes. The last effect is particularly acute in female voices (soprano and mezzosoprano). When singing high notes the singers often distort the vowels and consonants completely, so that the auditors could only correctly interpret a very few syllables. Due to the low percentage articulation in the upper registers, the overall percentage articulation of singing is reduced and hence, in singing in general the intelligibility is lower than in speech (investigations have shown that the mean syllable articulation of normal spoken speech under the same conditions is equal to 87.2% for the male group, 82.4% for the female group, 78.6% for the children's group). If now we examine the singing articulation at the same fundamental pitch as that of the singer's speaking voice, it turns out that the singing intelligibility at these notes is at least as good as the speech intelligibility and in a number of instances is even superior.

The reason for the inferior singing intelligibility of women in the upper voice range is apparently the high pitch of the vocally produced sound itself. When the fundamental tone is at the high c''' the singer's vocal chords vibrate at higher than 1000 cps. It is known, however, that many typical formants characterizing vowels (e.g., the Russian or Italian "u," like the "oo" in English "boot") lie in the interval below 1000 cps and hence are absent in the higher-pitched sounds. The highest notes produced by male voices are well below the highest fundamental tones produced by female voices (the tenor's high c'' corresponds to 524 vibrations per second), so that the male voice, unlike the female, does not disclose such a striking loss of intelligibility as the top notes of the voice range are approached.

Singing speech differs from ordinary spoken speech in a great many features. Specifically, as shown by Rzhevkin's investigations (3), the sound spectrum of the well-trained singing voice is characterized by the presence of a so-called high singing formant, i.e., appreciable reinforcement of the harmonic components of the spectrum in the interval from 2500 to 3000 cps. The high singing formant, which imparts a "brilliance" or "metallic" timbre to the singing voice, is present in any vowel at any pitch and is provided, in the opinion of acousticians, by resonance of the larynx. We found, utilizing four-octave band filters, that 30% of the entire acoustic energy is concentrated in the vicinity of the singing formant in the case of the brightest, or most sonorous, voices. Since the intensity of the singing formant is frequently strongly predominant over the intensity of the characteristic vowel formants, it is entirely conceivable that the phonetic discrimination of vowels is somewhat suppressed in voice production, a factor which also tends to reduce intelligibility.

It is quite possible that the speech intelligibility of singing is affected by the relative intensity levels of the vowels and consonants in singing. The vowel level at the high notes attains 90-110 dB, whereas the consonant level barely reaches 60-65 dB. It may be assumed that this wide rift between the intensities of vowels

Sounds produced by singer		Sounds correctly perceived by auditors, %			
		Initial consonant	Average %	Final consonant	Average %
Occlusives	Unvoiced: П, Т, К	81, 83, 80	81.3	54, 77, 60	63.6
	Voiced: Б, Г, Д, М, Н	68, 73, 91, 97, 93	84.4	– – – 47, 66	56.5
Fricatives	Unvoiced: С, Ф, Х, Ш	97, 73, 80, 87	84.2	97, 70, 47, 95	77.2
	Voiced: В, Ж, З, Л, Й	71, 65, 94, 98	81.7	– – – 86, 57	71.5
Affricates and trills	Ц, Ч, Щ, Р	40, 27, 73, 98	59.5	70, 80, 80, 93	80.7
Vowels	Between hard consonants: А, Э, Ы, О, У	97, 97, 97, 98, 97	96.2		
	Between soft consonants: Я, Э, И, О, У	97, 97, 96, 91, 95			

Table 2.

Sounds produced by singer		Sounds correctly perceived by auditors, %			
		Initical consonant	Average %	Final consonant	Average %
Occlusives	Unvoiced: П, Т, К	89, 84, 98	90.3	78, 92, 100	90
	Voiced: Б, Г, Д, М, Н	86, 87, 100, 87, 50	82	— — — 62, 25	43.5
Fricatives	Unvoiced: С, Ф, Х, Ш	100, 65, 75, 95	83.7	93, 98, 100, 83	93.5
	Voiced: Б, Ж, З, Л, Й	81, 100, 92, 70	85.7	— — 100 61, 55	72
Affricates and trills	Ц, Ч, Щ, Р	50, 96, 75, 100	80.2	75, 90, 87, 91	85.7
Vowels	Between hard consonants А, Э, Ы, О, У	81, 100, 94, 84, 72	85.4		
	Between soft consonants: Я, Э, И, О, У	86, 81, 82, 90, 84			

Table 3.

In Tables 2 and 3 the Russian Cyrillic letters have been preserved intact because of the loss of phonetic information that would be suffered in transliteration. An approximate idea of the sounds of the letters, as well as their ranges of variability, may be found by consulting the transliteration scheme found at the end of this arrangement. — Publisher.

and consonants (as much as 50 dB) produces the "self-masking" phenomenon in singing articulation; this obstructs perception of the consonants, and intelligibility suffers accordingly.

Our phonetic analysis of singing speech has demonstrated in a number of cases that the percentage articulation of males decreases mainly as a result of inaccurate consonant articulation on the part of singers (Table 2, wherein the subject is a bass). In the singing speech of females, on the other hand, there is also a significant distortion of the vowel sounds (Table 3, wherein the subject is a soprano). The disruptions in intelligibility in this case are especially severe in the upper registers of the voice and less so in the middle range.

It is known, however, that great masters of the art of singing often succeed in preserving a high measure of intelligibility of their words even when vocalizing at the highest notes. Apart from the sheer mastery of production, in seeking an explanation of this fact we must also recognize the much greater redundancy (of information) carried by the meaningful word and especially by the phrases of coherent speech in comparison with the syllables that make up the syllable articulation tables used in our experiments.

The experimental data presented herein on the intelligibility (articulation) of singing and its dependence on the fundamental voice pitch may prove to be of value in solving a number of practical problems associated with speech transmission over radio communication lines, as well as in voice and speech pedagogy.

LITERATURE CITED

1. Calculation and Measurement of the Intelligibility of Russian Speech, Trudy VKAS, 33 (1952).

2. N. B. Pokrovskii, Calculation and Measurement of Speech Intelligibility (in Russian) (Moscow, Svyaz'izdat, 1962), p. 15.

3. S. N. Rzhevkin, Certain Results of the Analysis of a Singer's Voice, Akust. Zhur., 2, 2, 205-210 (1956) (Soviet Physics — Acoustics, Vol. 2, p. 215).

*It is known from reported research on the interrelationship of the various modes of intelligibility (articulation) (2) that a syllable articulation of 80% or more corresponds to a phrase articulation of 99% or better, which is rated as "excellent."

An Investigation
Concerning Vowel Sounds
on High Pitches

William M. Triplett

It is well known that soprano singers have difficulty producing recognizable vowel sounds on high pitches. Any investigation which adds to the rather limited store of knowledge about this subject should be of interest to singers and teachers of singing. The writing of this article was prompted by an investigation of five vowel sounds on C_6 (the second leger line above the treble staff).

A significant contribution to the subject of vowels sung on high pitches has been made by Howie and Delattre.[1] In their article, and a previous one by Delattre,[2] very clear discussions of the formant theory of vowel recognition are presented. Formants are frequency regions of greater energy, in relation to other parts of the spectrum, which are present in the vowel sounds of speakers and singers. These intensified frequencies are represented on sound spectograms by relatively darker tracings. Formant frequencies remain stationary regardless of changes in the fundamental pitch of the sound. In the case of most vowels, it is the lowest two formants which cause the sound to be recognized. In vowels that have a high second formant, for example (i), the third formant plays a more significant role in making the vowel recognizable.

Howie and Delattre theorize that all vowel sounds produced on high C_6 will be heard as (a). Their explanation for this is that a listener effectively averages formant frequencies, and when a sound is heard that is midway between two formants, it is recognized as if both formants were actually present. Since high C_6 (1056 cps) is midway between the first two formants of (a), all vowels produced on that pitch are interpreted by the listener as (a). (Peterson and Barney[3] give the average frequencies for (a) in female voices as 850 cps for formant one, and 1220 cps for formant two.)

Two voice students at the University of Southern California volunteered to have their voices recorded. A tape recording was made in a sound-treated radio studio; the microphone and recording equipment used were capable of handling frequencies up to 18,000 cps.[4] The singers were given a card which had on it the five primary vowels in the following sequence: (i) — (ee) as in beet; (e) — (ay) as in date; (a) — (ah) as in father; (o) — (oh) as in tote; and (u) — (oo) as in boot. So that the singers might feel more at ease, the recording session was conducted rather informally. Each singer was asked to speak the series of vowels as printed on the card, and to sing the same series on each of the following pitches: C_4 (middle C), E_4, G_4, C_5, E_5, G_5, and C_6.

Having read the aforementioned article by Howie and Delattre, I was, at this point, somewhat skeptical about the outcome of this investigation. Indeed, the sounds produced on high C_6 by the first singer could be interpreted in no other way than "variations of (a)." However, the second singer was able to produce sounds which seemed to differ significantly enough from each other to warrant further investigation. Sound spectrograms were made of this singer's spoken vowels. Spectrograms and amplitude sections were made of the vowels sung on high C_6. A conference was then arranged with Dr. Delattre at his laboratory at the University of California, Santa Barbara.

Dr. Delattre examined the spectrograms very carefully, and then asked to hear one of the sounds on high C_6. Since he did not wish to be aware of what vowel he was to hear, the correct spot on the tape was found while the operator listened through a set of earphones. The first vowel in the sequence, as it was recorded, was (i), and this was thought to be a logical place to have Dr. Delattre listen. To his surprise, he identified the vowel correctly without any hesitation. He then recorded the last portion of the sound onto the tape of the sound spectrograph, deleting the initial second of phonation. When this part of the sound was played repeatedly for members of his staff who were called in to hear it, every one of them identified the sound as (a). I agreed that the final portion of the sound was definitely (a).

Dr. Delattre listened to the other vowels in the series. He identified these sounds as (a); and I, while not forced to agree, after listening as carefully as I possibly could, came to the same conclusion. Examination of the spectogram for the sound which was intended to be (u) showed that there was almost a total absence of upper partials;[5] the second partial was represented by a very light line, and the other partials were barely visible on the spectrogram. The tone that resulted possessed a more "flute-like" quality, but was nonetheless (a). It is highly possible that the rounding of the lips over the teeth while producing this sound created the dearth of partials other than the fundamental.[6]

The perception of (u) sung by this subject on high pitches is doubtless an illusion created by the flute-like quality in comparison with her other vowels at the same level. The vowel (u) is used pedagogically to induce light registration ("head voice" or falsetto) and while sopranos find it very difficult, some teachers feel that the discovery of this flute-like production is worth a great deal of patience. The low position of the larynx for (u) is another factor of benefit to the voice.

An attempt was then made to determine what factors were involved in making the initial portion of the (i) sound recognizable to the listener. Another spectrogram of the tone was made; this time care was taken to include the attack. In the initial part of the tone a rather significant phenomenon was observed (see Figure 1). Both the second and the third partials of the tone were stronger than the fundamental.

Complete accuracy in measuring the frequencies of the partials was made impossible by the vibrato in the singer's voice. The fundamental pitch centered around 1100 cps which indicates that the tone was somewhat sharp. The second partial was at approximately 2200 cps and the third was around 3300 cps. The strength of the second partial may have contributed something towards making the (i) sound, but no direct connection could be established. Peterson and Barney give 2790 cps as the average frequency of the second formant in female voices. Since the second partial was nearly 600 cps below that frequency, it is unlikely that this partial contributed to intelligibility.

Of greater significance is the strength of the third partial. The frequency of this partial was quite close to 3310 cps, which Peterson and Barney give as the average for the third formant of (i). Since the third formant makes a definite contribution to the identification of (i),[7] it is highly possible that the strength of the third partial was an important factor in making the sound recognizable.

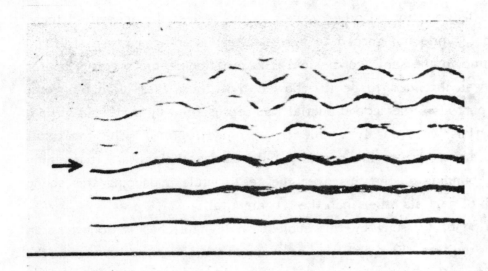

Figure 1.
The section of spectrogram above shows the attack of (i) sung on high C_6. Note that the intensity of the third partial, which corresponds to the third formant of (i), is greater than that of the fundamental.

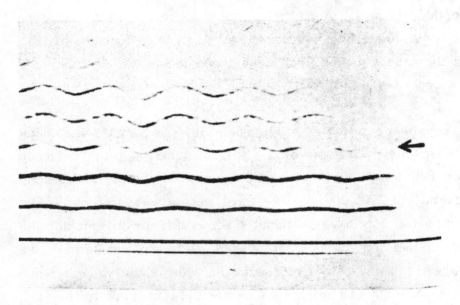

Figure 2.
The section of spectrogram above shows the end of (i) sung on C_6. The intensity of the third partial is considerably decreased, and this part of the sound is perceived as (a).

Delattre feels that a singer is constantly faced with two areas of concern, voice quality and vowel color, which are by no means compatible. Explaining this conflict in physiological terminology, he says:

"The best conditions for speaking vowels require the presence of constrictions along the vocal tract; the best conditions for singing require the absence of such constrictions in order to allow the high frequency overtones that characterize voice quality to be passed by the resonating cavaties."

The singer apparently had an unconscious conflict between these two contradicting tendencies as she was recording the (i) vowel. At the start of the tone she was intent on producing the vowel color, and somehow managed to do this by emphasizing the partial that corresponds to the third formant of (i), making the sound intelligible to the listener. Very soon, however, her desire for better voice quality becaue predominant; she allowed the intensity of the important partial to decrease, and the sound became (a) (see Figure 2). It is interesting to note that when the sound was heard in its entirety, the (i) seemed to carry throughout the tone in the mind of the listener. It was only when the first part of the sound was deleted that it was heard as (a). If this phenomenon were to be substantiated by further research, it would be an extremely valuable factor in the production of recognizable vowels on high pitches.

This investigation confirms the observation of Howie and Delattre that most vowels produced on high C are heard as (a). However, it has brought to light the distinct possibility that, in the initial stage of a tone it is possible for a singer to emphasize a partial which corresponds to a formant of a vowel; in this case, (i) was made intelligible by stressing the third formant. Although the third formant seems to play little part in the identification of the back vowels, it does play a significant role for front vowels; and if a singer could bring out this formant as she starts a tone, it appears possible that the front vowels, at least, could be produced so as to be recognizable on high pitches. It is even conceivable that there may be a particular formant of a back vowel that, when sufficiently emphasized, might make it recognizable. In any case, recognition would be aided by the fact that listeners appear to retain the original vowel color throughout tones of reasonably short duration.[9]

If a singer could learn to relegate voice quality to second place, and allow vowel color to predominate just for the split second it takes, at the beginning of a tone, to establish the vowel, more intelligible sounds could be sung on high pitches.

REFERENCES

1. HOWIE, J. and P. DELATTRE. "An Experimental Study of the Effect of Pitch on the Intelligibility of Vowels," The NATS Bulletin, 18, #4, 1962.

2. DELATTRE, P. "Vowel Color and Voice Quality," The NATS Buletin, 15, #1, 1958.

3. PETERSON, G. E. and H. L. BARNEY, "Control Methods Used in a Study of the Vowels," The Journal of the Acoustical Society of America, 24, #2, 1952, p. 183.

4. The recording was made in a studio of KUSC-FM on the campus of the University of Southern California, using an Altec microphone (Model 639), a Concertone tape recorder (Model 90), an Altec console (Model 230-B), and Scotch Brand recording tape (Tartan Series).

5. Upper partials are harmonics or overtones; accessory tones generated by the fundamental, which is considered the first partial.

6. HOWIE and DELATTRE, op. cit., p. 9.

7. DELATTRE, P. et al. "An Experimental Study of the Acoustic Determinants of Vowel Color," Word. 8, #3, 1962, p. 208.

8. DELATTRE, op. cit., p. 7.

9. To my knowledge, no one has defined tones of reasonably short duration. The tone under discussion lasted approximately 2.5 seconds. It would be worthwhile to know the average duration of high-pitched tones sung by sopranos in concert programs and operas.

ADDITIONAL BIBLIOGRAPHY

POTTER, R. K., G. A. KNOPP, and H. C. GREEN, Visible Speech. New York: D. Van Nostrand Co. Inc., 1947.

PULGRAM, E. Introduction to Spectrography of Speech. The Hague: Mouton & Co., 1964.

WILLIAM TRIPLETT earned his B.A. at the University of South Carolina and his Mus. M. at the University of Southern California. At the latter named university, he is now a candidate for his D.M.A. degree, studying voice with William Vennard and Acoustical Phonetics with Robert Kaplan.

He has had ten years experience as a choral director in the schools and churches of Columbia S.C. and Miami Beach, Florida. At present, he is a Lecturer in the School of Performing Arts, University of Southern California.

The Intelligibility
of Song

Research Results with a New Intelligibility Test[1]

Howard D. Nelson and William R. Tiffany

INTRODUCTION

While research in speech articulation and speech intelligibility has been notably energetic and fruitful in the past decade, the amount of <u>applied</u> research which could be of use to teachers and students of the art of singing has not been very impressive. Without question "articulation" in singing has remained a problem with which both singers and teachers continue to wrestle — but often without the benefit of such insights into the nature of speech perception as could be achieved by a closer relating of the general problems of speech perception to the special problems which result from the constraints imposed by the demands of artistic song.

The very nature of Western music as a complex, highly structured and formal pattern of frequency, intensity and time virtually insures that for any natural language sample upon which the formal musical structure is super-imposed there will be less than the optimal intelligibility. The reasons for this, while not yet completely understood in all details are becoming increasingly more clear as phonetic and linguistic research becomes more sophisticated.[2]

Any language clearly has its own <u>speech</u> melodies -- its "prosody" -- which constitute its own linguistically and culturally conditioned patterns of frequency, complexity and time, which cannot be altered without some degree of alteration of meaning, however slight. A rising pitch may change a statement into a question, the change in length of the steady-state portion of a vowel may change the perception of that vowel. <u>Cot</u> may become <u>cart</u> by an increase in the length of the vowel, for example.

Not only is normal conversational speech characterized by distinctive, flowing, pitch and time changes within the phrase, but also by distinctive phrasal stresses and by characteristic manners of flowing from syllable to syllable and word to word. A change of stress may change a noun to a verb. A change of blending or juncture can create linguistic havoc, as illustrated by many examples of what are termed "juncture contrasts," such as <u>I</u> <u>scream</u> vs. <u>ice</u> <u>cream</u>, <u>nitrate</u> vs. <u>night</u> <u>rate</u>, <u>cry</u> <u>doubt</u> vs. <u>cried</u> <u>out</u>, or <u>known</u> <u>ooze</u> vs. <u>no</u> <u>news</u>. It is obvious that composer and artist must both be aware of the considerable problems involved in the production of intelligible language superimposed on an artistic melodic line.

What is true in all song is compounded in "serious" -- especially operatic -- singing, where ranges of pitch and loudness are especially great, particularly in the higher registers, and where the human laryngeal and articulatory mechanisms are exploited to their utmost.

It is upon this problem of intelligibility in the upper register that there has been in recent years some scientific evidence to support the notion that not only do linguistic structures conspire to make intelligible song difficult, the basic acoustic nature of the high pitched voice wave form may also conspire against good and intelligible song. The evidence is not complete, not confined to English, and in any case presently available only for the singing of isolated speech segments (syllables and isolated vowels), but it must be considered, and if possible expanded to increasingly more reliable and valid statements which can be applied by students and teachers.

There have been at least three recent "applied" studies on this matter of singing intelligibility in the high registers, those of Howie and Delattre,[3] Morozov,[4] and Triplett.[5]

Howie and Delattre specifically studied the effect of pitch on the intelligibility of <u>isolated</u> sung vowels. Their point of departure was acoustic vowel theory, which has demonstrated that there are important cues for vowel identification contained in the pattern of overtones, particularly as defined by the first two resonance regions (the _formant_ regions), which result from the actions of the resonances of the vocal cavities on the laryngeal tone. The important speech resonances lie between about 300 and 3000 Hz. It is logical to assume, therefore, that if a singer produces a tone of such a high fundamental pitch that the lower resonance cavities cannot possibly have any effect on the tone, then the vowel sung might well be incorrectly identified. It was the application of this theory that Howie and Delattre tested by comparing the intelligibility of vowels sustained at pitches ranging from 132 to 396 Hz. for a baritone, and from 264 to 1056 Hz. for a soprano. They found that indeed the vowels did lose intelligibility as the pitch rose, and that the "theoretical assumption is generally correct that recognizable vowels cannot be produced with a fundamental frequency appreciably higher than the frequency of the first formant."

In a similarly motivated but independent study, V. P. Morozov evaluated the intelligibility of Russian consonant-vowel syllables sung by men, women, and children, over pitches ranging from 98 Hz to 988 Hz. Figure one, derived from the findings of that study, and simplified here, gives the results relating percent correct articulation of Russian syllables to voice fundamental frequency, for the men and the women.

Morozov's tests used standardized consonant-vowel syllables "normally applied to the investigation of speech over radio-telephone communication lines." The test results were summarized by Morozov as demonstrating that "optimum intelligibility in singing occurs at the middle notes of the voice range, becomes somewhat worse at the low notes, and declines considerably at the high notes. The last effect is particularly acute in female voices. . ."

One of the conclusions of the Howie and Delattre study of very high pitched vowels was that all vowel sounds produced on C_6 would tend to be heard as an "ah" vowel. This was the indication of the data as well as the prediction from the acoustic theory. In a subsequent study by Triplett, however, an important individual exception was found among singers at this pitch. In the case of one female singer an (i) (as in _feet_) sung at this very high pitch was reported to be clearly distinguishable as an (i). An acoustic analysis of that particular (i) showed that the factor apparently responsible for the distinguishing quality of (i) was a resonance _change_ following the initial onset of the sung tone, apparently a kind of special "dipthongization" which allowed for a compromise to be made between an

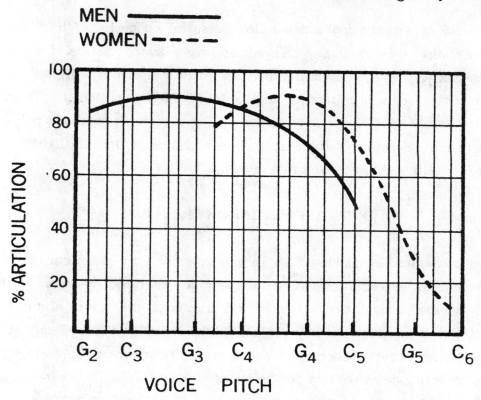

Figure 1.
Intelligibility-frequency curves redrawn from Morozov, showing per cent correct identification of Russian syllables as a function of fundamental voice frequency in male and female subjects.

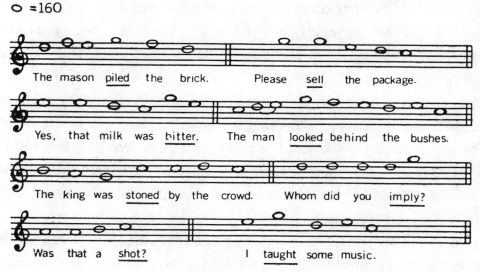

Figure 2.
Portion of score for the sung intelligibility test, showing eight of the 44 different phrases in the test. Underlining of key words did not appear on the singers' score.

initial clarity of articulation and a following sustained period of less "articulate" but better quality. It was, in any case, apparently a demonstration of an important difference suggesting the possibility that seriously degraded intelligibility may not be an immutable concommitant of high pitched singing provided articulation is appropriate to the special demands of the singing. Triplett's soprano's performance opens further the question of the practical significance of the relationship between singing and intelligibility at high pitch levels.

FURTHER RESEARCH PROBLEMS

From the three studies discussed above a number of very practical questions for research emerge. First, it is not at all clear yet that the measures of isolated vowel or syllable articulation are valid indications of the nature of the practical problems encountered in normal song. While it is true that sung tones are relatively stable acoustic phenomena, they are by no means completely so. There are many good phonetic reasons for believing that the cues to the recognition of vowels lie in the changes in quality of the vowel throughout its duration, as well as in the acoustic patterns of resonance as they may exist at some theoretical point of time. Hence, it would seem that to investigate the practical question of singing intelligibility, test items of greater validity should be used.

The matter of the practical significance of the loss in intelligibility which results from singing at very high pitch levels has not yet been fully assessed at a level which would shed light on the broad question of intelligibility of sung English, and which would be of practical assistance to those facing problems of composition, or problems of production of tones which are both beautiful and intelligible.

Other questions arise concerning the problem of intelligibility in singing. For example, there are questions concerning individual differences among singers, the degree of incompatibility between intelligibility and beauty, the relationships between effects of pitch per se and the effects of vocal strain which may accompany the production of pitches near the limits of a performer's ability, the relative influences of high pitch on vowels vs. consonants, and questions concerning the interactions of these variables and language structure. There can now be little question that pitch and intelligibility are related. In what way, and in what degree are questions which will require much more research than has yet been done in this area.

EXPERIMENTAL DESIGN

It was in an effort to shed a little more light on the matter of the intelligibility of singing at very high pitch levels that the experiment to be described in the following sections was done, using a "sung intelligibility test" (SIT), devised for the purpose, which consisted of short sung phrases rather than of isolated phonetic segments, and which was administered in such a way that the singers did not know that an intelligibility test was being given or which word was the test word.

Forty-four phrases, or "arias," were composed and set to music in such a way that certain key words in each phrase would fall upon either a very high (G_5-784 Hz) or a lower (C_5-523 Hz) pitch. The singers did not know which were the key words. A section of this "opera" is illustrated in Figure two -- eight items of the whole 44-item test actually used in the experiment. The test phrases were recorded by four experienced soprano solo artists and were judged for intelligibility by 40 listeners, half of whom were musically sophisticated.[6] Twenty-two of the test items were devised specifically to test vowel discrimination at two pitch levels, 22 to test consonant discrimination at the high level only. Intelligibility was tested in two ways by means of a "minimal-pair" (two choice) discrimination test, and by means of a "free-write-down" test of the entire phrase.

Half of the items of the SIT test constituted a vowel discrimination test. These were in the form of "minimal-pair" phrases in which one of the words -- the test word -- could be easily confused with a phonetically similar word which differed in terms of only one of the vowels in the word, and which was also appropriate in the context, and grammatically permissable. One example: "I discovered I was lost" differed from "I discovered I was last" only in the vowel contrast (ɔ-æ) of the words <u>lost</u> and <u>last</u>.

The vowel and consonant contrasts used in the SIT were chosen from among those previously found by Miller[7] and by Miller and Nicely[8] to be among the most easily confused in the intelligibility tests performed by them under relatively context-free conditions, with distorting transmission systems. For example, Miller's results predicted that under certain conditions, pairs of consonants such as (k) and (t) would be very difficult to discriminate. We took this data as a starting point from which to construct the SIT, using pairs which would present a challenging and difficult articulation task, while at the same time using a minimal-pair method of testing which would allow us to retain normal contextual conditions as well as isolation of single phoneme confusions to be tested. In this way it was hoped that test validity could be improved at the same time that some analysis of sources of articulation problems could be achieved. The fact that we have chosen to vary singers, vowels, consonants, and pitches, all in one short test design, makes it necessary to look upon this effort as primarily exploratory, of course.

In the preparation of the SIT recordings each of four singers sang the same 22 vowel phrases but with differing orders, each in a different random order. Two singers sang the vowel key words of half of the items at C_5 and the other half at G_5. The other two singers did the same, except that the vowels sung high by Singers One and Three were sung low by Singers Two and Four.

Because not all singers sang the same words at the same pitch, and because vowels are known to be important sources of variation in this kind of intelligibility task, there are essentially two different vowel tests of similar but not identical composition. The plan, a compromise designed to make maximum use of a few subjects, is illustrated in Table one, a table which provides a complete list of the words sung, together with the minimally contrasting item which appeared as the alternate item on the listeners' scoring sheet.

For the consonant tests minimal-pair phrases were constructed in a similar manner. There were 22 phrases which contained minimal consonant pairs. In this case the member of the pair sung was determined by chance, independently for each singer. The pairs were sung in phrases similar to those used in the vowel test. For example, "That is the best clue (cue)". A complete list of the consonant contrasts used may be found in Table two.

In the preparation of the SIT recordings the four singers sang the consonant contrasts in different random orders. Vowel and consonant phrases were randomly mixed together in the complete "opera." All of the consonant key words were sung on the high (G_5) pitch.

Intelligibility test scores were obtained by two different means for the recorded phrases of the four sopranos. The main measures were by the forty listeners, who simply listened to each sung phrase with the response form before them, on which was printed both of the possible keyword choices. Example "I discovered I was (lost last)." There was a five-second pause between phrases. Listeners simply circled the item which they believed to have been sung by the

	Per Cent Correct Responses. Test One			
	High Pitch		Low Pitch	
	S-1	S-3	S-2	S-4
Open Vowels				
/ o-ɔ / hole-haul	60	32	17	55
/ æ-ɑ / passible-possible	75	70	87	72
/ ɑ-æ / lost-last	97	85	100	100
/ ɔ-a / foyer-fire	35	55	92	92
/ a-ɔ / imply-employ	30	35	57	42
Close Vowels				
/ i-ɛ / bead-bed	57	40	100	97
/ ɛ-i / sell-seal	30	70	100	100
/ ɪ-ɛ / bitter-better	95	35	100	100
/ e-i / fate-feet	70	77	100	100
Others				
/ ʊ-ɜr / looked-lurked	70	52	100	100
/ ɔ-aɪ / law-lie	95	77	100	100

	Per Cent Correct Responses. Test Two			
	High Pitch		Low Pitch	
	S-2	S-4	S-1	S-3
Open Vowels				
/ æ-ɑ / Stack-stock	77	65	97	82
/ ɑ-o / ball-bowl	57	72	90	75
/ o-ʌ / stoned-stunned	60	85	92	97
/ ʌ-o / hull-hole	85	60	75	92
Close Vowels				
/ i-ɛ / heeded-headed	82	85	100	100
/ ɪ-ɛ / bill-bell	65	90	100	92
/ e-i / say-see	40	72	100	97
/ ɛ-æ / commend-command	82	90	97	100
Others				
/ ɑ-áʊ / shot-shout	92	95	100	100
/ u-ju / food-feud	97	100	100	100
/ aɪ-e / light-late	100	100	100	100

Table 1.
Two sets of minimal-pair contrast intelligibility test results, each for two different sopranos, two pitches, and two similar sets of vowel contrasts.

	Number of Incorrect Identifications			
Consonant Contrasts	Singer-1	Singer-2	Singer-3	Singer-4
/f-v/ face-vase	3	27	18	10
/k-p/ sucker-supper	7	1	24	20
/k-t/ pick-pit	15	8	19	3
/k-t/ pack-pat	14	13	11	5
/b-d/ bet-debt	0	8	18	14
/b-d/ buy-die	1	4	21	4
/k-p/ stock-stop	4	1	3	16
/r-j/ Ruth-youth	1	6	12	5
/k-t/ backer-batter	1	2	18	1
/b-p/ bill-pill	0	1	1	14
Total for all other* contrasts tested:	9	18	15	9
Total	55	89	160	101

	Mean Per Cent Correct Identification			
	94%	90%	82%	89%

*/p-t/ P-T	/s-t/ same-tame	/b-t/ bought-taught
/p-t/ piled-tiled	/ʃ-s/ shell-sell	/h-f/ hold-fold
/f-s/ feel-seal	/s-θ/ moss-moth	/g-k/ ghost-coast
/f-s/ foot-soot	/t-θ/ taught-thought	/l-j/ clue-cue

Table 2.
Analysis of 22 consonant minimal-pair choices showing number of errors made by 40 listeners for each of four different singers. Mean per cent correct identification scores are also given for each singer as averaged over all consonants.

soprano — having been previously told that the selection was a matter of pure chance.[9] This provided the main minimal-pair test results reported in this paper.

A second means of measuring intelligibility was to have ten listeners listen to each of the phrases and write down whatever they could hear or guess. Only singers One and Three were judged in this way. Half of the judges listened to Singer One first, the other half to Singer Three first. Each item was played only once as in the minimal-pair tests, but listeners were allowed all the time they wished for writing their responses.

RESULTS OF THE EXPERIMENT

The tables and figures which summarize the minimal pair contrast data show the proportion of correct responses obtained from 40 judges for the varying speech sound classes, pitches, and singers. A word of caution is necessary in the interpretation of these data. They are not to be confused with typical "intelligibility test" scores such as Morozov used. For the minimal-pair judgements a proportion of .5 correct judgments would indicate no demonstrated preference for either of the choices, and in this sense, no evidence of ability to discriminate between the two alternatives. Indeed, with 40 listeners each making a single judgment one would expect to get a proportion of .68 about one time out of twenty by chance alone. There is no satisfactory way of achieving with these data a single score value which would be equivalent to a typical "per cent articulation" score. Nevertheless, the comparative scores obviously reveal some interesting and reliable differences. In addition, it is a priori important to discover that in some conditions certain pairs can be discriminated at no better than the chance level, and that in others perfect discrimination may be achieved — on words which for the most part represent highly significant key words of the phrase.

The pitch effect is obviously an important one as demonstrated in Table one, but it is also obvious, as previous experiments have shown, that the extent of the effect is dependent upon the vowel contrast employed, and possibly upon individual differences among speakers as well. Use of such a high pitch as G_5 very seriously impaired minimal-pair vowel discrimination for the group of singers as a whole. The summarizing bar chart of Figure three shows, for example, that on the average the more simple vowels were identified at no better than a chance level at G_5 while the lower pitched pairs were substantially and consistently more easily idenfied — for all singers and both tests.

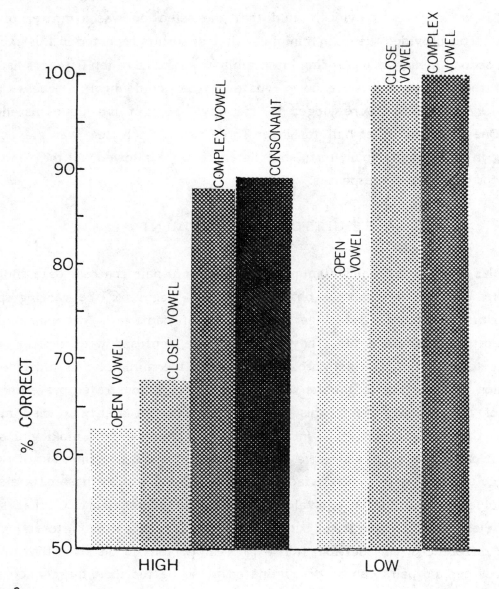

Figure 3.
Summary of minimal-pair sung intelligibility test results for high pitched vowel and consonant pairs and for low pitched vowel pairs.

	Vowels		Consonants
	Low	High	High
Singer One	92	39	60
Singer Three	89	33	60

Table 3.
Per cent correct identification of key words in the free-write-down test.

The fact that the influence of pitch is dependent upon phonetic structure is almost equally well demonstrated. Note from the table and chart the fact that only the open vowel pairs presented substantial difficulty at the low pitch level. Other vowels were identified at C_5 with nearly perfect consistency. It is perhaps of special interest to observe that the ability to differentiate between "complex" vowels such as (ɔ) vs. (aɪ) or (aɪ) vs. (e) is particularly good. Vowels which are necessarily or typically complex in speech and song present not only a resonance cue but also a kind of consonantal cue for their identification. The sound (a), for example, differs from sung (e) not only in the quality of the initial "stable" part of the sound, but also in the off-glide. Indeed, it is obvious that where such an off-glide occurs (and in context it may be more-or-less a part of most syllables) one may not have a "minimal" pair, but rather a duple. It also seems obvious that the addition of this cue helped the singers to resolve the ambiguity which might otherwise have made recognition difficult.

While we did not test the pitch effect on consonant-pair discriminations it seems obvious from the good identification scores obtained for the high pitched consonants that any differences which might have been revealed from a control group of consonants at C_5 would have been slight in comparison with that obtained for vowels. The average for all consonants and singers combined was nearly 90 percent correct, with difficulties for the most part centered around a very few of the pairs tested (See Table two).

Five of the 22 consonant pairs tested accounted for well over half of the errors. Of a total of 88 consonant pairs (22 by each of four singers) only 12 failed to show a statistically significant choice of the intended (correct) member of the pair. This may be compared with the vowels at the same pitch, where of a total number of 44 vowel pairs, 19, or nearly half, failed to be correctly identified at better than a statistical chance level. To say from this that vowels are almost three times more difficult than consonants at such high pitches would be a gross misuse of statistics in view of the fact that the tests do not have a phonetic structure exactly like the language as a whole, but it does appear clear that consonants are highly resistant to the distortion attendant upon the use of very high pitches when compared with vowels.

Unfortunately our data do not enable us to obtain a really clear evaluation of singer differences. There are strong hints, however, that individual differences may be significant as a generalization. The consonant data show that Singer Three, for example, accounted for almost three times as many errors as did Singer One. The vowel data do not seem to show this as clearly and in any case are quite ambiguous. They do, however, tend in the same direction. In this connection it was interesting to note that the informal preferences of listeners also tend to support Singer One over Singer Three. All evidences thus far point to important singer variations in intelligibility, not only in terms of degree, but also in terms of type of articulation problem. These results do appear to lend support to the notion of Morozov that the more extensive individual differences are to be found in articulation of the consonants.

The results of the free-write-down test of articulation are also not simple to analyze and interpret. Using a rigid criterion of perfect agreement on all words except the articles a and the, the average percent correct score for all subjects and conditions for the 44 phrases was 58 percent. If a less rigid criterion is used — say that of allowing for one error per phrase, then the score rises abruptly to 95 percent correct. That is, only five percent of the sentences had more than one important error as indicated by the write-downs of the listening panel. Such a score does, of course, appear to give an extremely favorable picture of the articulatory ability of our sopranos. It would be misleading, however, to jump to such a simple conclusion. The fact is that most of the errors were made on the very important test words, nearly all key nouns and verbs. For example, for both Singer One and Singer Three combined, listeners made an average of about 21 errors per test (not counting articles). Of these an average of 17 were key words. The reasons for this must be complex but are doubtless related to the deliberate choice of ambiguous pairs, as well as to the placement of the key words at the high pitch peak in 33 of the phrases.

Because such a high percentage of the errors made on the free-write-down tests were made on the same words used in the minimal-pair test it becomes possible to assess the relative difficulty listeners experienced with the vowels at the two different pitches and with the consonant key words, and to compare the results of the two methods of scoring. Table three presents a summary of the results of such an analysis for the three classes of key words: those used to test vowel contrasts sung at C_5, those used to test vowels at G_5, and those used to test consonants at the same high pitch level.

While the scores are, of course, different and do not represent directly consonant and vowel "confusion" it is clear that the orders of difficulty represented by the pitch and vowel vs. consonant conditions are similar to the results of the minimal-pair tests. Few write-down errors were made with the low pitched key words, vowel key words were more difficult than consonant key words. Singer One made somewhat fewer errors than Singer Three but the difference was slight and complex (and not on consonant words). It was interesting to note a bigger subject difference in the number of non-key word errors. Singer Three accounted for more than twice as many of this kind of error.

The results of the write-down test appear to support the major conclusions of the minimal-pairs test. They show the high intelligibility of soprano English at C_5, the considerable effect on the intelligibility of vowels of singing in the higher register, and the lesser effects on the consonants. A second kind of result can only be understood if the types of errors made on the write-down test are analyzed. While it is true that the listeners had considerable trouble with the consonant key words, the difficulty was apparently not because the consonants in those words were difficult, but because of the vowels in those same words. For example, of the approximately 85 errors made by all ten listeners to the consonant key words sung by Singer Three, only about ten errors were of a simple consonant confusion type. The others were complex, including both consonant and vowel errors, addition of syllables and omissions of the entire word.

A comparison of the write-down data with the results of Morozov is revealing. Morozov's curves show a decrease from about 75 percent to about 25 percent intelligibility as pitch rose from C_5 to G_5. This result was very close to ours considering the substantial differences in method.

CONCLUSIONS

It is obvious from these data that no easy generalizations are possible with regard to the problems of intelligible singing. The present and previous data certainly offer no support to the overgeneralization sometimes encountered that "You can't understand sung English anyway so why worry." For one thing the pitch effect influences Russian singing as well as English. In addition, the fact that most of the problem is with the simple vowels would seem to pretty well disqualify this argument when applied to languages which are supposedly more "musical" because of a "purer" vowel structure. It would seem that a tempting hypothesis might be that the greater the number of open and simple vowels in a language the more difficult that language would be to sing intelligibly. But even this hypothesis embodies an oversimplification. No language is without consonant and vowel complexity. Syllables in any language have some kind of boundary phenomena, and musical convention demands, generally, the holding of vowel tone on the steady state, treating these boundaries as essentially consonantal — in any of the major Western languages so far as we know. Interlinguistic comparisons of steady-state vs. boundary phenomena will require highly sophisticated techniques of phonetic analysis, if indeed they can ever be accomplished meaningfully.

Setting aside the value question of language "superiority" as a nonsense question at the present time, what do these and previous data suggest with regard to the singer's problem of articulation in general? They suggest, we believe, that the singer should be especially aware of the difficulties of articulation at high pitch levels, particularly in the case of simple and open vowels, and particularly where there is ambiguity in the language which can be resolved only by recognition of vowel quality. They seem to show the increased importance of clarity of consonant articulation in high register singing in order that such ambiguity may be reduced in the face of otherwise insurmountable acoustic problems. The results also may give warning to the composer that a key word which is both high pitched and vowel-ambiguous is a key word which will probably be a roadblock to understanding. If it is not clear from context whether "hole" or "haul" is sung, then placing that word well above C_5 is to invite misinterpretation. The use of a lower pitch or a word which is potentially less ambiguous may help solve such a problem.

The greatest difficulty appears to occur in words which differ in terms of a single articulatory feature only. This is the case among certain vowels, at least. If the problems of articulation are not understood, if beautiful tone is the only goal, then "pen" and "pain" may be nearly identical. An understanding of the American English vowel sound in "pain" as one which has not only a slightly different resonance, but also a different off-glide makes it possible to sing "pain" in a way which may retain the more open quality in the sustained portion of the vowel, but reveal the different vowel in the off-glide. Phonetically the difference may be best described as that between (pɛn) and (pɛjn) rather than between (pen) and (pɛn).

Of course, this discussion is going beyond the data of the present experiment at this point. What does not go beyond the data is the conclusion that singing at high registers presents great difficulties, that these difficulties are chiefly with steady-state vowel quality identification, that the actual kinds of problems which this presents in any given song are likely to be strongly influenced by language factors and by the articulation of consonants and the consonantal, or off-glide and on-glide, portions of syllables. It also suggests that there may be some rather complex individual differences among singers with respect to the kinds and extent of articulation problems. These are obviously worth much more careful study by phonetic scientists. The subject of articulatory and acoustic phonetics would also seem to be worth some careful study by singers and composers.

REFERENCES

1. This study is in part based upon a doctoral dissertation by the first author at the University of Washington. Additional data were collected during the second author's NINDB special fellowship year at the Communications Science Laboratory, University of Florida.

2. See for example, Lieberman, P., Intonation, Perception, and Language, Research Monograph No. 38, M.I.T. Press, 1967. See also Liberman, A.M., "Perception of the Speech Code," Psychological Review, 1968.

3. Howie, J. and Delattre, P., "An Experimental Study of the Effect of Pitch on the Intelligibility of Vowels," The NATS Bulletin, Vol. 18, No. 4, May, 1962, p. 6.

4. Morozov, V.P., "Intelligibility in Singing as a Function of Fundamental Voice Pitch," Translated from Akusticheskii Zhurnal, Vol. 10, No. 3, pp. 330-334, July-September, 1964, translation published in Soviet Physics-Acoustics, Vol. 10, No. 3, Jan.-March, 1965, pp. 279-283.

5. Triplett, W.M., "An Investigation Concerning Vowel Sounds on High Pitches," The NATS Bulletin, Vol. 23, No. 3, February, 1967, p. 6.

6. No significant differences were found in the judgments of these two types of listeners.

7. Miller, G.A., "The Perception of Speech," For Roman Jakobson; Essays on the Occasion of his Sixtieth Birthday. Compiled by Morris Halle. The Hague: Mouton and Co., 1965, pp. 353-359.

8. Miller, G.A., and Nicely, P.E., "Analysis of Perceptual Confusions Among Some English Consonants," Journal of the Acoustical Society of America, Vol. 27, No. 2, 1965, pp. 338-352.

9. The word to be sung was selected using a table of random numbers. Effects of the position of words on the scoring key were cancelled by the use of alternate scoring forms.

Howard D. Nelson, D.M.A., University of Washington, 1967, is presently soloist with the Zurich Opera Company, Zurich, Switzerland. William R. Tiffany, PhD., State University of Iowa, 1951, is Professor of Speech and director of the Speech Science Laboratory, University of Washington, Seattle, Washington.